Simply Physics

Terry Hall

Edward Arnold

© Terry Hall 1980

First published 1980
by Edward Arnold (Publishers) Ltd
41 Bedford Square, London WC1B 3DQ

Reprinted 1982,1983

ISBN 0 7131 0337 X

British Library Cataloguing in Publication Data

Hall, Terry
 Simply physics.
 1. Physics
 I. Title
 530   QC21.2

ISBN 0–7131–0337–X

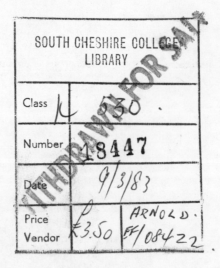

Set in 9/11 Univers by Parkway Group London and Abingdon
Printed in Hong Kong by
Wing King Tong Co Ltd

Preface

This book is based on the Nuffield Physics syllabus. It has been written for the wide ability range of students who now follow the Nuffield Physics course, C.S.E. as well as O'level. The text has been kept as simple as possible and extensive use is made of diagrams and photographs.

Simply Physics is intended to consolidate understanding which has been gained through experimentation and discussion. It explains the basic ideas which are developed in a Nuffield course, and helps pupils who need the security of a concise text.

At the end of each chapter are graded questions which relate to each subsection of the chapter. These questions are designed to test progress and are useful for revision. There are also 'Extra questions' on the general theme of the chapter: some of these have been selected from past Nuffield G.C.E. and C.S.E. papers, and others have been written to encourage pupils to use their understanding in tackling unfamiliar problems.

Note to the pupil

This book covers work done in a Nuffield Physics course. It will help you to understand topics you find difficult or have missed through absence, and be useful when you revise for exams.

There are graded questions at the end of each chapter.

* means **easy**
** means **fairly difficult**
*** means **difficult**

These grades are only a guide. Remember, what is easy for one person can be difficult for another. You may find that some questions are only easy if you look at an example or read through the topic first.

Acknowledgements

I would like to thank the following people:
Tim Hardingham for the advice and encouragement he has offered, for some original questions and for the contribution his ideas have made in writing certain of the chapters. Brian Matthews for the hours shared in writing *Involvement in Physics,* they clarified my thoughts and proved an inspiration for much of this new work and for his permission to use certain diagrams and questions we devised. Val, my wife, for her patience, perceptive criticism and help in checking proofs. My father for the part he played in checking the proofs.

The publishers would like to thank both the Oxford and Cambridge Schools Examination Board and the Metropolitan Regional Examination Board for permission to reproduce those examples indicated in the text by (*O. and C.*) and (*M.R.E.B.*) respectively.

The Publisher's thanks are also due to the following for permission to reproduce photographs:
Boxmag-Rapid Ltd, Birmingham: 10b; Crown Copyright reproduced by permission controller HMSO, courtesy Hydraulics Research Station, Wallingford, England: 21i; Electron Diffraction Group, Imperial College: 22d; Fulmer Research Institute Ltd: 22e; From *Geometrical and Physical Optics* by R. A. Longhurst (Longman): 21d,e,j,k; Griffin & George Ltd: 4b, 17c; Philip Harris Ltd: 4a; Dr. Judith Milledge, University College, London: 22a; National Physical Laboratory, U.K.: 226 From *Ripple Tank Studies of Wave Motion* by W. Llowarch (O.U.P. 1961): 19b, 21a,b,c; Tektronix: 15b.

Contents

Contents

1
Forces

1.1 Finding out about forces

Forces can make elastic objects stretch or change shape. By watching to see how an elastic object behaves we can tell something about the size or type of force.

For example, fig. 1.1 shows a block of rubber fixed at its base, first with no force acting on it and then with five different kinds of force in turn.

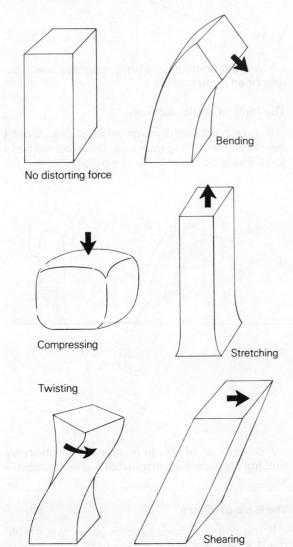

No distorting force

Compressing

Twisting

Bending

Stretching

Shearing

fig. 1.1

1.2 Hooke's law

When different sized weights are hung on an elastic band, it is found that double the weight makes the elastic band stretch twice as much and three times the weight makes it stretch three times as much, (see fig. 1.2). The amount by which the elastic band stretches is called the **extension**.

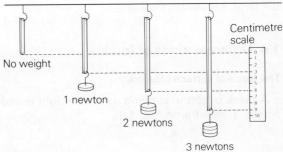

No weight

1 newton

2 newtons

3 newtons

Centimetre scale

fig. 1.2

This result is summed up by Hooke's law which says that 'the extension is proportional to the force which causes it'. Hooke's law is also true for springs provided that they, like elastic bands, are not over stretched.

Results from the elastic band experiment in fig. 1.2 can be used to draw a graph of extension against force (fig. 1.3).

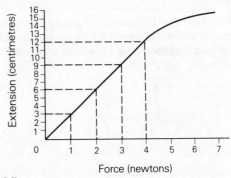

fig. 1.3

Notice that for this elastic band, Hooke's law is only true for forces up to 4 newtons. Above 4 newtons the graph line curves showing that stretch and force are no longer proportional.

1

1.3 Weight and mass

Weight is the force with which gravity pulls an object against the ground or a floor. It is measured in newtons.

A person might weigh 700 newtons on earth, be almost weightless while travelling to the moon and when he arrives on the moon find that his weight is less than 120 newtons. His weight depends on where he is at the time.

Mass is the amount of matter in an object. It is measured in kilograms.

If a person has a mass of 70 kilograms on earth, his mass will stay at 70 kilograms as he travels to the moon and still be 70 kilograms when he is on the moon. His mass does not depend on where he is at the time. It is always the same.

1.4 Different kinds of force

The force of surface tension

A piece of cotton carrying a small weight is tied across a wire frame (fig. 1.4).

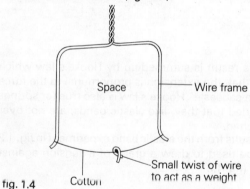

Space   Wire frame

Small twist of wire to act as a weight

fig. 1.4   Cotton

When the frame is dipped into soapy water so that a bubble is trapped between the frame and the cotton, it is noticed that the weight is pulled up towards the soap film (fig. 1.5).

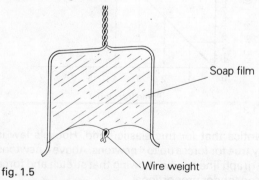

Soap film

Wire weight

fig. 1.5

This happens because the bubble surface is under tension and this 'surface tension' makes a force on the cotton.

The force of magnetism

You may have tried the experiment shown in fig. 1.6 where one end of a magnet is held up in the air by a magnetic force.

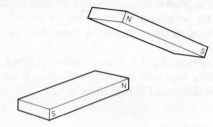

fig. 1.6

More experiments showing magnetic force are described in chapter ten.

The force of static electricity

If you rub a plastic comb on your sleeve and hold it near to water trickling from a tap, the water will feel a force and bend towards the comb (fig. 1.7).

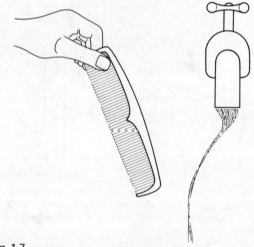

fig. 1.7

A description of how to make static electricity by rubbing plastic and cloth together is given in chapter eight.

The force of friction

If you pull your hand towards you across a table (fig. 1.8) you will feel the force of friction trying to stop it moving.

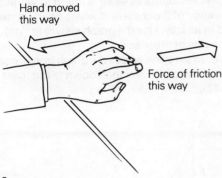

fig. 1.8

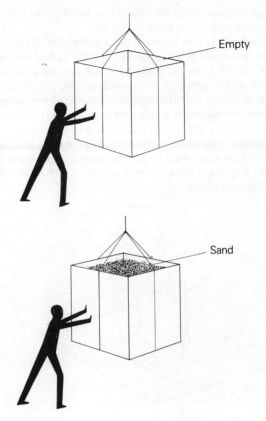

fig. 1.10

Friction is a special kind of force called a **reaction**. It always reacts against a force by pulling in the opposite direction. Stop pulling your hand towards you and the friction will stop.

Fig 1.9 shows a marble falling through glycerine. The marble falls slower than it would in air. This means that the liquid is making an upward force on the marble. Because this reaction is like the frictional force between two surfaces it is sometimes called **fluid friction**.

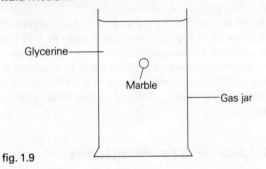

fig. 1.9

1.5 Inertia

Although two objects can look the same, one might be more difficult to move than the other. Fig. 1.10 shows a man who first pushes an empty box which is hanging on a long rope and then pushes the same box full of sand.

The full box is much more difficult to move than the empty box. The amount of difficulty in getting an object or mass to move is sometimes nicknamed 'unshovability': the correct term is **inertia**. Notice that the larger the mass the greater the inertia.

Photograph 1a shows an inertia balance whose sides are made of spring steel and whose tray contains three masses. If the tray is pushed to one side and then let go it will vibrate quite slowly. If one mass is taken out of the tray the side springs will have less to push and the tray will vibrate quicker.

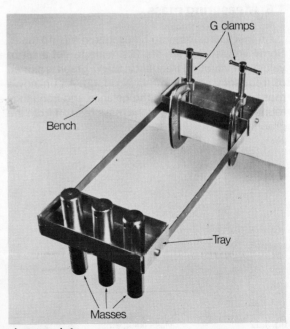

photograph 1a

Two masses in the tray have less inertia than three masses and so are easier to 'shove'.

Each mass can be hung on a string (fig. 1.11) so that its weight is supported by the string and not by the inertia balance. Even so it will still be pushed from side to side by the tray as it moves.

It is found that the rate of vibration is the same when the weight is supported as when it is not. This shows that inertia depends on mass and not weight.

Notice that in fig. 1.10 the weight of the box of sand was supported by a rope, so in that example it was the mass and not the weight which made it difficult to move.

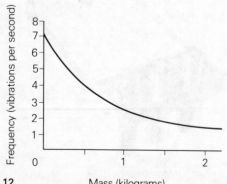

fig. 1.11

1.6 Measuring mass

An inertia balance can be used to measure mass. Some known masses are first used to get a set of values for vibrating frequency, then a graph is plotted of frequency against mass (fig. 1.12). An unknown mass can then be put in the balance, the frequency found and then the size of the mass read off from the graph.

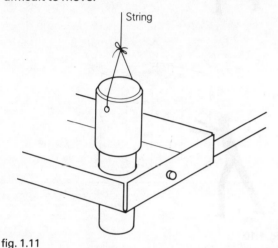

fig. 1.12

Example: An inertia balance is found to vibrate with a frequency of 2 per second when a certain mass is placed in its tray. Use the graph shown in fig. 1.12 to find the size of the mass.

Method: Draw a line across the graph from frequency 2 to meet the curve and then down to the mass axis. (fig. 1.13).

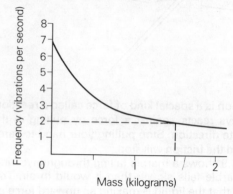

fig. 1.13

The line meets the mass axis at 1·5 showing that the object has a mass of 1·5 kilograms.

Note: In section 1.2 the graph for an elastic material shown in fig. 1.3 could have been used to find the size of an unknown weight. Now we have shown how an elastic material can be used to measure a mass. It is the spring steel sides of the inertia balance which are the elastic material in this case (photograph 1b).

1.7 Levers and balancing forces

Experience will tell you that the plank in fig. 1.14 will need a bigger force at B to balance it than it will at C.

fig. 1.14

If the wedge is put under the centre of the plank (fig. 1.15) there will be an equal weight of plank on each side of the wedge. Now the plank will balance.

fig. 1.15

A 5 newton weight on one end makes a **turning force** which will unbalance the plank. It can be rebalanced

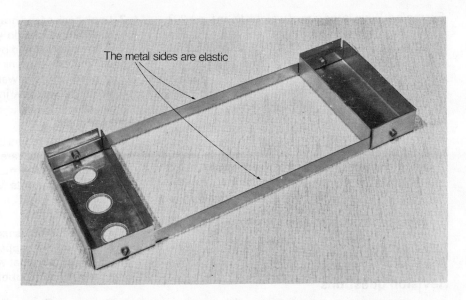

The metal sides are elastic

photograph 1b

by making a 5 newton force at C or a larger force at B (fig. 1.16).

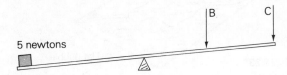

fig. 1.16

The size of force needed to rebalance a plank or lever depends on how far from the wedge or fulcrum the force is made. The rule is:

anticlockwise turning force × distance from fulcrum = clockwise turning force × distance from fulcrum

that is,

anticlockwise moment = clockwise moment

Example 1: What is the size of the weight, W, in fig. 1.17?

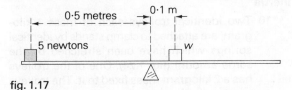

fig. 1.17

Calculation

anticlockwise moment = clockwise moment
force × distance = force × distance
$$5 \times 0.5 = W \times 0.1$$
$$\therefore W = 25 \text{ newtons}$$

Example 2: What is the distance, Y in fig. 1.18?

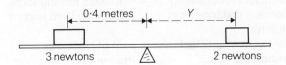

fig. 1.18

Calculation

anticlockwise moment = clockwise moment
$$3 \times 0.4 = 2 \times Y$$
$$1.2 = 2Y$$
$$\therefore Y = 0.6 \text{ metres}$$

If more than two weights are balanced on a lever we find that

the sum of the anticlockwise moments = the sum of the clockwise moments

Example 3: What is the size of weight, W, in fig. 1.19?

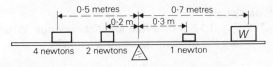

fig. 1.19

Calculation

sum of anticlockwise   = sum of clockwise
moments   moments
$$(4 \times 0.5) + (2 \times 0.2) = (1 \times 0.3) + (W \times 0.7)$$
$$2 + 0.4 = 0.3 + 0.7W$$
$$2.1 = 0.7\,W$$
$$\therefore W = 3 \text{ newtons}$$

5

Example 4: What is the size of weight, *W,* in fig. 1.20?

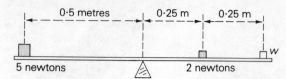

fig. 1.20

Calculation

sum of anticlockwise = sum of clockwise
moments   moments

$$5 \times 0\cdot5 = (2 \times 0\cdot25) + (W \times 0\cdot5)$$
$$2\cdot5 = 0\cdot5 + 0\cdot5W$$
$$2 = 0\cdot5W$$
$$\therefore W = 4 \text{ newtons}$$

Revision questions

Formula

anticlockwise turning   = clockwise turning force
force × distance from   × distance from fulcrum
fulcrum

or, sum of anticlockwise = sum of clockwise
moments   moments

Finding out about forces

* **1** Fig. 1.21 shows what a rubber band looked like after a force had been made on it.

fig. 1.21

   a What kind of force had been made on the rubber band?
   b What might have been the reason for making such a force?

Hooke's Law

* **2** Fig. 1.22 shows five identical springs. What are the missing values of weight?

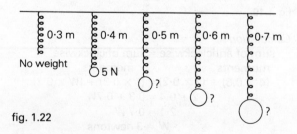

fig. 1.22

** **3** Look back at the graph shown in fig. 1.3
   a What weight do you think would stretch the elastic band by 7.5 centimetres?
   b What do you think would happen if a weight of 40 newtons were used?
* **4** Write Hooke's law in your own words.

Weight and mass

* **5** Experiments to find both the mass and weight of a metal object are done on earth and then repeated on the moon. What do you think these experiments will show?

Different kinds of force

* **6** A loop of cotton is fixed so that it will float on a flat bubble trapped in a wire frame (fig. 1.23). Explain what will happen to the cotton if the surface of bubble inside the loop bursts.

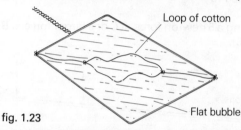

fig. 1.23

* **7** A girl blows up a balloon and is able to make it stick to the ceiling after first rubbing it against her sleeve. What might be the reason for this?
* **8** If you push a large wardrobe across the floor of a room, which way does the force of friction act; upwards, downwards, towards you, away from you or sideways?
* **9** If a person falls out of an aeroplane without a parachute he is not likely to fall much faster than 50 metres per second (110 miles per hour). Why is this?

Inertia

10 Two identical trolleys each of mass 1 kilogram, are attached to clamp stands by identical springs which have been stretched by the same amount (fig. 1.24). One of the trolleys has a 2 kilogram mass fixed to it. The trolleys are then both released.
   a Describe the motion of each trolley using the word 'inertia'.
   b Suppose that the experiment was repeated on the moon: compare these results from the moon experiment with those got on earth.

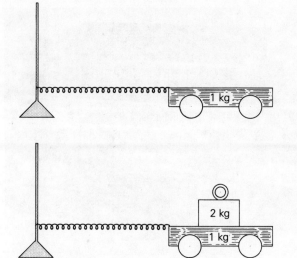

fig. 1.24

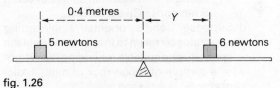

Measuring mass

*11 Look back at the graph shown in fig. 1.12. What vibrating frequency do you think the inertia balance would have with a mass of 0.5 kilograms in its tray?

Levers and balancing forces

*12 What force would be needed, first at B and then at C, to rebalance the plank in fig. 1.25?

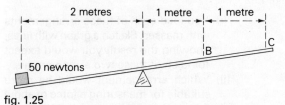

fig. 1.25

**13 What is the distance, Y, in fig. 1.26?

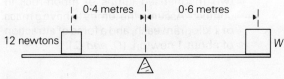

fig. 1.26

**14 What is the size of the weight, W, in fig. 1.27?

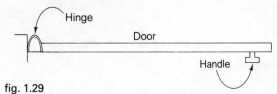

fig. 1.27

**15 What is the size of the weight, W, in fig. 1.28?

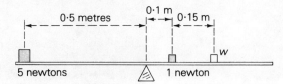

fig. 1.28

**16 Why is the handle of a door so far from the hinge (fig. 1.29)?

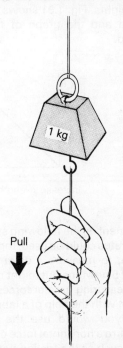

fig. 1.29

Extra questions

***17 A load of 1 kilogram is hung on a piece of strong thread and an extra piece of the thread is tied to the base of the load (fig. 1.30).

fig. 1.30

Why is it that a sharp pull downwards on the lower piece of thread will make it break below the load, while a slow pull will snap the thread above the weight?

photograph 1.c

**18 Explain why the middle book in a pile of books can be pulled out quickly without the top books falling over or coming with it (photograph 1.c).

***19 John does an experiment to measure the increase in length of a spring as he loads it with weights. Fig. 1.31 shows the apparatus he used and the graph of the results he obtained.

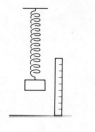 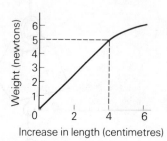

fig. 1.31

a Comment on the following statement. 'The apparatus could be used, together with the graph, to measure a downward force of about 5 newtons but might not be suitable for measuring greater forces.'

b Show, with the help of a labelled diagram, how you would use the apparatus to measure a horizontal force of about 3 newtons, such as the friction between a board and a bench.

c Given two springs of the kind that John

tested, they could be arranged either in series or in parallel, as shown in fig. 1.32.

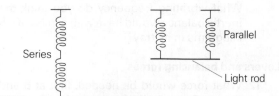

fig. 1.32

(i) You load each of these arrangements with masses. Sketch a graph with lines, showing the result you would expect for each of these two arrangements.

(ii) Which arrangement would be more suitable for measuring a force of about 0·5 newtons? Give a reason.

(iii) Which arrangement would be more suitable for measuring a force of about 9 newtons? Give a reason.

d Suppose John's original single-spring apparatus be taken to the moon. Would the apparatus be suitable for finding the weight of a sample of moon-rock of mass 1 kilogram? Give a reason.

e Would the apparatus be suitable for measuring the force of attraction between two magnetised lumps of moon-rock in contact? Assume the lumps to have a mass of 1 kilogram each, and a force of attraction of about 1 newton. (*O. and C.*).

2
Volume and Density

2.1 Measuring volume

The volume of an object is a measure of how much space it takes up. Volume can be measured in cubic centimetres (cm^3) or cubic metres (m^3). To find the volume of a small object we can see how many centimetre cubes would fit inside it. For some shapes this is easy.

The diagram in fig. 2.1 shows how an object can be divided into centimetre cubes. There are 24 cubes on the front face (6 × 4) and another two lots of 24 behind them: three lots of 24 altogether making a total of 72 cubes. The volume is 72 cubic centimetres.

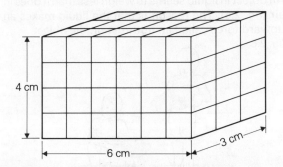

fig. 2.1

Notice that the volume of the object in fig. 2.1 could be found by multiplying its length, width and height.

$$\text{volume} = \text{length} \times \text{width} \times \text{height}$$
$$= 6 \times 3 \times 4$$
$$= 72 \text{ cubic centimetres}$$

The inside volume of a bottle can be found by filling it with water, pouring the water out and measuring the volume of the water (fig. 2.2).

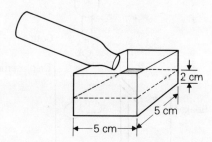

fig. 2.2

$$\text{volume of water} = \text{length} \times \text{width} \times \text{height}$$
$$= 5 \times 5 \times 2$$
$$= 50 \text{ cubic centimetres} (= \text{inside volume of bottle})$$

It is easier still to pour the water into a measuring cylinder which has volume measurements marked on its side.

The volume of a solid object can be found by lowering it into a measuring cylinder, partly filled with water and seeing how much the level of water rises (fig. 2.3).

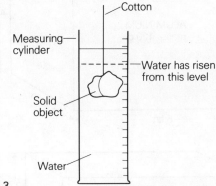

fig. 2.3

Although it is easy to measure the volume of small objects in cubic centimetres, scientists often prefer to measure in cubic metres. One cubic metre is a million times bigger than a cubic centimetre (fig. 2.4).

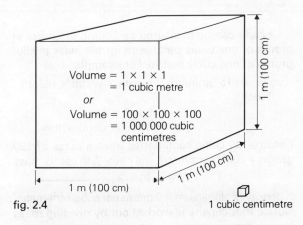

Volume = 1 × 1 × 1
= 1 cubic metre

or

Volume = 100 × 100 × 100
= 1 000 000 cubic centimetres

fig. 2.4

1 cubic centimetre

To change a measurement from cubic centimetres to cubic metres it must be divided by 1 000 000.

Example: What would 1500 cubic centimetres be equal to in cubic metres?

Calculation

$$1500 \div 1\,0000\,000 = 0.0015 \text{ cubic metres}$$

2.2 Density

The two blocks in fig. 2.5 each have the same mass of 120 grams (0.12 kilograms). The reason why the small block has the same mass as the large block is that iron is a more **dense** material than aluminium.

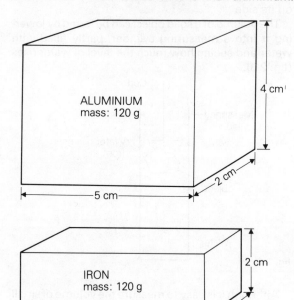

fig. 2.5

Density can be measured by finding the mass in grams of one cubic centimetre (or the mass in kilograms of one cubic metre). For example

volume of aluminium = length × width × height
block

$$= 5 \times 2 \times 4$$
$$= 40 \text{ cubic centimetres}$$

because 40 cubic centimetres have a mass of 120 grams 1 cubic centimetre will have $\frac{1}{40}$ th of this mass

$$120 \div 40 = 3$$

∴ density of aluminium = 3 grams per cubic centimetre. Notice that density is worked out by dividing mass by volume.

$$\text{density} = \frac{\text{mass}}{\text{volume}}$$

$$\left(\text{grams per cubic centimetre} = \frac{\text{grams}}{\text{cubic centimetres}}\right.$$
$$\left.\text{or, kilograms per cubic metre} = \frac{\text{kilograms}}{\text{cubic metres}}\right)$$

For the iron block

volume = length × width × height
$$= 5 \times 1.5 \times 2$$
$$= 15 \text{ cubic centimetres}$$

$$\text{density} = \frac{\text{mass}}{\text{volume}}$$
$$= \frac{120}{15}$$
$$= 8 \text{ grams per cubic centimetre}$$

2.3 Upthrust

An object in liquid seems to weigh less than it does in air (fig. 2.6). The reason is that the liquid makes an upward force called an **upthrust** on the object.

fig. 2.6

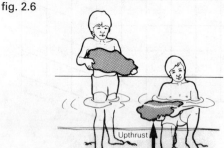

The upthrust is the difference between an object's weight in air and its weight in the liquid. Upthrust

fig. 2.7

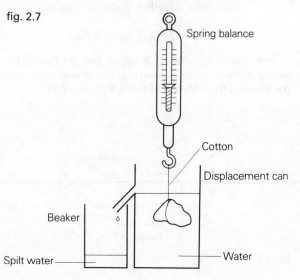

can be measured using the apparatus in fig. 2.7. If the water spilt from the displacement can is collected and weighed, its weight will be found to equal the upthrust. **Archimedes principle** states that the upthrust on a body is equal to the weight of liquid displaced.

2.4 The density of air

Air is a substance and has mass and density. Its density can be measured using the apparatus in photograph 2.a.

The polythene container is pumped up hard then put on a lever balance to find its mass. The extra air is then bubbled off into an upturned, water filled, perspex box of volume 0.001 cubic metres (fig. 2.8).

The volume of air let out is calculated by counting how many times the perspex box fills with air. When this extra air has bubbled out, the polythene container is put on the balance again and the mass of the extra air calculated. From values of the mass and volume of this air, its density is calculated.

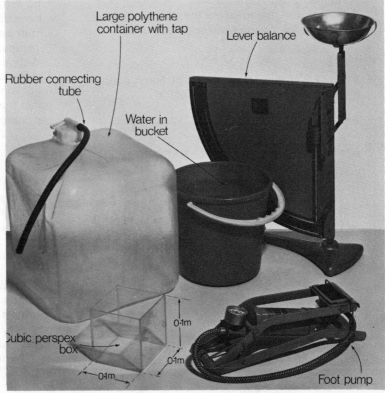

photograph 2.a

fig. 2.8

Revision questions

Formulae

volume = length × width × height

$$density = \frac{mass}{volume}$$

Measuring volume

* **1** A room is 5 metres long, 4 metres wide and 2·5 metres high; what is its volume in **a** cubic metres, **b** cubic centimetres?
** **2** How would you measure the volume of an oddly shaped wooden object which floats?

Density

** **3** Fig. 2.9 shows three blocks of equal size. Calculate the density of each block.

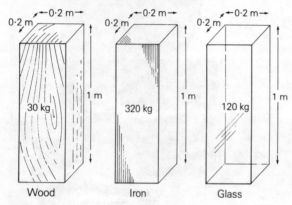

fig. 2.9

** **4** Which metal is more dense, iron or copper (fig. 2.10)?

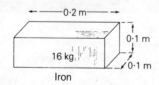

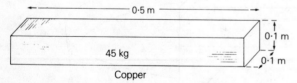

fig. 2.10

Upthrust

* **5** Why can a ship in sea water be loaded with more cargo than it can when it is in fresh water?

The density of air

*** **6** The following results are from the experiment described in section 2.4:

mass of container with = 0·427 kilograms
extra air
mass of container with = 0·418 kilograms
no extra air
volume of perspex box = 0·001 cubic metres
number of times the = 7·5
perspex box filled
with air

Use these results to calculate the density of air.

* **7** Calculate the mass of air in your living room given that the density of air is 1·2 kilograms per cubic metre.

Extra questions

*** **8** How might you find the density of air using a vacuum pump and a strong bottle?
** **9** The height of the atmosphere is about 10000 metres. Estimate the area of table you are working at and calculate **a** the volume of air above the table **b** the mass of air above the table.

(Density of air = 1·2 kilograms per cubic metre)

*10 Two non-scientists are having an argument. One says, 'Iron is heavier than glass', and the other says, 'Glass is heavier than iron. I have a glass bowl which is heavier than any iron nail'. Which person, if either is correct and what might you say to settle the argument?

3
Atoms and Molecules

3.1 Models of a theory

Scientists believe that solids, liquids and gases are made up of tiny particles which they call atoms or molecules.

Note: An **atom** is the smallest possible particle of an element. A **molecule** is a number of atoms bonded together.

This belief about atoms and molecules is called a theory. It can be illustrated by models and is supported by experimental evidence.

Model 1 'Ball and spring'

Fig. 3.1 is a model of a solid. Balls stand for the atoms, springs stand for the forces which hold a solid together. If a solid is heated enough it will expand first, then melt and finally vaporise.

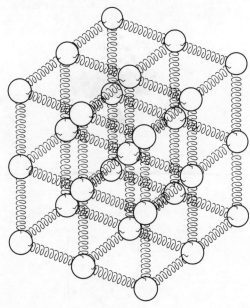

fig. 3.1

The theory is that its atoms and molecules vibrate more and more, until the forces between them cannot hold the solid together any longer. The ball and spring model can show this. If it is shaken it will take up more room. If it is shaken hard enough the springs will undo and the model fly apart.

Model 2 'Marbles in a tray'

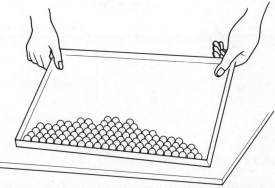

fig. 3.2

Fig. 3.2 is another model of a solid. If the tray is shaken slowly the marbles will begin to move around like molecules in a liquid. Some marbles will jump up from the top layer, like liquid molecules evaporating from a surface. If the tray is shaken hard the marbles will move apart to be like the molecules of a gas.

3.2 A model of a crystal

Instead of making a flat, two-dimensional model, marbles in a smaller tray (fig. 3.3) can be built up into a pyramid (fig. 3.4).

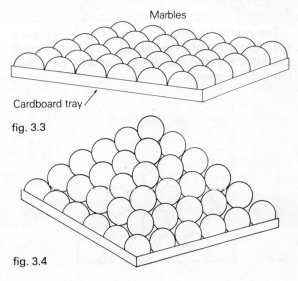

Marbles

Cardboard tray

fig. 3.3

fig. 3.4

As the pyramid builds up layer by layer, it increases its size but keeps its same basic shape.

If a crystal is grown from seed in copper sulphate solution (fig. 3.5), it increases its size but keeps its same basic shape. This is evidence that the marble pyramid is a good model of a crystal.

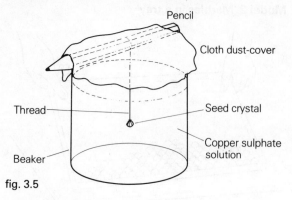

fig. 3.5

A crystal of calcite can only be split (cleaved) by tapping a blade held parallel to one of the crystal's faces (fig. 3.6).

fig. 3.6

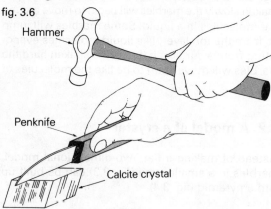

The marble pyramid can also only be 'cleaved' parallel to one of its faces (fig. 3.7). This is more evidence that the model is good and the theory behind it is correct.

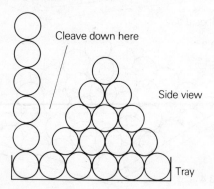

fig. 3.7

3.3 A model of a gas

The 'kinetic theory' of gases is based on the idea of moving molecules. A model of the theory is shown in photograph 3.a. Ball bearings are made to fly about inside a glass tube.

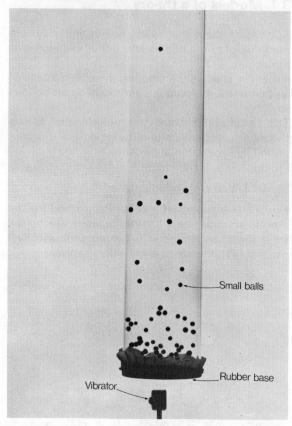

photograph 3.a

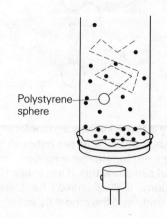

fig. 3.8

We cannot see air molecules but the ball bearing model gives a clue how to find evidence for them.

If a polystyrene sphere is put into the glass tube it is knocked about by the ball bearings (fig. 3.8). This jerky movement can be seen from a distance even when the ball bearings are too far away to show up. This is the principle of the smoke cell experiment.

The smoke cell experiment

If smoke is run into a small glass cell and looked at through a microscope (fig. 3.9), the particles of smoke can be seen making jerky movements called **Brownian motion** (fig. 3.10).

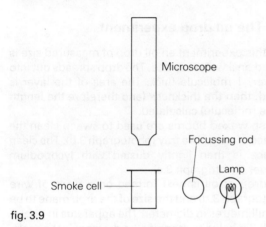

fig. 3.9

Particles of smoke
seen through a microscope

fig. 3.10

This is evidence that the kinetic theory of gases is correct. The small particles of smoke are being knocked about by tiny, fast moving molecules of air. Our ball bearing model is a useful one.

The kinetic theory is mentioned again in section 4.6 and is taken up in greater detail in chapter seven.

3.4 Surface tension

The effect of surface tension can be seen when a drop of water is formed (fig. 3.11).

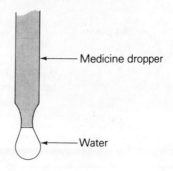

Medicine dropper

Water

fig. 3.11

The water is pulled into a spherical shape when it falls from the dropper, as if there is an elastic skin around it.

This surface tension effect can be explained by thinking of the liquid as being made of molecules, all attracted to one another. A molecule near the centre of the liquid will be attracted in all directions (fig. 3.12) and the forces will balance.

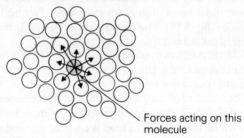

Forces acting on this molecule

fig. 3.12

A molecule on the surface will only be attracted sideways and downwards (fig. 3.13).

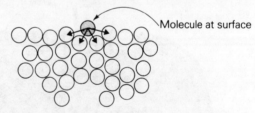

Molecule at surface

fig. 3.13

The result of this is that the surface is under tension and pulls inwards on the liquid.

3.5 Reducing surface tension

By heat

Fig. 3.14 shows a red hot poker being held near the surface of some water. The water has been lightly dusted with lycopodium powder to show if it moves.

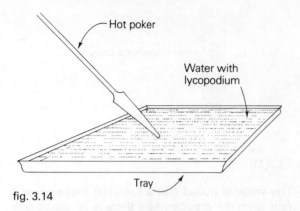

fig. 3.14

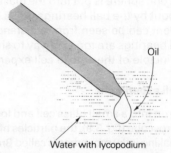

fig. 3.15

The lycopodium powder moves towards the edges of the tray. This means that the surface tension gets weaker where the water is heated.

By oil

A small drop of oil is placed on the surface of water which has been lightly dusted with lycopodium powder (fig. 3.15). The powder moves back as the oil drop is pulled out into a large patch.

A large patch is made because the surface tension of the water under the oil is weaker than the surface tension round the edges.

The patch of oil stops spreading when it cannot get any thinner. The thinnest possible layer must be only one molecule thick. This idea is used to calculate the length of a molecule in the oil drop experiment.

3.6 The oil drop experiment

In this experiment an oil drop of measured size is placed on a water surface. The drop spreads out into a layer, 1 molecule thick. The area of the layer is found, then the thickness (and therefore the length of the molecule) calculated.

First, waxed booms are used to sweep clean the surface of water in a tray (photograph 3.b). The clean surface is then lightly dusted with lycopodium powder (photograph 3.c).

A drop of oil is next formed on a piece of wire (photograph 3.d) and the size of the drop made to be 0.5 millimetres in diameter. The apparatus in photograph 3.e helps to magnify the drop against a scale.

The drop is then placed in the centre of the water

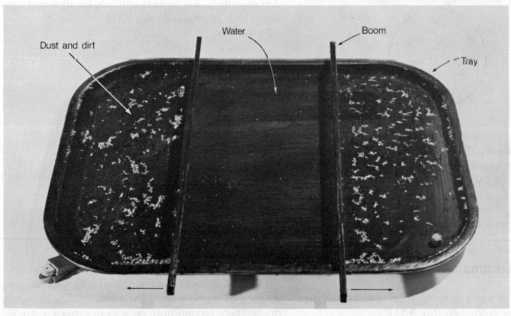

photograph 3.b.

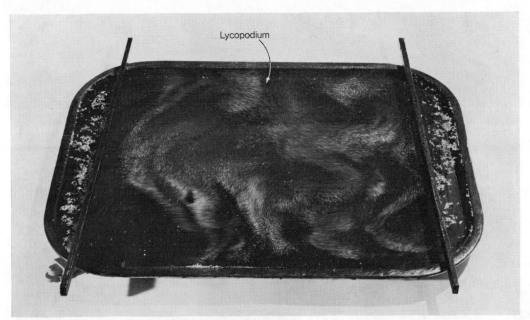

photograph 3.c

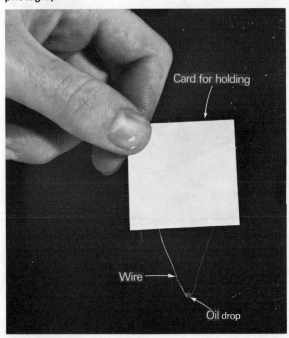

photograph 3.d

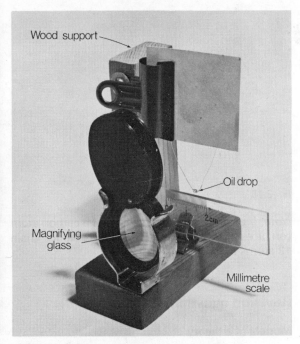

photograph 3.e

surface (fig. 3.16). It spreads into a patch (photograph 3.f) and the patch diameter is measured.

Theory: Although the oil has changed shape from a drop to a patch, its volume has stayed the same. The volume of the drop can be calculated from its diameter. The volume of the patch is its area × depth. Area can

be found from the diameter of the patch, so in the relation

volume of drop = area × depth of patch

depth is the only unknown and can be calculated.

Because the patch is only one molecule thick the result of the calculation gives the length of a molecule.

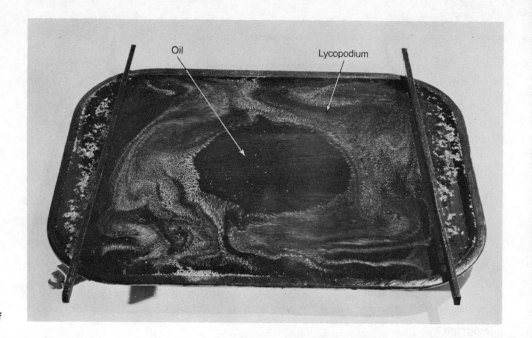

photograph 3.f

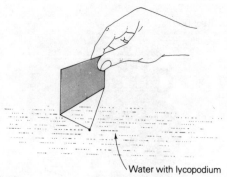

fig. 3.16

Note: If olive oil is used, the width of a carbon atom can be estimated. Olive oil is based on a carbon chain 12 atoms long.

Revision questions

Models of a theory

* **1** Explain how marbles in a tray can be used to illustrate a solid, a liquid, evaporation and a gas.

A model of a crystal

* **2** Photograph 3.g shows a small pyramid of marbles. It has sides, edges and a point just like a crystal.

photograph 3.g

    a Can the pyramid be built bigger and still keep its same basic shape?

    b What happens to the shape of a real crystal as it is grown from seed?

** **3** Diamond cutters must be careful not to try cleaving their gems at the wrong angle, or they may smash them. Explain why a diamond can only be cleaved in certain directions.

A model of a gas

** **4** Describe the smoke cell experiment and explain what it shows.

** **5** A physics student notices that a light bulb hanging from the ceiling is vibrating slightly. He wonders if this is because of air molecules hitting against it or vibrations from the room above. Explain which is the most likely reason.

Surface tension

** **6** Surface tension is sometimes wrongly described as 'a skin over the surface'. Give a better explanation in terms of the forces between the molecules of a liquid.

Reducing surface tension

** **7** In section 3.5 (fig 3.14), why did the water surface move outwards when its surface tension was made weaker by heating? (*Hint: not all the surface was heated*).

* **8** When a drop of oil is placed onto clean water, what happens to the surface tension of the water beneath the oil?

* **9** What is the thinnest an oil patch on water can spread to and what would happen if it tried to spread out even more?

The oil drop experiment

*10 Does the volume of an oil drop increase, decrease or stay the same when it spreads out into a patch?

***11 Here are some results from an oil drop experiment. Use them to calculate the length of an oil molecule. (*Hint: It will help you to look back at section 3.6*).

Formulae you may need:

volume of a sphere $= \frac{4}{3}\pi r^3$ area of a circle $= \pi r^2$

Results:

diameter of oil drop = 0.5 millimetres
(5×10^{-4} metres)
diameter of patch = 24 centimetres
(24×10^{-2} metres)

Extra questions

**12 Robert Brown first observed Brownian motion with pollen grains in water. What information does this give us about water?

***13 Movement can be seen when smoke particles in air are suitably illuminated and viewed through a microscope.

a Describe briefly, with the aid of a diagram, the type of movement which can be seen.

b Someone suggests that the movement is due to bombardment of the smoke particles by the light used to illuminate them. Either suggest a simple experiment that might show whether this suggestion is right or wrong, or give a theoretical reason for agreeing or disagreeing with it.

c One of the bright specks seen in the microscope can be viewed for a second or two, then it may become blurred or even disappear. Account for this.

d Some of the particles show less movement than others. Are these the larger particles or the smaller particles? Give reasons for your answer. (*O. and C.*)

4
Pressure

4.1 Pressure in gas and liquid

The rubber of a balloon stretches all ways when it is blown up (fig. 4.1). This is because gas pressure acts in all directions.

Fig. 4.2 shows a can with three holes in it. The weight of water acting **downwards** in the can makes a pressure which pushes the water out sideways. The

fig. 4.1

deeper the water, the greater its weight and the greater the pressure.

If the can is dented, some water will squirt upwards (fig. 4.3). This shows that pressure in a liquid acts in all directions.

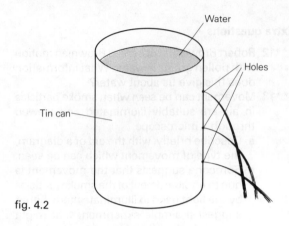

fig. 4.2

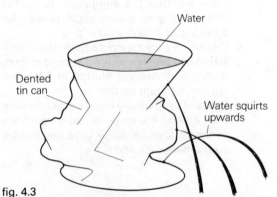

fig. 4.3

4.2 Calculating pressure

Photograph 4.a shows two syringes joined together. When the pistons of both syringes are pressed the pressure of the squashed air makes an even force on every square centimetre of the inside surface. Because the piston of the large syringe has a bigger area it is more difficult to hold in than the small piston.

Example 1: The syringe pistons in photograph 4.a have areas of 5 square centimetres (large) and 2 square centimetres (small). The force pushing the smaller piston is 6 newtons. Calculate **a** The pressure inside the syringes **b** The force pushing the large piston.

Calculation

a The force on 2 square centimetres is 6 newtons so, the force on 1 square centimetre is 3 newtons ∴ the pressure is 3 newtons per square centimetre

b Because the pressure makes a force of 3 newtons on 1 square centimetre, the force on 5 square centimetres will be five times greater = 15 newtons

Note: The answer to part **a** was got by dividing force by area. That is

$$\text{pressure} = \frac{\text{force}}{\text{area}}$$

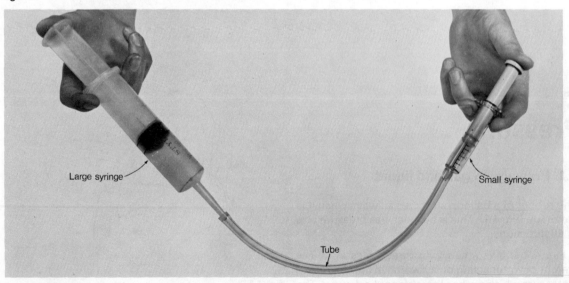

photograph 4.a

(newtons per square centimetre $= \dfrac{\text{newtons}}{\text{square centimetres}}$

or newtons per square metre $= \dfrac{\text{newtons}}{\text{square metres}}$)

Example 2: A man who weighs 1200 newtons stands on an air pillow (fig. 4.4). The total area of the soles of his shoes is 0.1 square metres. What must be the pressure of the air inside the pillow if it is to support him?

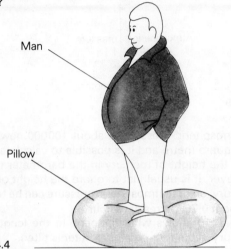

fig. 4.4

Calculation

pressure $= \dfrac{\text{force}}{\text{area}}$

$= \dfrac{1200}{0.1}$

$= 12\,000$ newtons per square metre (above normal atmospheric pressure)

photograph 4.b

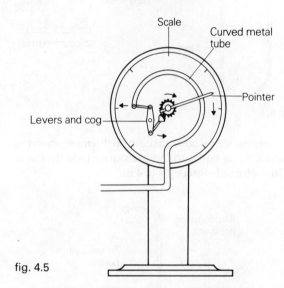

fig. 4.5

4.3 The Bourdon gauge

In industry pressure is often measured using a Bourdon gauge (photograph 4.b). Inside the gauge is a curved tube of thin metal which tends to uncurl as the pressure inside it increases (fig. 4.5). This movement drives a pointer across a scale.

4.4 The manometer

A simple instrument for measuring pressure is the manometer. It is a U-tube of glass or clear plastic, half filled with liquid. High pressure on one side makes the liquid move round. Pressure is measured by the difference in liquid levels between the two sides of the U-tube (fig. 4.6).

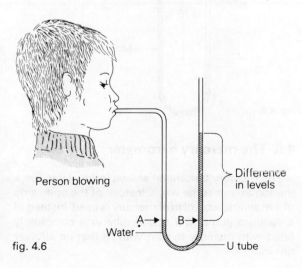

fig. 4.6

In fig. 4.6 the pressure of the boy's blow at A was the same as the pressure caused by the weight of water pressing down on B.

If a **mercury** manometer is connected to a vacuum pump and all the air removed from one side (fig. 4.7) the mercury will move up towards the vacuum.

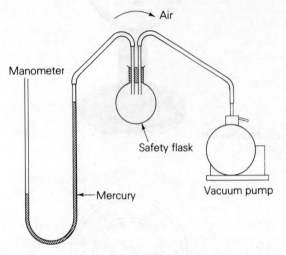

fig. 4.7

Atmospheric pressure pushing on the mercury in the open side, is equal to the pressure made by about 0·76 metres of mercury (fig. 4.8).

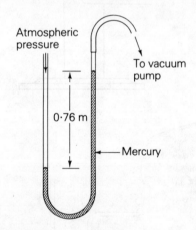

fig. 4.8

4.5 The mercury barometer

The mercury barometer shown in fig. 4.9 is like a manometer in some ways. Instead of the open side of a manometer, a dish of mercury is used. Instead of a vacuum pump, the sealed tube was completely filled with mercury to start with so that no air ever got in.

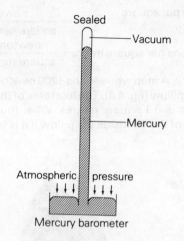

fig. 4.9

Atmospheric pressure is about 100 000 newtons per square metre and it is possible to calculate this from the height of mercury in the barometer tube. However, it is usual just to quote the height of the mercury, so that atmospheric pressure can be taken as about 0·76 metres of mercury.

Fig. 4.10 shows what happens to the length of mercury in the tube as a barometer is tilted.

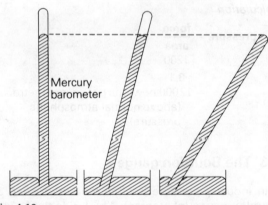

fig. 4.10

The height of the atmosphere

Mercury is used in barometers because it is a very dense liquid: 13 600 kilograms per cubic metre. The density of air is 1·2 kilograms per cubic metre: 11 300 times less dense than mercury. Because of this the atmosphere must be 11 300 times higher than a 0·76 metre column of mercury to make the same pressure. Therefore

height of atmosphere = 11 300 × 0·76
                     = 8588 metres (about six miles)

4.6 Pressure by bombardment

The smoke cell experiment in section 3.3 was evidence for the kinetic theory of gases, in which air is thought of as small, fast moving molecules. How can separate molecules of air make a steady atmospheric pressure? The simple story given here may help answer this question.

A person hit by one tennis ball will feel a quick force (fig. 4.11). When hit by a stream of tennis balls, a lot of forces will be felt one after the other (fig. 4.12).

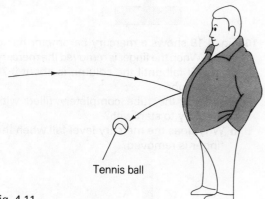

Tennis ball

fig. 4.11

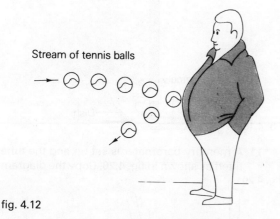

Stream of tennis balls

fig. 4.12

If the rate at which the balls hit is increased, the effect of one ball will not have worn off before another ball hits. All the forces then begin to feel like one steady force.

Revision questions

Formula

$$\text{pressure} = \frac{\text{force}}{\text{area}}$$

Pressure in gas and liquid

* **1** What would happen to the blown up balloon in fig. 4.13 if the pressure inside it pushed harder to the right than to the left? How do we know that the pressure inside a balloon acts evenly in all directions?

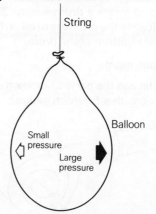

String

Small pressure

Large pressure

Balloon

fig. 4.13

* **2** Fig. 4.14 shows a fish under the water. What would happen to the fish if water pressure only acted downwards and not in all directions?

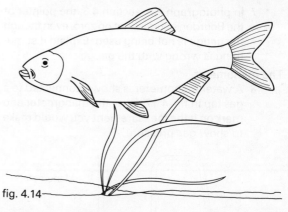

fig. 4.14

Calculating pressure

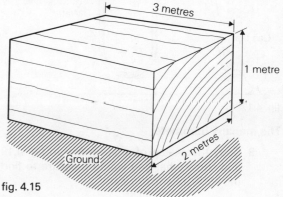

3 metres

1 metre

2 metres

Ground

fig. 4.15

* **3** The large block of wood in fig. 4.15 weighs 30 000 newtons. Calculate the pressure it makes on the ground.

** **4** By turning the block in fig. 4.15 to stand on different sides, it can be made to make different pressures on the ground. Calculate the greatest pressure it can make.

** **5** The oil inside a drum weighs 3000 newtons. Calculate the pressure of oil on the 0·6 square metre bottom of the drum.

The Bourdon gauge

* **6** What has the party toy shown in fig. 4.16 got to do with a Bourdon gauge?

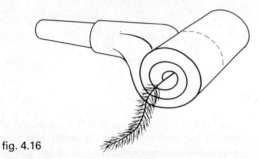

fig. 4.16

* **7** In photograph 4.b, section 4.3, the pointer of the Bourdon gauge is not on zero, even though the gauge is not being used. Explain if something is wrong with the gauge.

The manometer

* **8** A water manometer is shown connected to a gas tap in fig. 4.17. Copy the manometer and mark on it the measurement you would make to show gas pressure.

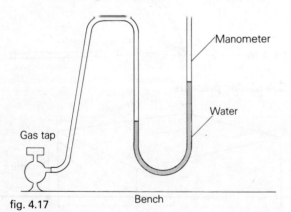

Manometer

Water

Gas tap

Bench

fig. 4.17

The mercury barometer

* **9** Copy the sketch of a barometer in fig. 4.18 and show what you would measure to find the atmospheric pressure.

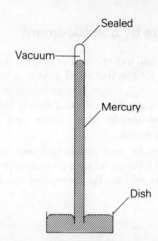

Sealed

Vacuum

Mercury

Dish

fig. 4.18

**10 Fig. 4.19 shows a mercury barometer being set up. When the finger is removed the mercury level will fall until the column is about 0·76 metres high.

  a Why is the tube completely filled with mercury to start with?

  b Why does the mercury level fall when the finger is removed?

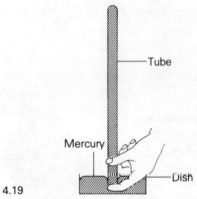

Tube

Mercury

Dish

fig. 4.19

*11 A mercury barometer is set up and the tube tilted as shown in fig. 4.20. Copy the diagram

fig. 4.20

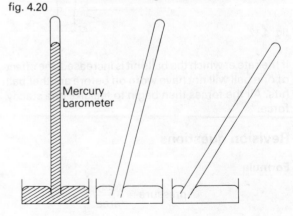

Mercury barometer

and mark in the levels of mercury in each of the three positions. Explain your answers.

**12 Mercury is 13·6 times more dense than water. Atmospheric pressure will support 0.76 metres of mercury in a barometer tube. How high will a water barometer need to be?

Pressure by bombardment

*13 If the atmosphere makes its pressure by bombarding us with molecules, why don't we feel lots of little forces all over us?

Extra questions

**14 A pressure cooker has a 2 newton weight on it which plugs a 0·2 square centimetre hole in the lid. What is the maximum increase in pressure above atmospheric pressure that can build up in the cooker?

**15 When the syringe piston in fig. 4.21 is pushed with a force of 12 newtons, the Bourdon gauge measures an increase in pressure of 4 newtons per square centimetre. What is the area of the piston?

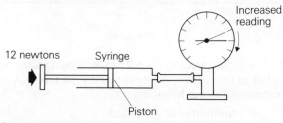

fig. 4.21

**16 A vacuum pump is connected to a tin can (fig. 4.22) and the air pumped out from inside it. When the can collapses Jane says, 'The can has been pulled in by the vacuum'. What do you think?

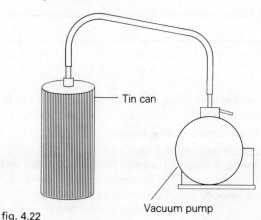

fig. 4.22

**17 If the air in the bell jar in fig. 4.23 is removed, explain what will happen to the sealed polythene bag. Why is a wire support needed for the bag?

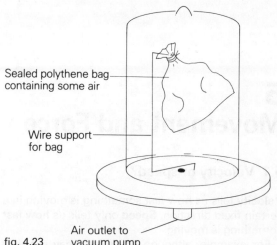

fig. 4.23

**18 Why does lemonade rise up the straw when the person in fig. 4.24 starts to suck?

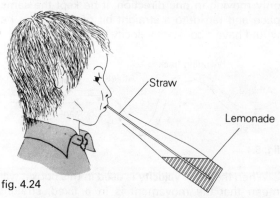

fig. 4.24

***19 Explain what would happen if a person tried to drink lemonade through a straw, sealed into the neck of a bottle by a bung (fig. 4.25).

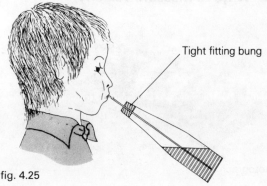

fig. 4.25

Comment on the following statement: The air in a room exerts a pressure. In the open air outside there is a much greater mass of air overhead because of the atmosphere above.

There will therefore be a greater pressure on the outside of a window than on the inside. (*O. and C.*)

5
Movement and Force

5.1 Velocity or speed?

Velocity tells us how fast something is moving in a certain fixed direction. **Speed** only tells us how fast something is moving.

For example, although an athlete may run at a constant (steady) **speed** along a winding track, it would be wrong to say that he was running with a constant **velocity** because this would mean he was only moving in one direction. If he kept the same pace and ran onto a straight bit of track, then he would have a constant velocity there. (fig. 5.1).

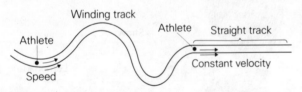

fig. 5.1

When the word **velocity** is used in this book it will mean that the movement is in a fixed, straight direction.

5.2 Ways to measure velocity

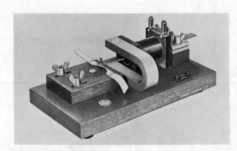

photograph 5.a

Using a tickertimer

If a piece of tickertape is pulled through a tickertimer a dot will be made on the tape every $\frac{1}{50}$ second. The time between dots is called a **tick**. A tick of time is $\frac{1}{50}$ second.

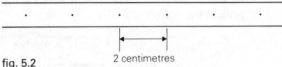

fig. 5.2

The tape shown in fig. 5.2 moved 2 centimetres in a tick of time. The velocity shown by the tape can be calculated in the following way:

2 centimetres in $\frac{1}{50}$ second
∴ it would move 50 times as far in a whole second
it would move 100 centimetres in a second
∴ its velocity is 100 centimetres per second
    or   1 metre per second

It is usual to measure lengths of tape which have 10 gaps (a '10-tick' length).

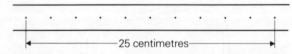

fig. 5.3

The tape shown in fig. 5.3 moved 25 centimetres in 10 ticks of time.

25 centimetres in $\frac{10}{50}$ second
is 25 centimetres in $\frac{1}{5}$ second
∴ it would move 5 times as far in a whole second
it would move 125 centimetres in a second
∴ its velocity is 125 centimetres per second
    or   1·25 metres per second

Sometimes the dots on a tickertape are not evenly spaced because the velocity is changing. A calculation made from a length of such a tape, shown in fig. 5.4, would give an **average** velocity for that length.

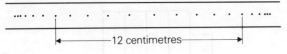

fig. 5.4

The tape shown in fig. 5.4 moved 12 centimetres in 10 ticks of time.

12 centimetres in $\frac{10}{50}$ second

is 12 centimetres in $\frac{1}{5}$ second

∴ it would move 5 times as far in a whole second
it would move 60 centimetres in a second

∴ its average velocity is 60 centimetres per second

or   0·6 metres per second

Note: in all the calculations of velocity so far the answers have been reasoned out step by step. The same answers would be got using the formula

$$\textbf{velocity} = \frac{\textbf{distance}}{\textbf{time}}$$

$$(\text{centimetres per second} = \frac{\text{centimetres}}{\text{seconds}}$$

$$\text{or,}\quad \text{metres per second} = \frac{\text{metres}}{\text{seconds}})$$

For example, in the last calculation where distance = 12 centimetres and time = $\frac{1}{5}$ second

velocity = $12/\frac{1}{5}$

= $12 \times \frac{5}{1}$

= 60 centimetres per second

or 0·6 metres per second

You may like to check the other calculations using the formula

Using a scaler-timer

A scaler-timer will time to an accuracy of $\frac{1}{100}$ or $\frac{1}{1000}$ second. It can be started and stopped by making or breaking electric circuits. Fig. 5.5 shows a scaler-timer being used to time a rifle bullet between two foil contacts 5 metres apart. The bullet starts the timer by breaking foil A and stops it by breaking foil B.

The timer records 0.025 seconds

Calculation

$$\text{velocity} = \frac{\text{distance}}{\text{time}}$$

$$= \frac{5}{0.025}$$

(Multiply the top and bottom of the fraction by 1000 to make the calculation easier)

$$= \frac{5000}{25}$$

= 200 metres per second

5.3 Measuring acceleration

Acceleration tells us how quickly velocity is changing. It may be calculated using the formula

$$\textbf{acceleration} = \frac{\textbf{change in velocity}}{\textbf{time taken for that change}}$$

$$(\text{centimetres per second per second} = \frac{\text{centimetres per second}}{\text{seconds}}$$

$$\text{or,}\quad \text{metres per second per second} = \frac{\text{metres per second}}{\text{seconds}})$$

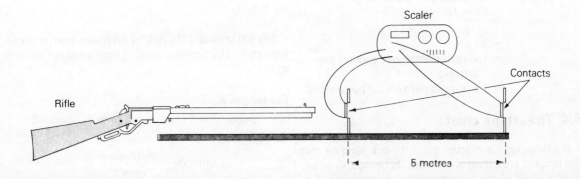

Scaler

Contacts

Rifle

5 metres

fig. 5.5

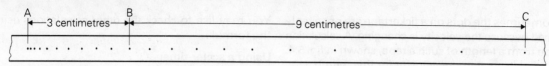

fig. 5.6

Measurements from a tickertape can be used to calculate acceleration. Fig. 5.6 is of tickertape showing acceleration. It has been marked off in '10-tick' lengths.

Between A and B

distance = 3 centimetres, time = $\frac{1}{5}$ second

Calculation

$$velocity = \frac{distance}{time}$$

$$\therefore \text{ average velocity} = \frac{3}{\frac{1}{5}}$$

$$= 3 \times \frac{5}{1}$$

$$= 15 \text{ centimetres per second}$$

Between B and C

distance = 9 centimetres, time = $\frac{1}{5}$ second

Calculation

$$velocity = \frac{distance}{time}$$

$$\therefore \text{ average velocity} = \frac{9}{\frac{1}{5}}$$

$$= 9 \times \frac{5}{1}$$

$$= 45 \text{ centimetres per second}$$

The time taken to change from the first average velocity (half way between A and B) to the second average velocity (half way between B anc C) is $\frac{1}{5}$ second.

Calculation

$$acceleration = \frac{change \ in \ velocity}{time \ taken \ for \ that \ change}$$

$$= \frac{45 - 15}{\frac{1}{5}}$$

$$= 30 \times \frac{5}{1}$$

$$= 150 \text{ centimetres per second per second}$$

$$\text{or } 1\cdot5 \text{ metres per second per second}$$

5.4 Tickertape charts

If a tickertape is marked off in '10-tick' lengths and the lengths are cut off and stuck side by side, in order, then a chart of the movement has been made. Fig. 5.7 is a '10-tick' chart. It shows constant acceleration, followed by constant velocity, followed by a deceleration which is not constant.

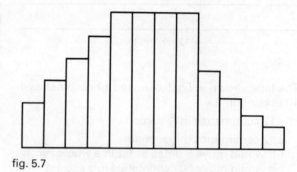

fig. 5.7

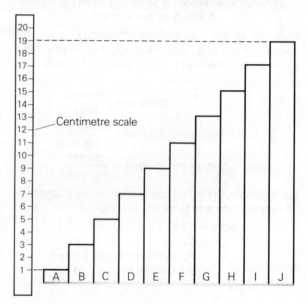

fig. 5.8

Fig 5.8 shows a '10-tick' chart made from a tickertape pulled by a trolley moving with constant acceleration.

For length A

distance = 1 centimetre, time = $\frac{1}{5}$ second

Calculation

$$velocity = \frac{distance}{time}$$

$$\therefore \text{ average velocity} = \frac{1}{\frac{1}{5}}$$

$$= 5 \text{ centimetres per second}$$

For length J

distance = 19 centimetres, time = $\frac{1}{5}$ second

Calculation

$$\text{velocity} = \frac{\text{distance}}{\text{time}}$$

$$\therefore \text{ average velocity} = \frac{19}{\frac{1}{5}}$$

$$= 95 \text{ centimetres per second}$$

The time taken to go from the average velocity of A to the average velocity of J is $\frac{9}{5}$ second. (If A and J were side by side the time would have been $\frac{1}{5}$ second but there are eight complete lengths between A and J making an extra $\frac{8}{5}$ second.)

To calculate acceleration between A and J:

$$\text{acceleration} = \frac{\text{change in velocity}}{\text{time taken for that change}}$$

$$= \frac{95 - 5}{\frac{9}{5}}$$

$$= 90 \times \frac{5}{9}$$

$$= 50 \text{ centimetres per second per second}$$

$$\text{or } 0\cdot5 \text{ metres per second per second}$$

The total distance moved by the trolley is the same as the total length of tape it pulls. If all the lengths on the chart in fig. 5.8 are added up they total 100 centimetres. This shows that the trolley moved 1 metre.

5.5 Velocity–time graphs

The chart shown in fig. 5.8 could be drawn as a line graph of velocity against time (fig. 5.9).

The shaded area under the graph line (a triangle)

$$= \tfrac{1}{2} \times \text{base} \times \text{height}$$
$$= \tfrac{1}{2} \times 2 \times 100$$
$$= 100$$

The distance travelled by the trolley was found from the chart (fig. 5.8) to be 100 centimetres. So distance can also be calculated by

distance = area under graph line

The gradient (slope) of the graph line

$$= \frac{\text{height}}{\text{base}} \text{ of the triangle}$$
$$= \frac{100}{2}$$
$$= 50$$

The acceleration of the trolley was found from the chart (fig. 5.8) to be 50 centimetres per second per second. So acceleration can also be calculated by

acceleration = gradient of graph line

Example: Fig. 5.10 shows the motion of a car accelerating from rest, moving with constant velocity, then decelerating to rest again. Calculate the distance it moves and its acceleration in the first 8 seconds.

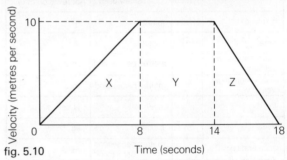

fig. 5.10

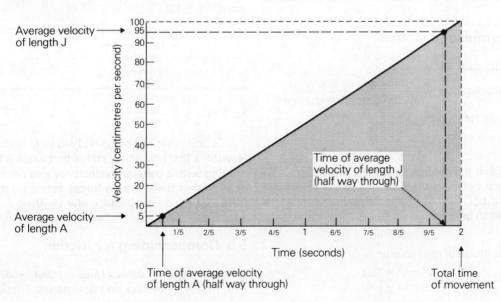

fig. 5.9

The total distance moved is equal to the total area under the graph line. This is found by adding the areas of the triangle X, the rectangle Y and the triangle Z.

$$\text{total area} = (\tfrac{1}{2} \times 8 \times 10) + (6 \times 10)$$
$$+ (\tfrac{1}{2} \times 4 \times 10)$$
$$= 40 + 60 + 20$$
$$= 120$$

∴ total distance = 120 metres

The acceleration in the first 8 seconds is equal to the gradient of the line.

$$\text{gradient} = \frac{\text{height}}{\text{base}} \text{ of triangle}$$
$$= \frac{10}{8}$$
$$= 1 \cdot 25$$

∴ acceleration = 1·25 metres per second per second

5.6 Symbols and units

	Symbol	Unit usually used	Abbreviation of unit
distance	s	metre	m
time	t	second	s
initial (or starting) velocity	u	metres per second	m/s
final (or ending) velocity	v	metres per second	m/s
force	F	newton	N
mass	m	kilogram	kg
acceleration	a	metres per second per second	m/s²

5.7 Formulae of motion

A formula such as

$$\text{acceleration} = \frac{\text{change in velocity}}{\text{time taken for that change}}$$

may be written in symbols

$$a = \frac{v - u}{t}$$

(Notice that the change in velocity is written as the difference between the final and initial velocities). The 'symbol' formula for acceleration can be re-arranged to be

$$v = u + at$$

Other formulae of motion are:

$$v^2 = u^2 + 2as$$
$$s = ut + \tfrac{1}{2}at^2$$

5.8 Newton's first law

Fig. 5.11 shows an experiment with a marble and curtain rail, based on an idea by Galileo.
When the marble is let go from A the pull of the earth makes it accelerate towards the bottom of the slope, then decelerate as it rolls up to level B. Galileo

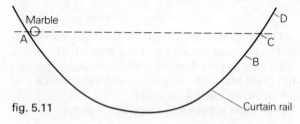

fig. 5.11

reasoned that if there was no friction a ball would roll up to C on the same level as A, no matter what the steepness of the second slope.

Suppose that the right hand side of the rail was horizontal and never reached the level of A (fig. 5.12).

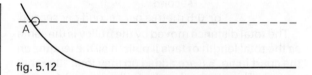

fig. 5.12

The marble would accelerate down to the bottom of the slope and then roll on for ever at a constant velocity.

Notice that while a ball is rolling at a constant velocity there is no force keeping it going. Gravity pulls it down onto the rail but does not push it forward (fig. 5.13).

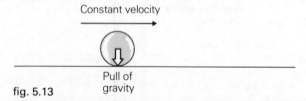

Constant velocity

Pull of gravity

fig. 5.13

This and other experiments help us to understand Newton's first law which states that **when a body is moving with a constant velocity or else not moving at all, either there are no forces acting on it or the forces which do act balance one another.**

5.9 Compensating for friction

Friction is an unwanted force in most experiments with trolleys, runways and tickertapes. Friction can-

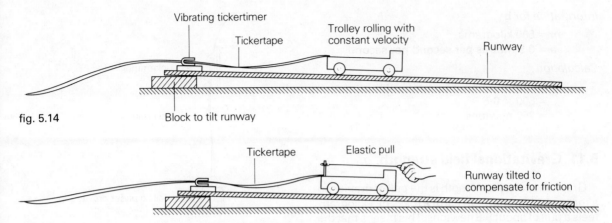

fig. 5.14

Vibrating tickertimer
Tickertape
Trolley rolling with constant velocity
Runway
Block to tilt runway

Tickertape
Elastic pull
Runway tilted to compensate for friction

fig. 5.15

not be removed but if the runway is tilted slighty, the force of friction which tries to hold the trolley back can be balanced by the effect of gravity, which tries to make the trolley roll down the slope.

When a trolley is correctly compensated for friction it will not roll down the runway unless started with a push: if it is started then it will roll with a constant velocity.

While the runway is being tilted to find the correct slope, a strip of tickertape from the trolley should be threaded through a vibrating tickertimer because this is also a source of friction and must be compensated for (fig. 5.14).

5.10 Newton's second law

Fig. 5.15 shows a trolley, which is correctly compensated for friction, being pulled down a runway by one elastic pull which is kept stretched to the front edge of the trolley.

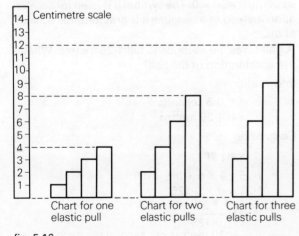

Centimetre scale

Chart for one elastic pull
Chart for two elastic pulls
Chart for three elastic pulls

fig. 5.16

The experiment is then repeated using two elastic pulls to give twice the force on the trolley, and then with three elastic pulls to give three times the force. '10-tick' charts from each experiment are shown in fig. 5.16.

If the constant acceleration shown by each chart is calculated it is found that for double the force there is twice the acceleration, and for three times the force there is three times the acceleration. This shows that force is proportional to acceleration ($F \propto a$), provided that the mass being accelerated does not change.

The results of these and other experiments with trolleys and elastic pulls are summed up in Newton's second law, which states that **the acceleration of an object is directly proportional to the force acting on it, and inversely proportional to the mass of the object.**

This law can be written as the formula
$$F = ma$$
(newtons = kilograms × metres per second per second)

Example: A car of mass 500 kilograms accelerates from 10 metres per second to 20 metres per second in 20 seconds. Calculate **a** the car's acceleration **b** the force making it accelerate.

Information for **a**

$u = 10$ metres per second
$v = 20$ metres per second
$t = 20$ seconds

Calculation

$$a = \frac{v - u}{t}$$
$$= \frac{20 - 10}{20}$$
$$= 0.5 \text{ metres per second per second}$$

   $m = 500$ kilograms
   $a = 0.5$ metres per second per second

Calculation

   $F = ma$
   $= 500 \times 0.5$
   $= 250$ newtons

5.11 Gravitational field strength, *g*.

Gravitational field strength is the pull of gravity on a mass of 1 kilogram. On earth a mass of 1 kilogram feels a pull of about 9·8 newtons. This means that the earth's gravitational field strength is 9·8 newtons per kilogram. *Note:* this is often approximated to $g = 10$ newtons per kilogram.

Example: On a certain planet a 60 kilogram rock feels a pull of 120 newtons due to gravity. (It weighs 120 newtons). What is the gravitational field strength of that planet?

Calculation

If 60 kilograms weigh 120 newtons
1 kilogram will weigh 60 times less than 120 newtons
1 kilogram will weigh (feel a pull of) 2 newtons
∴ the gravitational field strength of the planet is 2 newtons per kilogram

5.12 Gravitational acceleration

Gravitational acceleration (also given the symbol, *g*) is the acceleration with which objects fall towards the earth when there is no air resistance. This acceleration of 9·8 metres per second per second is often approximated to 10 metres per second per second.

Ways to measure gravitational acceleration

Using a tickertimer

Let a mass fall under gravity and pull a tape through a tickertimer (fig. 5.17). Then calculate the acceleration from the spacing of the dots on the tape (see section 5.3). *Note:* Friction between the tape and tickertimer may lead to a poor result.

Using a scaler-timer

A metal ball held at A completes a circuit across two metal contacts (fig. 5.18).
   When the ball begins to fall the circuit is broken and the scaler-timer starts to count. When the ball

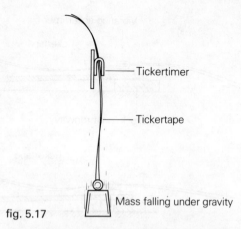

fig. 5.17

hits a metal gate at B it knocks it open and breaks a second circuit, which stops the scaler-timer counting.

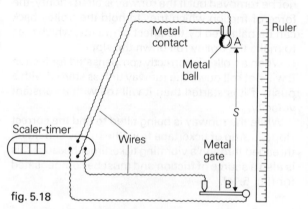

fig. 5.18

This gives an accurate time for the ball falling through a measured distance, *s*. *g* is calculated using the formula

$$s = \tfrac{1}{2}gt^2$$

(Notice that this is really the formula $s = ut + \tfrac{1}{2}at^2$ but because the ball is not moving at the start, $u = 0$, and so *ut* must also $= 0$. The symbol *g* is used for acceleration instead of *a* because it is **gravitational** acceleration.

A ball takes 0·5 seconds to fall 1·25 metres. What is the acceleration of the ball?

Information

   $t = 0.5$ seconds
   $s = 1.25$ metres

Calculation

   $s = \tfrac{1}{2}gt^2$
   $1.25 = \tfrac{1}{2} \times g \times 0.5 \times 0.5$
   $1.25 = g \times 0.125$
   $g = \dfrac{1.25}{0.125}$
   $= 10$ metres per second per second

fig. 5.19

5.13 Newton's third law

Twins sit on trolleys of equal mass and each holds the end of a rope (fig. 5.19).
Steven holds the end of his rope tight while Peter tries to pull him towards the left. Peter expects to remain still but finds that both trolleys move towards each other. Peter has not been able to make a force on Steven without Steven making a force on Peter.

This result demonstrates Newton's third law which states that **where a force acts there will always be an equal and opposite force.**

5.14 Component velocities

An insect crawls across a wall from corner D to corner B as shown in fig. 5.20.

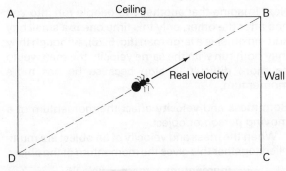

fig. 5.20

Although the insect is not going straight up towards the ceiling it gets closer to it all the time. The same is true towards the wall BC.

Instead of stating the real velocity of the insect, its velocity towards the ceiling AB and its velocity towards the wall BC could be used to describe how it moves (fig. 5.21).

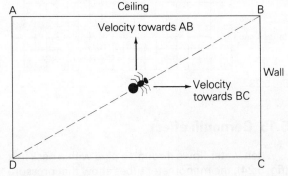

fig. 5.21

These two velocities are **components** of the real velocity. The velocity towards AB is the **vertical component** and the velocity towards BC is the **horizontal component.**

In the experiment shown in fig. 5.22 the ruler is moved quickly sideways so that penny 1 falls straight down and penny 2 is knocked sideways.
Both coins hit the floor at the same time. This means that the vertical component of the motion of penny 2 must be an acceleration the same as that of penny 1, which falls freely under gravity. The horizontal component of the motion of penny 2 is a constant velocity, which takes the coin sideways while it is accelerating downwards.

A multiflash photograph of the two coins falling is drawn in fig. 5.23. Notice how the coins stay level with each other as they fall.

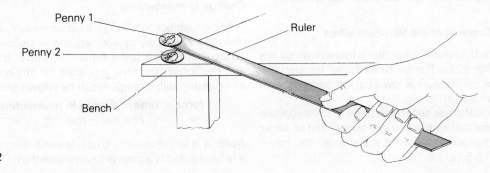

fig. 5.22

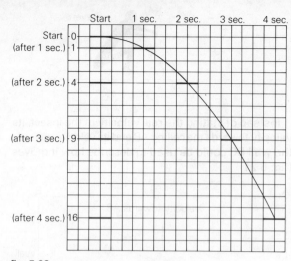

fig. 5.23

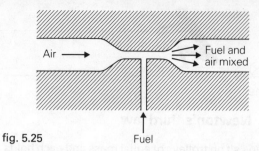

fig. 5.25   Fuel

Because of this, the pressure is higher below the wing than above it, and this helps to lift the aeroplane.

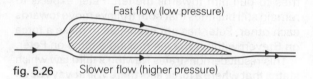

fig. 5.26   Slower flow (higher pressure)

5.15 Bernoulli effect

When water flows through a pipe with a neck in it (fig. 5.24), the manometer tubes show that pressure in the neck where the water moves quickly, is lower than it is in the wider parts of the tube where the water moves slowly.

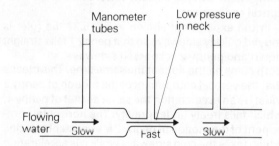

fig. 5.24

This is an example of the Bernoulli effect which is true for gases as well as for liquids. It can be summed up as **the faster the flow the lower the pressure.**

Two applications of the Bernoulli effect

a In the carburettor of a car, fuel is mixed with air in a **venturi** (fig. 5.25). The air flows faster through the neck and so its pressure is low. Fuel is therefore drawn up into the stream of air.

b The special cross sectional shape of an aeroplane wing means that air has to travel further and so faster over the top surface than it does under the lower surface (fig. 5.26).

5.16 Momentum

Imagine that a person who is running very quickly bumps into you. Then another person, of similar size, runs into you slowly (fig. 5.27). The fast moving person would be more difficult to stop because he has more momentum.

Next imagine that another two people run into you one after the other, only this time one is a small boy and the other is a large man (fig. 5.28). Although they may both run with the same velocity the man would be more difficult to stop because he has more momentum.

Both **mass** and **velocity** affect the momentum of a moving person or object.

When the mass and velocity of an object are multiplied together this gives the momentum of the object.

$$\textbf{momentum} = \textbf{mass} \times \textbf{velocity}$$

Note: because momentum is calculated by multiplying kilograms by metres per second it is measured in **kilogram metres per second (kg m/s).**

Change in momentum

For an object to change its momentum, it must change its velocity by accelerating or decelerating. To do this it must feel a force. The larger the force and the longer the time it pushes for, the more the momentum will change. It can be shown that

$$\textbf{force} \times \textbf{time} = \textbf{change in momentum}$$
$$\text{or} \qquad Ft = mv - mu$$

Note: u is initial velocity so mu is initial momentum. v is final velocity so mv is final momentum.

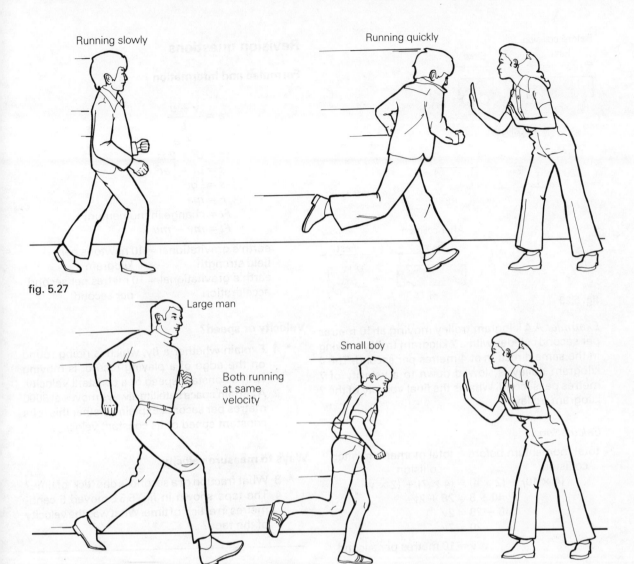

Running slowly

Running quickly

fig. 5.27

Large man

Small boy

Both running at same velocity

fig. 5.28

Impulse

When an object is given a change in momentum the force × time causing the change is called an **impulse**.

$$\text{impulse} = \text{force} \times \text{time}$$

Note: because impulse is calculated by multiplying newtons by seconds it is measured in **newton seconds (Ns)**.

5.17 Conservation of momentum

If two trolleys moving in the same direction collide and move apart again as in fig. 5.29, the force which

makes one go faster is equal and opposite to the force which makes the other slow down. (See Newton's third law, section 5.13).

Because both trolleys must feel the same size of force for the same length of time, and because

$$\text{force} \times \text{time} = \text{change in momentum}$$

the gain in momentum of m_2 must be equal in size to the loss in momentum of m_1. The total momentum after the collision is therefore the same as it was before. We say that momentum has been conserved.

This is a very useful result because in any calculation between two colliding objects we can assume that

total momentum before = total momentum after collision   collision

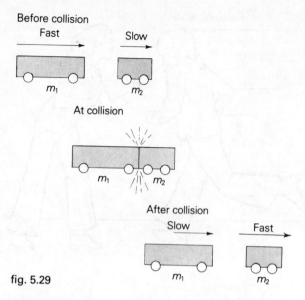

fig. 5.29

Example: A 4 kilogram trolley moving at 10 metres per second collides with a 2 kilogram trolley moving in the same direction at 4 metres per second. The 4 kilogram trolley is slowed down to a velocity of 7 metres per second. What is the final velocity of the 2 kilogram trolley?

Calculation

total momentum before = total momentum after
collision   collision

$$(4 \times 10) + (2 \times 4) = (4 \times 7) + (2 \times v)$$
$$40 + 8 = 28 + 2v$$
$$48 - 28 = 2v$$
$$20 = 2v$$
$$\therefore v = 10 \text{ metres per second}$$

The direction of momentum

Before firing, the total momentum of a gun and its bullet is zero. For momentum to be conserved the total momentum after firing must also be zero. This is made possible by the fact that the gun recoils (fig. 5.30) so that its momentum is equal and opposite to that of the bullet. The gun's velocity and momentum are negative and the bullet's velocity and momentum are positive.

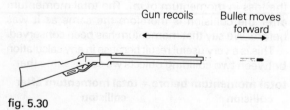

Gun recoils   Bullet moves
                     forward

fig. 5.30

Revision questions

Formulae and Information

$$a = \frac{v - u}{t}$$
$$v = u + at$$
$$v^2 = u^2 + 2as$$
$$s = ut + \tfrac{1}{2}at^2$$
$$s = \tfrac{1}{2}gt^2$$
$$F = ma$$
$$Ft = \text{change in momentum}$$
$$Ft = mv - mu$$

earth's gravitational = 10 newtons per
field strength   kilogram
earth's gravitational = 10 metres per second
acceleration   per second

Velocity or speed?

* **1** Explain whether a fly, which is riding round on the edge of a playing record, is moving with a constant speed or a constant velocity.
* **2** A certain space satellite always moves at 3000 metres per second. Explain whether this is its constant speed or its constant velocity.

Ways to measure velocity

* **3** What fraction of a second is one 'tick' of time?
* **4** The tape shown in fig. 5.31 moved 5 centimetres in a 'tick' of time. What was the velocity of the tape?

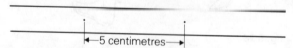

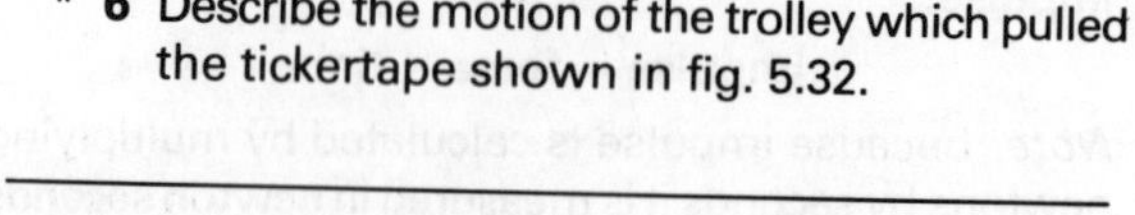

←—5 centimetres—→

fig. 5.31

* **5** A '10-tick' length of tape measures 8 centimetres. What was the velocity of the trolley that pulled the tape?
* **6** Describe the motion of the trolley which pulled the tickertape shown in fig. 5.32.

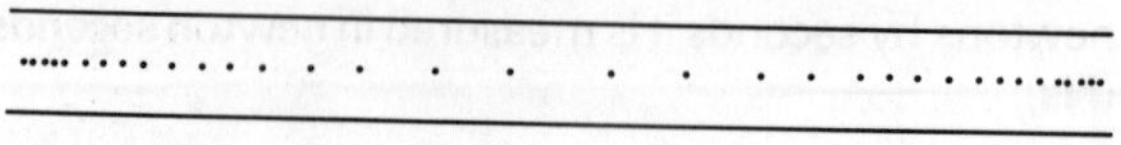

fig. 5.32

* **7** The tickertimer which made the dots on the tape in fig. 5.32 vibrated at 50 times a second. Use a ruler to help you calculate the fastest velocity shown on the tape.

** **8** Use a ruler to help you calculate the average velocity of the trolley which pulled the tape in fig. 5.32.

Measuring acceleration

** **9** Fig. 5.33 is of a tickertape showing acceleration. It has been marked off in '10-tick' lengths. Calculate the acceleration shown by the tape.

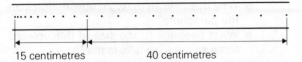

15 centimetres   40 centimetres

fig. 5.33

* **10** A racing car increases its velocity from 30 metres per second to 40 metres per second in 2·5 seconds. What is its acceleration?

** **11** A bicycle slows from 8 metres per second to 3 metres per second in 10 seconds. What is its deceleration?

Tickertape charts

* **12** Describe the motion shown by the '10-tick' chart in fig. 5.34.

fig. 5.34

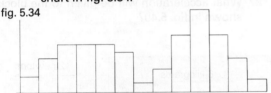

* **13** The '10-tick' chart shown in fig. 5.34 is drawn full size. Use a ruler to help you calculate the fastest velocity it shows.

** **14** Calculate the constant acceleration shown by the '10-tick' chart in fig. 5.35.

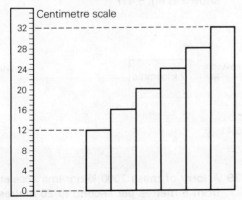

fig. 5.35

Velocity-time graphs

* **15** Fig. 5.36 shows the first 5 seconds of motion of a van. What is the total distance travelled in this time?

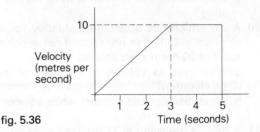

fig. 5.36

* **16** What distance is travelled in fig. 5.37?

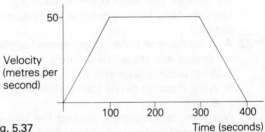

fig. 5.37

Symbols and units

* **17** Copy the table below and fill in the missing words, symbols and units.

	Symbol	Unit normally used	Abbreviation of unit
			m/s^2
mass			
	s		
		second	
initial velocity			
			N
	v		

Formulae of motion

** **18** A graph of motion is shown in fig. 5.38. Use formulae to calculate **a** the acceleration **b** the distance travelled.

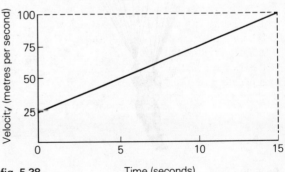

fig. 5.38

**19 A motorbike travelling at 20 metres per second accelerates steadily at 2 metres per second per second for 6 seconds.
   a What is its velocity after this time?
   b What distance does it travel while accelerating?

**20 A car which has accelerated steadily for 4 seconds at 3 metres per second per second reaches 30 metres per second.
   a What was its velocity at the start of its acceleration?
   b What distance did it travel while accelerating?

**21 A bicycle travelling at 12 metres per second arrives at a hill down which it accelerates at 0·2 metres per second per second for 10 seconds. How fast is it going at the bottom of the hill?

***22 A cyclist riding at 10 metres per second applies his brakes and stops in 4 seconds.
   a What was his deceleration?
   b What distance did he travel while decelerating?

   Note: more problems needing the use of **formulae of motion** will be found in the set of questions on **gravitational acceleration**.

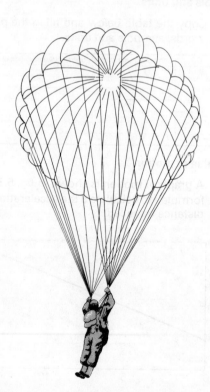

fig. 5.39

Newton's first law

*23 What force is needed to keep a book sliding with constant velocity across a desk if there is a frictional force of 9 newtons opposing the motion; is it less than 9 newtons, exactly 9 newtons, or more than 9 newtons?

**24 A man starts to fall using a parachute (fig. 5.39). He is pulled down by a force due to gravity (his weight).
   a Why does the air make an upward force on the parachute?
   b What happens to the size of this upward force as the man falls faster?
   c Why does the man eventually stop getting faster and fall with a constant velocity?

**25 Write Newton's first law in your own words.

Compensating for friction

*26 If you were using a friend's apparatus for a trolley, tickertape and runway experiment, how would you check that it was correctly compensated for friction?

Newton's second law

*27 What acceleration will be given to the block shown in fig. 5.40?

fig. 5.40

*28 What acceleration will be given to the block shown in fig. 5.41?

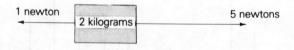

fig. 5.41

**29 A lorry of mass 2000 kilograms accelerates from 5 metres per second to 20 metres per second in 5 seconds.

a What is the acceleration of the lorry?

b What is the size of the force making it accelerate?

Gravitational field strength, g

*30 What is the force due to earth's gravity on **a** an 8 kilogram mass **b** a 0·5 kilogram mass?

*31 On another planet a mass of 4 kilograms has a weight of 20 newtons. What is the gravitational field strength of that planet?

**32 On earth a mass of 5 kilograms is needed to stretch the spring of the apparatus in fig. 5.42 so that the plank is exaclty level. What mass would be needed if the plank and spring were taken to the planet mentioned in question 31?

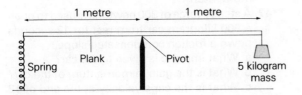

fig. 5.42

Gravitational acceleration

*33 There is a legend that Galileo dropped two different sized masses from the Leaning Tower of Pisa, to see if they would fall with the same acceleration. If he had used a coin and a feather as his masses, then the coin would have reached the ground first. Under what conditions will a coin and a feather fall with the same acceleration?

**34 A scaler-timer shows that a ball bearing takes 0·8 seconds to fall from the ceiling to the floor

of a laboratory. What is the approximate height of the ceiling?

35 How far will an object fall towards the earth in **a 1 second **b** 2 seconds **c** 3 seconds?

**36 A rock falls from the top of a cliff 80 metres high.

a How long does it take to fall?

b How fast does it hit the sea?

**37 A pebble thrown down a well with a velocity of 5 metres per second reaches the water in 3 seconds.

a How deep is the well?

b How fast does the pebble hit the water?

38 A girl who has just answered questions **34 to **37** *correctly* says, 'If the things in these questions really did happen and measurements were made to check my answers then I would have got them all wrong.' What does she mean?

Newton's third law

*39 Identical twins sit on trolleys of equal mass and each holds the end of a rope (fig. 5.43). If Peter was to pull his end of the rope hard whilst Steven held his end firm, where would the front ends of the trolleys meet?

*40 How does the force acting on Peter and his trolley compare with that acting on Steven and his trolley?

*41 Write Newton's third law in your own words.

Component velocities

**42 A hunter fires at a monkey which is hanging in a tree 300 metres away (fig. 5.44). The monkey lets go of the branch the instant that the bullet leaves the gun barrel; even so the bullet hits the monkey. Was the hunter aiming

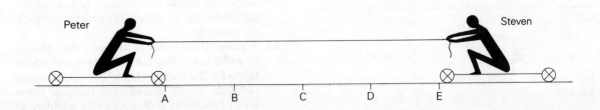

fig. 5.43

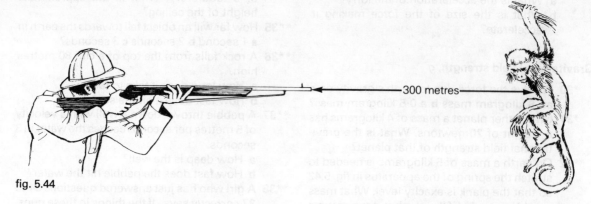

fig. 5.44

300 metres

directly at the monkey, slightly above it or slightly below it? Explain your answer.

Bernoulli effect

*43 A boy blows hard over a piece of paper (fig. 5.45). Explain what happens to the piece of paper.

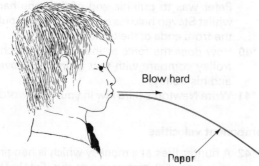

Blow hard

Paper

fig. 5.45

**44 A boat tries to run parallel and near to the side of a dock (fig. 5.46). Explain why the boat has to steer away from the dockside in order to move parallel to it.

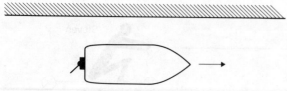

fig. 5.46

Momentum

*45 What are the units of momentum?

*46 An object has a mass of 6 kilograms and is moving at 3 metres per second: what is its momentum?

**47 A steady force of 300 newtons is used to push a 900 kilogram car from rest for 12 seconds down a friction compensated slope.
a What impulse is given to the car?
b What is the gain in momentum of the car?
c What is the car's velocity at the end of 12 seconds?

*48 Two boys of equal mass jump from the same window ledge onto the ground. One bends his legs while landing and the other keeps his rigid. What difference do the boys notice in the force they feel? Explain your answer.

Conservation of momentum

**49 A 5 kilogram trolley moving at 6 metres per second collides with a 1 kilogram trolley moving in the same direction at 2 metres per second. After the collision the 1 kilogram trolley has speeded up to 7 metres per second. What is the velocity of the 5 kilogram trolley after the collision?

**50 Two skaters, one of 80 kilograms, the other of 60 kilograms, and both moving at 2 metres per second collide head on. They manage to keep their balance by clinging to each other. Calculate the velocity with which they slide on together.

***51 A scaler-timer used to measure the velocity of a rifle bullet (fig. 5.47) shows that the time taken for the bullet to travel between the two contacts is 0·01 seconds.The bullet of mass 0·001 kilograms then sticks into a trolley of mass 0·199 kilograms. Calculate the velocity with which the bullet and trolley move off together.

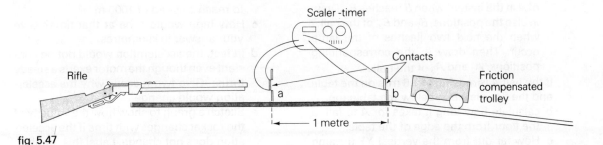

fig. 5.47

*52 A pupil learning physics is puzzled by what happens to the momentum of a boulder which hits the ground after falling from the top of a high cliff. She asks her teacher if this is an exception to the rule of conservation of momentum. What answer would you give the pupil?

*53 A stationary 100 kilogram cannon on wheels fires a 2 kilogram cannon ball at 80 metres per second. What is the velocity of the cannon's recoil after firing?

Extra questions

*54 Explain why a high jumper might be able to clear 4 metres easily on the moon even though he was wearing a space suit.

**55 Would a long jumper be able to jump further on the moon than on earth? Explain your answer.

56 If you step off a bus before it has stopped moving you are likely to fall over. **Explain which way you would fall. What must you do to stop yourself falling?

**57 A man of mass 70 kilograms is standing in a lift on bathroom scales which are calibrated in newtons.
  a What do the scales read when the lift is stationary?
  b What do the scales read when the lift is moving steadily upwards?
  c Under what conditions would the scales read zero?

***58 Read the following account, then answer the questions at the end:
  A number of people are sitting by the side of a large lake, watching a girl skiing on the water, towed by a speed boat. Someone asks 'What keeps her up?' Five answers are given to this question.
  a 'The water is at atmospheric pressure, and this pressure keeps her up.'
  b 'It's a displacement effect. She sinks a little

and this produces an upthrust equal to the weight of water displaced. This keeps her up.'
  c 'It's like a rifle bullet. She travels so fast she doesn't have time to sink.'
  d 'She places herself so that the skis slope upwards at the front, and then the water has an upward force. This supports her weight.'
  e 'It's a Bernoulli effect. Water rushes under the skis, and because it is moving faster the pressure is greater, and this keeps her up.'
  Comment on each of these answers, giving the reason why you consider some to be entirely wrong, and assessing the degree of truth in the others. Say why the girl sinks if the boat stops. (*O. and C.*)

***59 A ball *A*, illuminated by a flashing lamp, is rolling towards the edge of a horizontal table. Fig. 5.48 represents part of a photograph of the motion of *A*. At the instant when *A* reaches the edge of the table, another ball, *B*, is allowed to fall freely from rest. At the next flash of the lamp *B* appears at B_1.

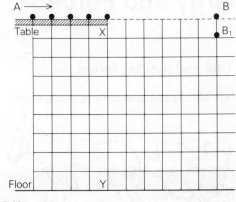

fig. 5.48

  a Make a careful copy of fig. 5.48 on a sheet of graph paper and draw in the position A_1

41

of A at the instant when B reaches B_1. Draw in also the positions, B_2 and B_3, of the ball B when the next two flashes of the lamp occur. Then draw in the corresponding positions, A_2 and A_3 of the ball A.

If the ball A is moving at 1.8 m/s on the table and the floor is 0.8 m below the table top,

b calculate how long it takes for A to fall to the floor from the edge of the table.

c How far out from the vertical XY through the edge of the table will the ball hit the floor? (O. and C.).

***60** Throughout this question, ignore air resistance on the rocket and assume that the Earth is not moving.

A rocket whose total mass is 2400 kg, is launched vertically from the Earth's surface. The rocket motor exerts a constant force (thrust) of 30 000 N.

a What is the acceleration of the rocket at blast-off (when it leaves the surface of the Earth)?

b If the rocket had continued with this acceleration, how long would it take the rocket to reach a speed of 1000 m/s?

c How high would it be at that time? Give your answer in kilometres.

d In fact, the acceleration would not be constant even though the motor exerts a steady thrust. Give two reasons why the acceleration would change.

e Sketch a graph to show how the velocity of the rocket changes with time if the acceleration does not change. Label this graph X. On the same axes, sketch another graph to show how the velocity changes with time according to your answer in part (d). Label that graph Y.

f State how you could find the height of the rocket after a certain time, from a graph like graph Y, if the values of velocity and time were marked on the axes.

g Before blast-off the rocket has no momentum, but after blast-off it has momentum upwards. How do you explain that in terms of the law of conservation of momentum?

h What has happened to the chemical energy of the fuel consumed? (O. and C.)

6
Energy and Force

6.1 Still and moving forces

Here are some examples of force being used:

fig. 6.1 A donkey pulling a cart along a track

fig. 6.2 A propeller forcing a boat through the water

fig. 6.3 A tightened clamp holding a glued joint together

fig. 6.4 A wood support propping up a wall

Notice that figs. 6.1 and 6.2 need a supply of energy in the form of food or petrol to keep them moving, but figs. 6.3 and 6.4, which are still, will keep doing their jobs without needing a supply of energy.

If the force doing the job moves then a supply of energy is needed.

If the force doing the job does not move then no supply of energy is needed

Forces that need a supply of energy are doing work.

6.2 Calculating the energy used

One way to calculate the energy used is by using the formula

energy = force × distance moved in direction of force

(joules = newtons × metres)

Example A: How much energy does a horse use to pull a cart with a force of 1200 newtons through a distance of 500 metres along a level road?

Information

force = 1200 newtons
distance = 500 metres

Calculation

energy = force × distance moved in direction of force
= 1200 × 500
= 600 000 joules

Example B: How much energy is needed to lift a 40 newton weight up by a distance of 3 metres?

Information

force = 40 newtons
distance = 3 metres

Calculation

energy = force × distance moved in direction of force
= 40 × 3
= 120 joules

In these examples the distance moved has been in the direction of the force: suppose now it is not. For example, suppose a person walks up stairs as shown in fig. 6.5.

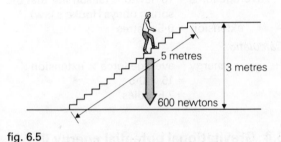

fig. 6.5

He is lifting his weight of 600 newtons upwards by 3 metres, so although he moves 5 metres altogether, force × distance moved in direction of force
= 600 newtons **upwards** × 3 metres **upwards**
= 1800 joules

6.3 Energy used in stretching a spring

In section 1.2 we saw that the force needed to stretch a spring gets gradually greater as the spring gets longer. This is now illustrated in fig. 6.6.

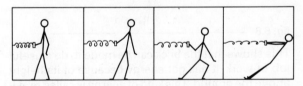

fig. 6.6

Because the force is changing all the time, it is the **average** force on a spring which must be used when energy is calculated. The formula is

energy = average force × extension

(joules = newtons × metres)

Example: How much energy is needed to stretch a spring by 0.5 metres until the force on it is 30 newtons (fig. 6.7)?

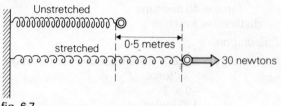

fig. 6.7

Information

        starting force = 0 newton
        final force = 30 newtons
    ∴ average force = 15 newtons (assuming that the
                     spring obeys Hooke's law)
        extension = 0.5 metres

Calculation

$$energy = average\ force \times extension$$
$$= 15 \times 0.5$$
$$= 7.5\ joules$$

6.4 Gravitational potential energy (P.E.)

If a brick held above the ground is tied to a small load by a piece of string passing over a pulley (fig. 6.8), the load will be lifted by the brick as it falls.

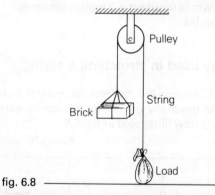

fig. 6.8

This shows that the brick can be made to do a useful job of work. It has got energy because of its height above the ground. This kind of energy is called **gravitational potential energy.**

Since
energy = force × distance moved in direction of force
then
    gravitational potential energy = weight × height
$$= m \times g \times h$$
$$P.E. = mgh$$

Example: Calculate the gravitational potential energy of a 3000 newton statue which has been lifted up 12 metres onto a column.

Information

        weight = 3000 newtons
        height = 12 metres

Calculation

    gravitational potential energy = weight × height
$$= 3000 \times 12$$
$$= 36000\ joules$$

6.5 Kinetic energy (K.E.)

If a trolley rolling freely along a desk is tied by slack string to a load on the floor (fig. 6.9),

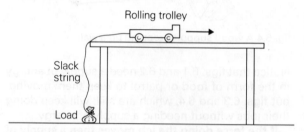

fig. 6.9

the trolley will be slowed to a stop when the string gets tight and the load lifts off the floor (fig. 6.10).

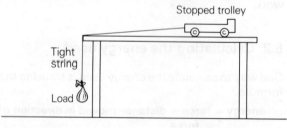

fig. 6.10

This shows that the trolley can be made to do a useful job of work. It has got energy because it is moving. This kind of energy is called **kinetic energy.** The kinetic energy of an object of mass m kilograms moving with a velocity of v metres per second can be calculated using the formula

$$K.E. = \tfrac{1}{2}mv^2$$

Example: A girl of mass 50 kilograms is running at 4 metres per second. What is her kinetic energy.?

Information

        m = 50 kilograms
        v = 4 metres per second

Calculation

$$K.E. = \tfrac{1}{2}mv^2$$
$$= \tfrac{1}{2} \times 50 \times 4 \times 4$$
$$= 400 \text{ joules}$$

6.6 Different kinds of energy

Energy can be in different forms. Here is a list of some of the kinds of energy, including those already mentioned:

Gravitational potential energy—energy due to a high position. Example: a boy at the top of a slide (fig. 6.11).

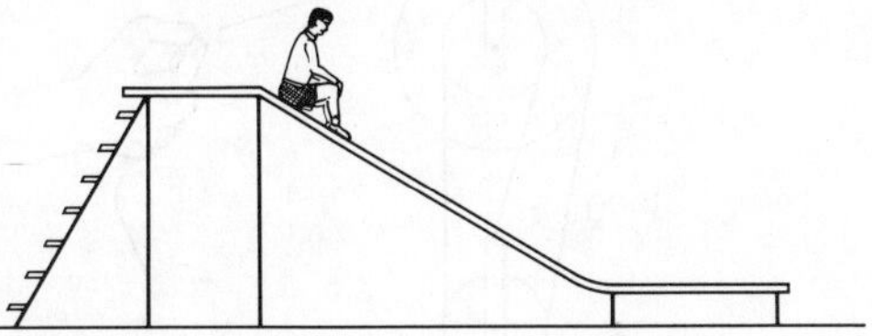

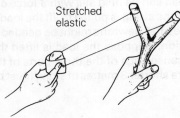

fig. 6.11

Kinetic energy—energy due to movement. Example: an arrow flying through the air (fig. 6.12).

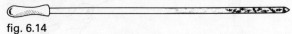

fig. 6.12

Strain energy—energy stored in something which is stretched or squashed. Example: the stretched elastic of a catapult (fig. 6.13).

Stretched elastic

fig. 6.13

Heat energy—energy due to the atoms of a substance vibrating (see sections 12.5 and 13.1). Example: the atoms in the red hot end of a poker (fig. 6.14).

fig. 6.14

Chemical energy—energy which can be released by chemical reactions. Example: gunpowder (fig. 6.15).

fig. 6.15

Electrical energy—energy due to electric charge. Example: electric charge flowing through a lamp to make heat and light (fig. 6.16).

fig. 6.16

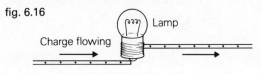

Lamp

Charge flowing

Light energy—energy in the form of electromagnetic waves. Example: light coming from the sun (fig. 6.17).

fig. 6.17

Sound energy—energy carrried away from a source by waves of vibrating molecules. Example: the noise of gun fire travelling through the air (fig. 6.18).

fig. 6.18

Nuclear energy—energy stored in the nucleus of an atom. Example: the source of energy in an atomic bomb (fig. 6.19).

fig. 6.19

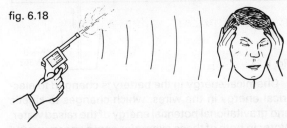

6.7 Energy changes

It is sometimes said that energy is used to do a job of work: this is not exactly true. What really happens is that energy changes from one form to another. Here are some examples of energy change:

A catapult fires a stone straight up into the air (fig. 6.20).

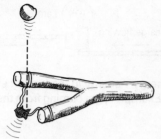

fig. 6.20

Strain energy in the elastic is changed to kinetic energy of the moving stone, which then changes to gravitational potential energy of the stone as it gets higher.

A battery drives an electric motor, which works a pump to lift water from a bucket (fig. 6.21).

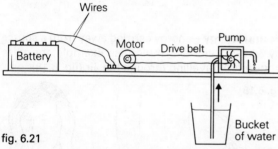

fig. 6.21

Chemical energy in the battery is changed to electrical energy in the wires, which changes to kinetic and gravitational potential energy of the raised water. *Note:* in both of these examples some energy would be changed to heat and sound by the moving parts.

6.8 Work

Instead of using the words 'energy change' the everyday word 'work' can be used. The amount of work done is equal to the amount of energy changed. *Example:* How much work is done in lifting a 40 newton load through 3 metres?
Information
      force = 40 newtons
      distance = 3 metres

Calculation

work done = (energy change) = force × distance
                           moved in
                           direction of force
           = 40 × 3
           = 120 joules

6.9 Machines

Machines will change one kind of energy into another, and are often useful because they make it easier to do work. This does not mean that more energy is got from a machine than is put into it: in fact because some energy is changed to heat in the moving parts, a machine will always do less work than the work put into it.

Pulleys as a machine

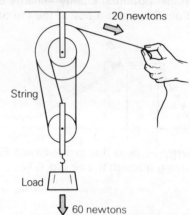

fig. 6.22

In fig. 6.22 the 60 newton load is hanging on three parts of the string which share the weight. This is why the load can be held still with a force of only 20 newtons. If the string is pulled to lift the load higher a larger force of 25 newtons might be needed because of the friction. Suppose the load is lifted through 1 metre. Because each of the three parts of the string gets 1 metre shorter 3 metres of string must be pulled (fig. 6.23).

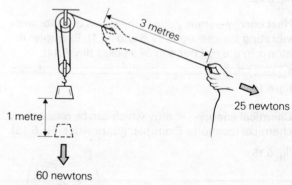

fig. 6.23

The work done by the pulleys in lifting the load, (60 newtons × 1 metre), is 60 joules. The work done by the person pulling the string, (25 newtons × 3 metres), is 75 joules. So although the machine makes it easier to lift the load, the person does more work than he would do lifting the load by hand.

The lever as a machine

Just as a set of pulleys make it easier to lift a load so does a lever. The force needed to balance the load in fig. 6.24 would be 3 newtons (section 1.7).

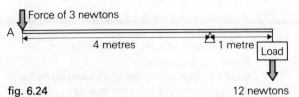

fig. 6.24   12 newtons

Example: If the end A of the lever shown in fig. 6.24 was pushed down to 1 metre below its present level, how far up would the 12 newton load be lifted (if there was no friction)?

Calculation

  assuming energy put in = energy gained by load
     3 newtons × 1 metre = 12 newtons × height lifted
        ∴ height lifted = 0·25 metres

6.10 Power

A man can easily and quickly lift a load. A boy can lift the same sized load through the same distance but not so easily or quickly (fig. 6.25).

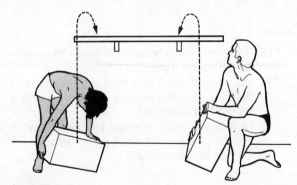

fig. 6.25

The boy does the same amount of work as the man but it takes him longer. The man is more powerful than the boy because he works faster.

Power measures how quickly work is done, that is, how many joules of work are done each second. Power measured in watts, can be calculated using the formula

$$\text{power} = \frac{\text{work done}}{\text{time taken}}$$

$$\left(\text{watts} = \frac{\text{joules}}{\text{seconds}}\right)$$

Example: A man lifts a 120 newton load through 2 metres in 3 seconds.
a How much work does the man do?
b What is his power?

Information for **a**

      force = 120 newtons
   distance = 2 metres

Calculation

  work done = force × distance moved in direction
                 of force
          = 120 × 2
          = 240 joules

Information for **b**

     work done = 240 joules
     time taken = 3 seconds

Calculation

$$\text{power} = \frac{\text{work done}}{\text{time taken}}$$

$$= \frac{240}{3}$$

$$= 80 \text{ watts}$$

The power of vehicles is often measured in **horse power**

     1 horse power = 746 watts

Electrical power can be calculated using the formula (see section 10.15)

    power = potential difference × current
    (watts = volts × amperes)

Revision questions

Formulae and information

    energy = force × distance moved
               in direction of force
    work done = force × distance moved
               in direction of force
  gravitational potential = weight × height
   energy
       or, P.E. = mgh
  kinetic energy, K.E. = $\frac{1}{2}mv^2$
    strain energy = average force ×
                 extension
$$\text{power (watts)} = \frac{\text{work done (joules)}}{\text{time taken (seconds)}}$$
  gravitational field = 10 newtons per kilogram
   strength, g,

Still and moving forces

* **1** In the list below, which things need a supply of energy to do their jobs and which do not?
  the foundations of a house   a picture hook
  a paper weight   a watch spring
  an aeroplane propeller   a tin opener
  the girders of a bridge   an egg whisk
* **2** What is a useful way of telling if energy is needed to do a job?

Calculating the energy used

** **3** How much energy is used **a** to push a car with a force of 150 newtons 20 metres along a road, **b** to lift a 45 newton weight up through a height of 4 metres, **c** by a 480 newton girl climbing 3 metres up a rope in the gym, **d** by a train engine pulling carriages a distance of 3 kilometres (3000 metres) with a force of 5000 newtons?

** **4** A prisoner weighing 800 newtons climbs from the gutter to the chimney of a prison roof (fig. 6.26). How much energy does he use to do this?

fig. 6.26

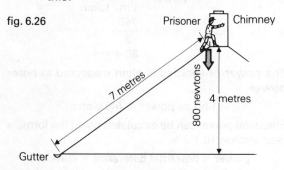

Energy used in stretching a spring

** **5** How much energy is needed to stretch a spring by 0·3 metres, until the force on it is 20 newtons?

** **6** A person needs to make a force of 110 newtons to stretch his chest expander by 0·2 metres. How much energy does he use in stretching the chest expander?

Gravitational potential energy

* **7** Calculate the potential energy of a 15 newton weight, which has been lifted 2 metres above the floor.

** **8** The brass weight of a grandfather clock falls 1·4 metres in a week and the clock needs 2 joules of energy a day to keep going. What is the size of the brass weight in newtons?

Kinetic energy (K.E.)

* **9** A dog of mass 9 kilograms is running at 6 metres per second. What is its kinetic energy?

* **10** A cannon ball of mass 2 kilograms is fired at 80 metres per second. What is its kinetic energy?

Different kinds of energy

* **11** What different kinds of energy are each of the following an example of?
  a The noise of a door slamming
  b An atomic reactor
  c The stretched rubber of a blown up balloon.
  d A glider flying through the air
  e A book balanced on top of a door
  f A hot iron
  g The beam of a search light
  h A message travelling along telephone wires

Energy changes

Make a list of the energy changes which happen for each of the questions 12 to 14.

** **12** Wind blows the sails of a windmill round, which works a dynamo, which makes electricity to run an electric fire.

** **13** Some water is boiled inside a sealed can, until pressure makes the lid fly off into the air before coming down to land on a tin tray.

** **14** A boy swings backwards and forwards on a rope.

Work

* **15** How much work is done in lifting a 25 newton load through 2 metres?

* **16** How much work is done by a person who drags a sack of potatoes 4 metres, using a force of 30 newtons?

* **17** How much work is done by the 4 newton weight of a cuckoo clock as it drops by 1·1 metres during the day?

Machines

* **18** Why might a person choose to use a set of pulleys to lift a load instead of lifting it by hand?

* **19** A man pulling on a pulley rope with a force of 70 newtons is able to lift a load of 250 newtons. Explain if this means he is using less energy than he would use if he lifted the load by hand.

Power

**20 An engine lifts a 600 newton load by 5 metres in 2 seconds.

   a How much work does the engine do?

   b What is its power output?

**21 A 54 kilogram girl walks up stairs to the next floor 3 metres above. She takes 6 seconds.

   a How much work does she do?

   b What is her useful power?

Extra questions

***22 A boy sits on a sledge at the top of a snowy bank 4 metres high. The mass of the boy and his sledge together is 60 kilograms.

   a What is his potential energy at the top of the slope?

   b If he slides down the slope what will be his kinetic energy when he reaches the bottom? (If no energy is changed into other forms).

   c How fast will he be moving at the bottom?

**23 In what form is the energy of the wind? Explain where it gets its energy from.

*24 On a freely running 'big dipper' (or switchback) at the fairground, Tom said that the last summit was the highest, but Dick was sure that it must be the first which was the highest. Explain who you think is correct.

***25 When a force is applied to one end of a light spring about 50 cm long which is fixed at the other end (fig. 6.27), an extension of the spring takes place. The graph in fig. 6.28 shows the relationship between the force and the extension (or increase in length).

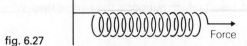

fig. 6.27

   a What would you expect the extension to be for a force of 7·5 newton? Give your reason.

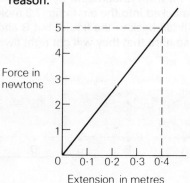

fig. 6.28

   Force in newtons

   Extension in metres

b Why is it unwise to estimate the extension for a force of 75 newton?

c If the potential energy stored in the spring due to the extension is given by

$$\text{potential energy stored} = \text{average force} \times \text{extension}$$

calculate the energy stored when the force is increased from zero to 5 newton.

fig. 6.29

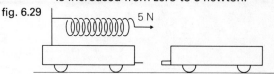

This spring is now attached to a trolley (mass 0·5 kg), held stationary on a friction compensated slope as shown in fig. 6.29 and stretched until the force exerted is 5 newton. The trolley is then released and the spring becomes unhooked when the tension in it is zero.

d What is the speed of the trolley at the moment the spring becomes unhooked?

e The trolley then collides with a trolley of mass 1·0 kg at rest and they stick together. What is their velocity after the collision?

f Calculate the kinetic energy of the trolleys before and after the collision and comment on the values you obtain. (*O. and C.*)

***26 a Fig. 6.30 shows the side view sketch of a 'big dipper'.

fig. 6.30

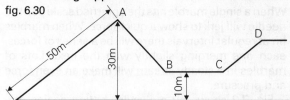

A car is pulled to point A and then released. Describe the **motion** of the car as it moves along the track from A to D.

b The mass of the car and passengers is 600 kilograms. i What is the earth's gravitational pull on the car? ii Calculate the gain in potential energy of the car as it is pulled from the bottom to the top of the track at A. iii The frictional forces which oppose the motion of the car are 500 newton. Calculate the total work done on the car by the device which pulls the car to the top of the track. iv If friction and other forces which oppose the motion of the car can be neglected calculate the kinetic energy of the car at B. (*M.R.E.B.*)

7
Kinetic theory

7.1 How molecules of gas make a pressure

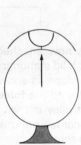

fig. 7.1   a) Falling marble   b) Marbles falling at regular intervals   c) Steady stream of marbles

The kinetic theory describes gas as being made of molecules which are flying about in all directions. A 'ball bearing' model of this theory was shown in section 3.3. In the same section **the smoke cell experiment** gave evidence to support the theory.

In section 4.6 it was suggested that molecules of a gas make a pressure by bombardment. This argument is illustrated in fig. 7.1.

When a single marble hits the upturned scale pan the needle will jerk to show a quick force. When marbles hit at regular intervals there will be a series of forces, each one merging slightly with the next. Lots of marbles in a steady stream will make an even force and pressure.

Fig. 7.2 shows air molecules hitting against the inside of a container to make a pressure.

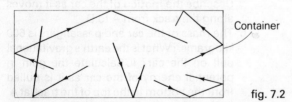

Container

fig. 7.2

If the molecules bounced back with slightly less speed each time they hit a wall, the forces would get weaker and weaker and the pressure eventually fall to zero. But pressure does not drop, so the molecules must make **elastic collisions** and bounce back with the same speed as they hit. This is one of the basic assumptions of the kinetic theory, which are:

1 The molecules of a gas are very small.
2 They collide elastically so do not lose kinetic energy.
3 Their collisions make a pressure.

7.2 Heat and pressure

The kinetic theory says that when a gas is heated its molecules will gain kinetic energy and move faster. Faster molecules will hit harder and so make a bigger pressure. In the experiment in photograph 7.a, the pressure gauge reading quickly rises as the air gets hotter. A result which supports the kinetic theory.

7.3 Evaporation

Molecules near the surface of a liquid may sometimes be hit from underneath by other molecules, and get knocked into the air. In fig. 7.3 molecules A and C will fall back to the liquid, but B and D have been hit so hard that they will get right away.

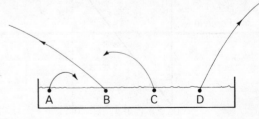

A   B   C   D

fig. 7.3

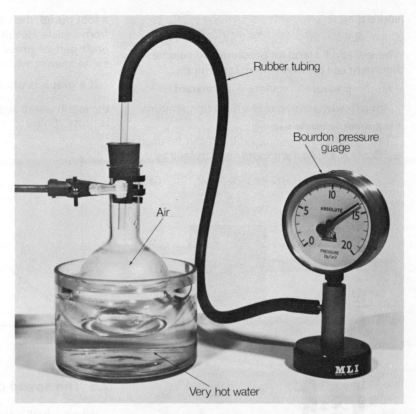

photograph 7.a

A liquid evaporates by molecules escaping. If a wind blows across the surface, molecules which would have fallen back get carried away (fig. 7.4). In this way the liquid evaporates quicker.

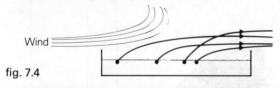

Wind

fig. 7.4

For every molecule which gains momentum as it is knocked out of the surface, other molecules must be slowed down. (Conservation of momentum, section 5.17). Because of this, the average speed (and therefore energy) of the molecules left behind will get less and less. This means that an evaporating liquid gets colder.

The experiment in fig. 7.5 shows that evaporating liquids do cool down.

fig. 7.5

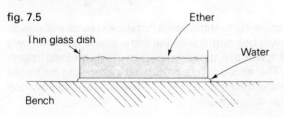

Ether

Thin glass dish

Water

Bench

The ether is made to evaporate quickly by blowing across its surface. Soon the dish gets frozen to the bench. The ether has got so cold that it has turned the water to ice.

7.4 Pressure and volume

Fig. 7.6 shows some molecules trapped in a box by a piston.

Gauge

Piston

fig. 7.6

If the piston is pushed in so that the molecules only have half the volume, they will hit the walls twice as often and the pressure will double (fig. 7.7).
By the same argument, if the volume goes to one third the pressure will be three times greater; a quarter the volume will give four times the pressure, and so on.

51

Notice that
$$P \times V = 2P \times \tfrac{1}{2}V = 3P \times \tfrac{1}{3}V = 4P \times \tfrac{1}{4}V$$

Where P and V stand for pressure and volume. This argument can be summed up by writing

pressure × volume = a constant

for a fixed mass of gas at a fixed temperature.

It is known as **Boyle's law.**

The apparatus in photograph 7.b can be used to test Boyle's law. As the pressure is increased by using a foot pump, the volume of air gets less and is read from a scale. Results from this experiment show that each pair of pressure and volume values give the same answer when multiplied together.

If a graph is plotted of pressure against $\dfrac{1}{\text{volume}}$ the result is a straight line (fig. 7.8). This shows that P is proportional to $\dfrac{1}{V}$.

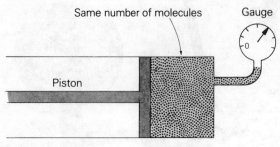

Same number of molecules

Gauge

Piston

fig. 7.7

Half the volume

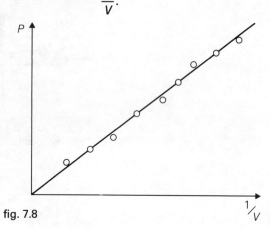

fig. 7.8

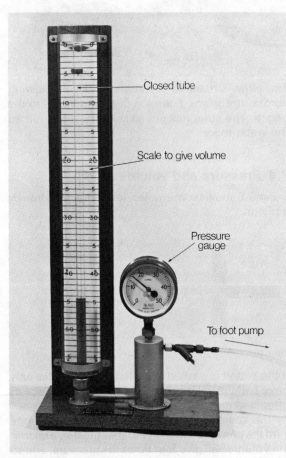

Closed tube

Scale to give volume

Pressure gauge

To foot pump

photograph 7.b

7.5 The speed of an air molecule

When a ball is thrown up into the air and caught again (fig. 7.9), its energy changes from kinetic to gravitational potential and back to kinetic.

fig. 7.9

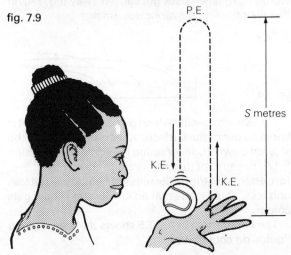

P.E.

K.E.

K.E.

S metres

Assuming that the ball is not slowed by air resistance, it will be caught with the same speed it was thrown at. It was this speed which took it to its greatest height, s. This speed can be calculated by knowing the height it falls through on its way down, and the acceleration due to gravity.

This is the basis of one method for finding the speed of an air molecule. In section 4.5 the height of the atmosphere was calculated as 8588 metres (about 6 miles). The speed an air molecule needs to get this high, is the same as the speed it will land with after falling through 8588 metres under gravity.

Information

s = 8588 metres
a = 10 metres per second per second
u = 0

Calculation

$v^2 = u^2 + 2as$
$v^2 = 0 + 2 \times 10 \times 8588$
$v^2 = 171760$
$\therefore v$ = 415 metres per second

Note: 415 metres per second is an average speed, because some air molecules move faster and some slower after they collide with each other.

7.6 Diffusion through porous material

In the experiment in fig. 7.10 carbon dioxide will leak (diffuse) in through the tiny holes in the porous pot, and hydrogen will diffuse out. The water manometer will show any change in pressure.

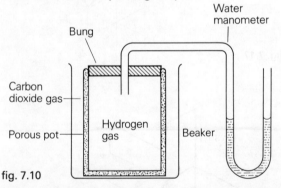

fig. 7.10

The water levels inside the manometer soon change to show that the pressure inside the porous pot has fallen. Hydrogen has diffused out more quickly than carbon dioxide has diffused in (fig. 7.11).

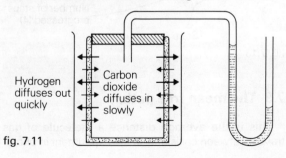

fig. 7.11

The reason for this is that hydrogen is a less dense gas than carbon dioxide. Hydrogen, for example, can be used in weather balloons because it is lighter than air (fig. 7.12).

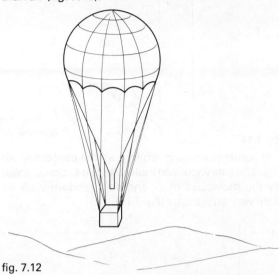

fig. 7.12

Carbon dioxide is heavier than air as the shadow of the gas being poured from a beaker shows (fig. 7.13).

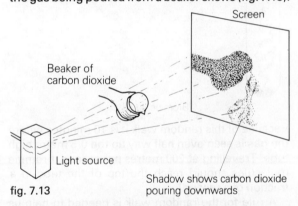

fig. 7.13

The kinetic theory tells us that molecules of both gases in fig. 7.10 hit against the porous pot to make a pressure. Because hydrogen is less dense, its smaller molecules must move faster to make the same pressure as the carbon dioxide. This is why hydrogen diffused through the pores in the pot more quickly.

7.7 Bromine diffusion through air

Liquid bromine vaporises to give a dense brown gas at normal temperature. Because its molecules have a large mass they only move at about 200 metres per second; half the speed of air molecules.

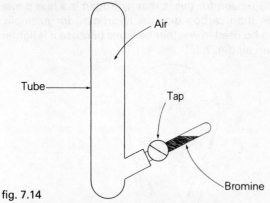

fig. 7.14

Air

Tube

Tap

Bromine

If liquid bromine is run into a tube containing air (fig. 7.14), its vaporised molecules are knocked about by the molecules of air and do a **random walk** on their way up the tube (fig. 7.15).

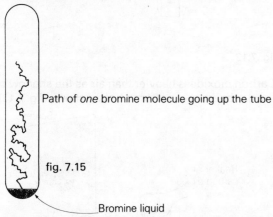

Path of *one* bromine molecule going up the tube

fig. 7.15

Bromine liquid

Because of this random walk it is 10 minutes before the gas is seen even half way up the 0·5 metre high tube. Travelling at 200 metres per second, bromine molecules should reach the top of the tube in a fraction of a second!

A rule for the random walk is needed to help us understand.

7.8 The random walk rule

A dice and isometric graph paper (fig. 7.16) are used to draw a random walk. Where the lines cross on the graph paper there are always six possible directions to draw the path of the walk. The direction taken at each step is decided by the throw of the dice.

Fig 7.17 shows the path of a walk when the first five dice throws gave 3, 1, 6, 6, 2.

Fig. 7.18 shows the path of a walk, 25 steps long. The direct distance moved (shown by the dotted line) can easily be found.

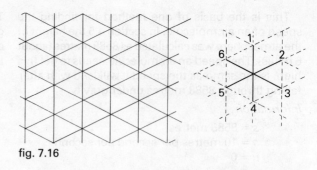

fig. 7.16

If many 25-step random walks are drawn in this way, the average of the direct distances moved will be 5 steps (or $\sqrt{25}$).

The rule is that on average the direct distance moved is the square root of the number of steps taken. If N equal length steps are taken at random, the average distance moved will, on average, be $\sqrt{N}$ steps.

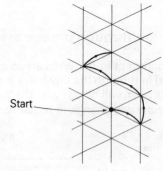

Start

fig. 7.17

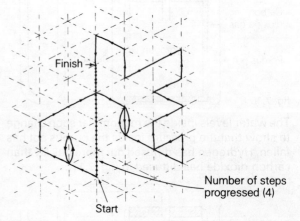

Finish

Number of steps progressed (4)

Start

fig. 7.18

7.9 The mean free path, y

This is the average distance a molecule of gas travels between collisions. In the experiment in photo-

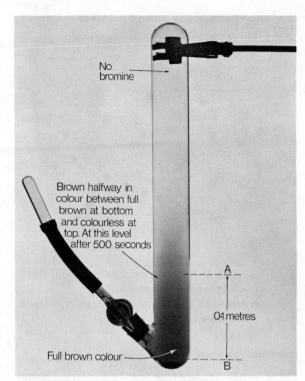

No bromine

Brown halfway in colour between full brown at bottom and colourless at top. At this level after 500 seconds

A

0·1 metres

Full brown colour

B

photograph 7.c

graph 7.c bromine has been run into a tube, and after 500 seconds the average direct distance travelled by the gas is 0·1 metres. This is judged by measuring from the liquid to the 'half brown' position.

The actual distance travelled by a bromine molecule moving at 200 metres per second for 500 seconds

$$= 200 \times 500$$
$$= 100\,000 \text{ metres}$$

If there are N collisions and y, the mean free path, is the average length of each step then

$$N \times y = 100\,000 \qquad (1)$$

The random walk rule says that the direct distance moved, 0·1 metres, is equal to the square root of the number of steps × the length of each step (fig. 7.19).

$$\therefore \sqrt{N} \times y = 0·1 \qquad (2)$$

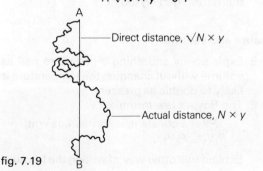

A

Direct distance, $\sqrt{N} \times y$

Actual distance, $N \times y$

B

fig. 7.19

If equation (2) is squared and rearranged it becomes

$$N = \frac{0·01}{y^2}$$

Substituting for N in equation (1) gives

$$\frac{0·01}{y^2} \times y = 100\,000$$

This rearranges to give

$$y = \frac{0·01}{100\,000}$$
$$= \frac{1}{10\,000\,000} \text{ metres}$$
$$\text{or} \quad 10^{-7} \text{ metres}$$

A very small distance indeed!

The molecules themselves which move around and collide, must be even smaller in size than 10^{-7} metres.

7.10 Change of volume from liquid to gas

To find out how much more space a molecule has when a liquid turns to a gas, the apparatus in fig. 7.20 is used.

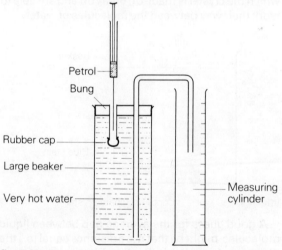

Syringe

Petrol

Bung

Rubber cap

Large beaker

Very hot water

Measuring cylinder

fig. 7.20

0·1 cubic centimetres of petrol are injected through the rubber cap into the hot water. The petrol vaporises, pushing out nearly 100 cubic centimetres of water into the measuring cylinder. We see then that petrol takes up about 1000 times more volume when it turns to a gas. This means that molecules have about 1000 times more space to move about in when they are a gas than when they are a liquid.

In a liquid the molecules must have only $\frac{1}{1000}$ th of the mean free path they have in a gas.

$$\therefore \text{ mean free path in a liquid} = 10^{-7} \times \frac{1}{1000}$$
$$= 10^{-10} \text{ metres}$$

7.11 The size of a molecule

Fig. 7.21 is a picture of molecules in a solid (A) and molecules in a liquid (B).

 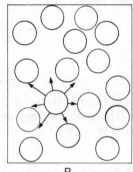

A   fig. 7.21   B

The molecules in a liquid are further apart. This explains how a blue stain diffuses from a copper sulphate crystal, even in still water (fig. 7.22). The particles which the crystal is made of, break off and are able to work their way between the molecules of water.

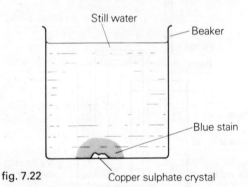

Still water

Beaker

Blue stain

fig. 7.22   Copper sulphate crystal

A good guess for the average gap between liquid molecules, might be that it is a distance equal to $\frac{1}{3}$ the diameter of a molecule. But this distance is the 'mean free path' in a liquid. So

$\frac{1}{3}$ of a molecule diameter $= 10^{-10}$ metres

$$\therefore \text{ a molecule diameter} = 3 \times 10^{-10} \text{ metres}$$

Although this is just an estimate, it gives us an idea of just how small molecules are.

Revision questions

Formulae   K.E. $= \frac{1}{2}mv^2$
$PV =$ a constant
or, $P_1V_1 = P_2V_2$

How molecules of gas make a pressure

** **1** Fig. 7.23 is a drawing of gas molecules inside a box.

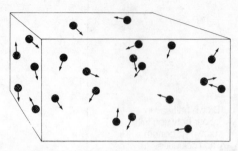

fig. 7.23

a In what ways is this drawing good, and in what ways is it poor?
b How do gas molecules make a pressure inside a box?

Heat and pressure

*** **2** A balloon held near to a fire is seen to expand. Gary says, 'The hot molecules of gas have got bigger and pushed the balloon out'. Ralph says, 'The balloon rubber has got softer and isn't able to squash the gas inside so much'. Emma says, 'You are both wrong. The heat has speeded up the gas molecules so they hit the rubber harder and make a greater pressure'. Comment on the amount of truth in each person's opinion.

Evaporation

* **3** Even when the air temperature is higher than the water temperature, we often feel colder coming out of the sea than we are swimming. Why is this?
* **4** Athletes often perspire. How does this stop them from getting too hot?

Pressure and volume

** **5** Explain why squashing a gas up to half its volume without changing the temperature is likely to double its pressure.
** **6** The Boyle's law formula,

$PV =$ a constant, is sometimes written
$P_1V_1 = P_2V_2$

Explain this other way of writing the formula.

* **7** 25 cubic centimetres of air at atmospheric pressure are expanded at constant temperature until the pressure has fallen to $\frac{1}{4}$ atmospheric pressure. What is its new volume?

* **8** 40 cubic centimetres of air at atmospheric pressure are compressed at constant temperature until the pressure has increased to 8 times atmospheric pressure. What is its new volume?

** **9** 20 cubic centimetres of gas at atmospheric pressure (100 000 newtons per square metre) are compressed to 4 cubic centimetres without a change in temperature. What is the new pressure?

The speed of an air molecule

** **10** The average speed of an air molecule near the earth is 415 metres per second. How high would a **ball** go if it were thrown vertically upwards with this speed, ignoring air resistance? (**Hint:** Use the formula, $v^2 = u^2 + 2as$. Acceleration will be -10 metres per second per second, and its velocity at the top of the flight will be zero.)

* **11** The answer to question 10 is the approximate height of the atmosphere. If an air molecule fell down through this distance what would be its fastest speed? (**Hint:** You need not calculate the answer).

Diffusion through porous material

** **12** Fig. 7.24 shows how a diffusion experiment is set up. The levels of water inside the mano-meter soon begin to change. Will the level **A** rise or fall? Explain your answer.

Bromine diffusion through air

* **13** Compare and explain carefully what will happen if bromine is run into each of the tubes in fig. 7.25.

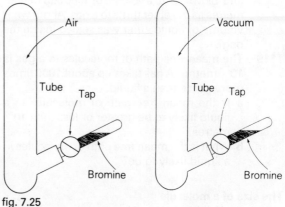

fig. 7.25

The random walk rule

** **14** A regiment of drunken soldiers are stood in the centre of a parade ground. They are dismissed and walk drunkenly away, taking 25 steps at random.
  a How many steps on average, and measured in a straight line, will they move from their starting places?
  b How many steps on average, will they need to get to the edge of the parade ground, 100 paces away?

** **15** A pupil who has heard of the random walk rule tries taking 16 steps at random and ends up back where he started. 'This means', he says, 'that the rule is wrong!' How would you answer this?

The mean free path, y

* **16** How can fig. 7.26 be used to explain mean free path?

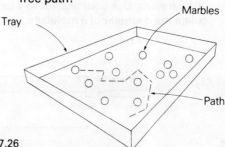

fig. 7.26

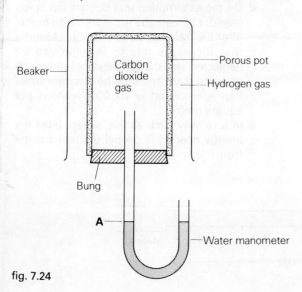

fig. 7.24

*17 The mean free path of molecules in a gas is 10^{-7} metres. Is the size of a gas molecule likely to be greater or smaller than this value?

Change of volume from liquid to gas

*18 Some liquid ether is sealed in a collapsed polythene bag. The bag is put into hot water and 'blows up' to a volume of 1000 cubic centimetres as the ether turns to a gas. About what volume of liquid ether was sealed inside the bag?

**19 The mean free path of molecules in a gas is 10^{-7} metres. A gas takes up about 1000 times more space than a liquid.

  a Is the mean free path of molecules in a liquid likely to be greater or less than 10^{-7} metres?

  b What is the mean free path of molecules in a liquid likely to be?

The size of a molecule

***20 Fig. 7.27 shows a sketch of molecules in a liquid.

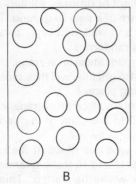

fig. 7.27

  a Guess what is their average distance apart; $\frac{1}{4}$ molecule diameter, $\frac{1}{3}$, $\frac{1}{2}$, $\frac{3}{4}$, 1 molecule diameter, or what?

  b This average distance apart must be the mean free path of molecules in a liquid, 10^{-10} metres. Use your answer to **a** to calculate the diameter of a molecule.

Extra questions

***21 Read the following account, look at the diagrams, and answer the questions **a** to **f** below.

An underground railway has been designed to work between two cities, X and Y, 85 miles apart (fig. 7.28). It is expected to cover this distance, start to stop, in about quarter of an hour.

The train, shown at rest in station X, is a good fit (like a piston) in the tunnel, the clearance between it and the walls being less than 2·5 centimetres all round. Two flaps, at X and Y, seal off the main tunnel from the stations. Atmospheric pressure in the station is about 100 000 newtons per square metre. A pump is used to reduce the pressure in the tunnel to about 2000 newtons per square metre. The train at station X has one end just inside the tunnel, as shown. The flap X is then opened.

  a What happens to the train, and why? Why may this be called an atmospheric railway?

  b When the train is 5 miles inside the tunnel, flap X is closed again, and the train continues to move rapidly towards flap Y, which is still closed. Fig. 7.29 shows how the pressure behind and in front of the train varies as the train travels from X to Y. Why are the portions AB and CD straight? Give an explanation of the rest of the graph.

  c At what distance from A was the train moving with zero acceleration? Where was it moving most rapidly? Where was its forward acceleration greatest? Where was its deceleration greatest?

  d On the assumption that Boyle's law is followed, estimate the pressure in the tunnel after the train has gone through. (Assume that increases due to leakage can be neglected, that the temperature is the same as at the start, and that the pressure when flap X is closed is 100 000 newtons per square metre.

  e In a railway such as this, where does the energy needed to propel the trains come from?

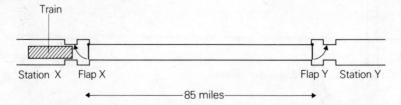

fig. 7.28

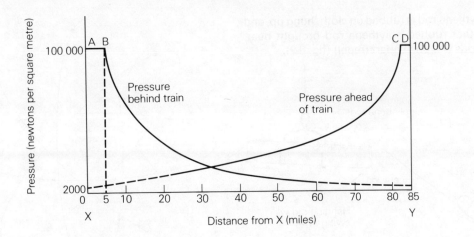

fig. 7.29

f Such a train would attain a speed of, say 420 m.p.h., while a conventional train of the same mass reaches 60 m.p.h.. How many times greater is the kinetic energy of this train, compared with the kinetic energy of the conventional train? What happens to the kinetic energy of an ordinary train? What happens to the kinetic energy of the train described here? (*O. and C.*)

***22 **a** The air in each of the four tyres of a motor car exerts a pressure above atmospheric of 3×10^5 N/m². Each tyre is in contact with the ground over an area of 80 cm² (0·008 m²) Estimate the mass of the car.

b What would happen to the area of contact between the tyres and the ground if the temperature rose? Explain your answer. (*O. and C.*)

8
Static electricity

8.1 Charging by friction

When a nylon shirt is pulled off, it often crackles and makes tiny sparks which can be seen in the dark. It has rubbed against other clothing to become charged with static electricity.

If a plastic comb is rubbed on cloth, it becomes charged and can be made to pick up small pieces of paper (fig. 8.1).

Acetate and polythene rods are useful for experimenting with static electricity.

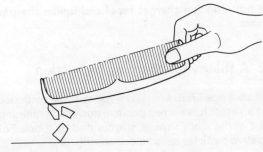

fig. 8.1

If a polythene rod is rubbed on cloth, hung up, and then another rubbed polythene rod brought near, the two rods will push apart (repel) (fig. 8.2).

fig. 8.2

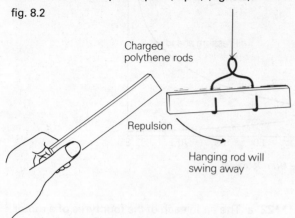

Charged polythene rods

Repulsion

Hanging rod will swing away

Two charged acetate rods will also repel, but a charged acetate rod and a charged polythene rod will pull together (attract) (fig. 8.3).

fig. 8.3

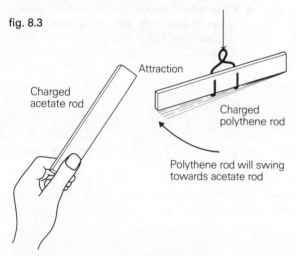

Attraction

Charged acetate rod

Charged polythene rod

Polythene rod will swing towards acetate rod

It seems there are two kinds of static electricity. The charge on the acetate is called **positive** (+). The charge on the polythene is called **negative** (−).
We find that **like charges repel and unlike charges attract.**

8.2 A theory for charging by friction

In sections 17.16 and 17.17 you will see evidence that an atom has a small positive nucleus containing most of the atom's mass, surrounded by a cloud of negative particles called electrons (fig. 8.4).
The size of positive charge in the nucleus equals the

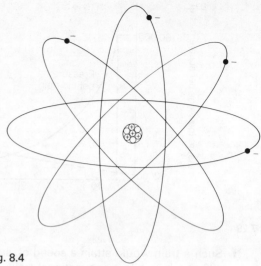

fig. 8.4

total negative charge of all the electrons, so an atom has no overall charge.

When an acetate rod is rubbed it becomes positive, because some electrons are rubbed **off** it onto the cloth. (If the cloth is tested, it is found to be negative).

When a polythene rod is rubbed it becomes negative because some electrons are rubbed **onto** it from the cloth. (If the cloth is tested, it is found to be positive).

8.3 The gold leaf electroscope

The gold leaf electroscope (fig. 8.5) has a piece of gold leaf joined to a metal strip. A metal plate is fixed to the top of the strip which is insulated from the case by a plastic plug. The wooden case is earthed by being stood on a bench. There are glass sides to the case to protect the gold leaf from draughts while it is being used.

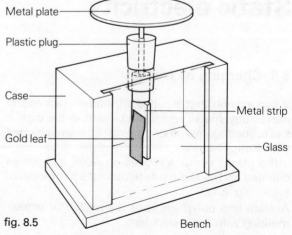

Metal plate

Plastic plug

Case

Gold leaf

Metal strip

Glass

fig. 8.5

Bench

8.4 Charging an electroscope by contact

The atoms of the metal plate, strip and gold leaf in an uncharged electroscope, have equal numbers of positive and negative charges (fig. 8.6).

fig. 8.6

photograph 8a

When a charged polythene rod is rubbed onto the plate (fig. 8.7), some of its negative charge is scraped off.

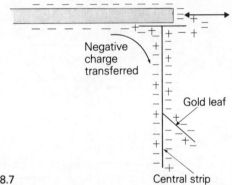

fig. 8.7

The charge spreads out over the strip and leaf and because both get an overall negative charge they repel (fig. 8.8).

fig. 8.8

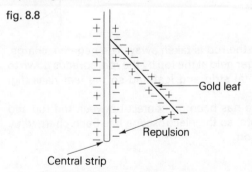

8.5 Charging by induction

It is possible to charge two metal cans without touching them with a rod. The uncharged cans are

made to touch each other as they stand on two non-conducting tiles (photograph 8a).

A charged polythene rod is held near them so that some negative charge is repelled from the can closest to the rod, into the can which is furthest away (fig. 8.9).

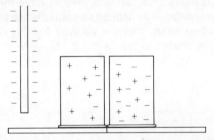

fig. 8.9

While the polythene rod is held near, the cans are pulled apart by moving a tile (photograph 8.b). The rod is then taken away.

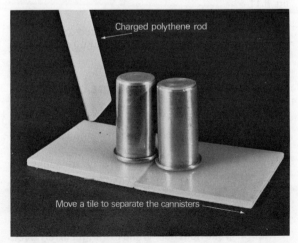

photograph 8.b

To test the cans for charge, an electroscope is first charged by contact with the polythene rod until its gold leaf is at an angle of about 45° (fig. 8.10).

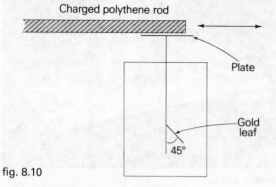

Charged polythene rod

Plate

Gold leaf

45°

fig. 8.10

Each can is then brought in turn, close to the top plate of the electroscope. One can makes the leaf go down slightly, the other can makes the leaf go up slightly.

Bringing up the can which was furthest from the rod has the same effect on the leaf as bringing up the rod itself. This can and the rod have the same kind of charge. This happens because when the cans are pulled apart, there is no way for the repelled negative charge to return (fig. 8.11).

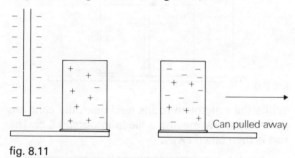

Can pulled away

fig. 8.11

We say that charge has been **induced** on each can, or that the cans have been charged by **induction**.

8.6 Charging an electroscope by induction

A charged acetate rod is held near the top plate of an electroscope. This attracts negative charge up from the leaf and metal strip (fig. 8.12). Because the leaf and metal strip are left positive they repel and the leaf rises.

While the acetate rod is held near the top, the plate is touched to earth it (fig. 8.13).

The rod is still held near while the finger is removed (fig. 8.14).

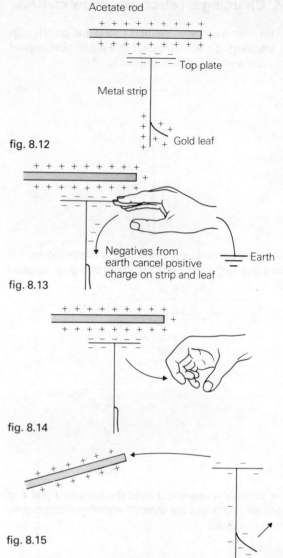

Acetate rod

Top plate

Metal strip

Gold leaf

fig. 8.12

Negatives from earth cancel positive charge on strip and leaf

Earth

fig. 8.13

fig. 8.14

fig. 8.15

Now the rod is taken away. The negative charge, no longer held at the top by the rod, spreads down to the metal strip and leaf and so the leaf rises (fig. 8.15).

There has been no contact between the rod and the plate, so the electroscope has been charged by **induction**.

8.7 Electric fields

A diamond shape, cut from a piece of stiff paper and pinned to a piece of wood (fig. 8.16), can be used to show that where there is a potential difference across a gap, there is an electric field.

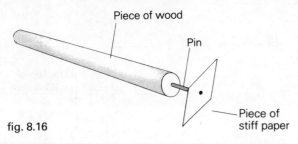

fig. 8.16

A **field** in science is a space where something feels a force.

In a **gravitational field** a **mass** feels a force (section 1.3).

In a **magnetic field** a **magnetic material** feels a force (section 10.3).

In an **electric field** an **electric charge** will feel a force.

If the paper diamond is held between two electrical plates, the point nearest the positive plate will have an induced negative charge and the opposite point will become positive. The charged points will feel forces towards the plates (fig. 8.17) and the diamond will turn until it shows the direction of the electric field.

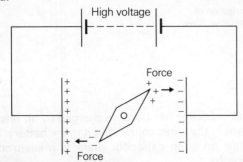

fig. 8.17

In the same way, semolina seeds floating on oil between electrodes will line up to show the direction and pattern of an electric field (photograph 8.c).

The electric field pattern may be drawn as in fig. 8.18.

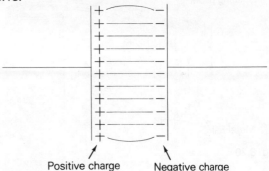

Positive charge   Negative charge

fig. 8.18

8.8 Capacitors

A simple form of capacitor is two metal plates separated by air (fig. 8.19).

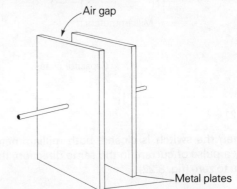

fig. 8.19

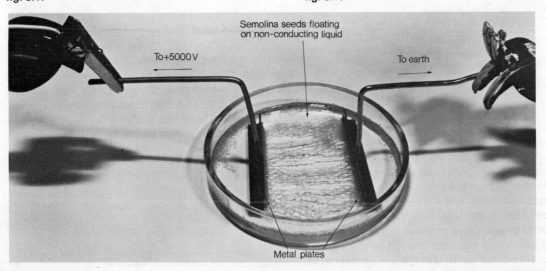

photograph 8.c

If the plates are made of foil and kept apart by insulating paper, the capacitor can be wound to take up less space (fig. 8.20).

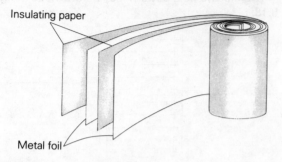

fig. 8.20

The symbol for this type of capacitor is ⊣⊢. A capacitor is put in the circuit shown in fig. 8.21.

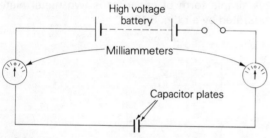

fig. 8.21

When the switch is closed, both milliammeters show a pulse of current in the same direction, then return to zero (fig. 8.22).

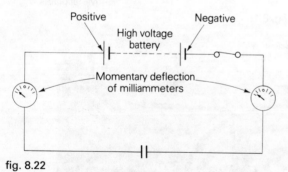

fig. 8.22

It seems as if electricity has jumped the gap between the capacitor plates. What has really happened is that negative charge has moved from the battery onto one of the plates, until that plate is at the same potential as the negative terminal (fig. 8.23).

Negative charge has also moved to the battery from the other plate until it is at the same potential as the positive terminal (fig. 8.24).

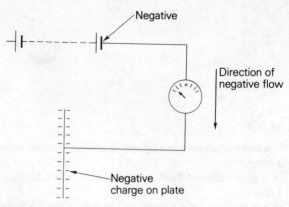

fig. 8.23

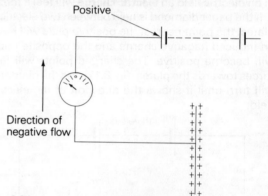

fig. 8.24

The capacitor has become charged by an electric current in the wires connecting it to the battery. The charge on each capacitor plate is measured in **coulombs**.

8.9 Static and current electricity

In fig. 8.22 milliammeters showed a current of electricity as charge flowed to and from the capacitor plates. If a capacitor is connected to a high voltage battery (fig. 8.25) and then its leads touched together, a spark will be seen (fig. 8.26).

If the capacitor is then connected to a working Van

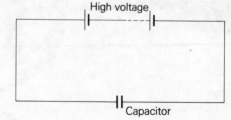

fig. 8.25

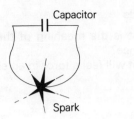
fig. 8.26

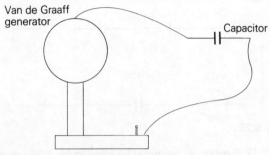
fig. 8.27

de Graaff generator (which generates static electricity) (fig. 8.27), then its leads touched together, a spark will be seen again (fig. 8.26).

The result is the same whether the capacitor is charged from a supply designed to give current electricity, or a supply designed to give static electricity. Here is evidence that there is no difference between the two types of electricity. In current electricity the coulombs of electricity move, in static electricity the coulombs are still.

Revision questions

Charging by friction

* 1 Sometimes dust seems attracted to a newly polished table. Why is this?
* 2 The sides of a strip of polythene, rubbed on cloth and hung over a string, do not hang straight down but push apart (fig. 8.28). Why is this?

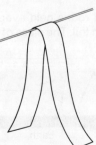
fig. 8.28

* 3 What does the rule, 'like charges repel and unlike charges attract' mean?

A theory for charging by friction

* 4 A piece of dry glass rubbed on silk becomes positively charged. Explain this in terms of electrons.

The gold leaf electroscope

* 5 Why is it important for the gold leaf of an electroscope to be protected from draughts?
* 6 Why must the centre strip of an electroscope be insulated from the case?

Charging an electroscope by contact

** 7 Explain carefully how charge rearranges, when an electroscope is charged positively by contact with an acetate rod.

Charging by induction

*** 8 Two metal spheres, each mounted on a plastic stand (fig. 8.29), have to be charged by induction using a polythene rod. Use a series of sketches to explain how this can be done, and show which sphere will end up with the same negative charge as the polythene rod.

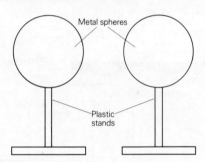
fig. 8.29

Charging an electroscope by induction

*** 9 In fig. 8.30 an electroscope is earthed to make sure that it is not charged. Figs. 8.31 to 8.34

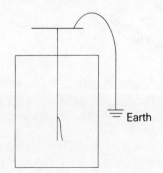
fig. 8.30

show how the electroscope is then charged by induction, using a negatively charged polythene rod. Refer to the diagrams and explain carefully why the electroscope becomes charged.

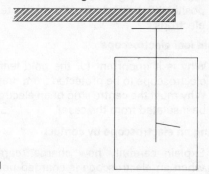

fig. 8.31

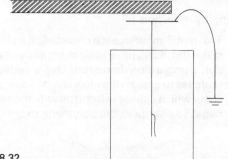

fig. 8.32

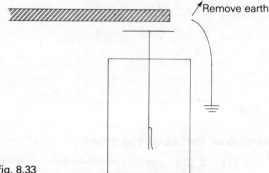

fig. 8.33

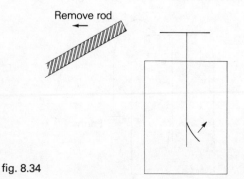

fig. 8.34

Electric fields

*10 What is the meaning of the term 'field' in science?

*11 What will feel a force in an electric field?

Capacitors

*12 Explain what might be seen in fig. 8.35 when the switch is closed.

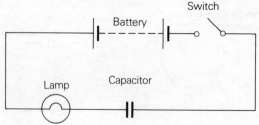

fig. 8.35

**13 Explain what might be seen in fig. 8.36 when the switch is closed (*Hint:* The current from an alternating supply changes direction, back and forth, very quickly).

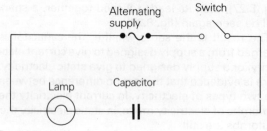

fig. 8.36

Static and current electricity

*14 A capacitor is first connected to a 240 volt, direct current supply and then to a low power mains lamp. The lamp flashes. Why is this?

15 Might the experiment in question **14 work if a Van de Graaff generator is used in place of the 240 volts supply? Explain your answer.

Extra questions

***16 A charged rod is held over a small piece of aluminium foil. The piece of foil jumps up and

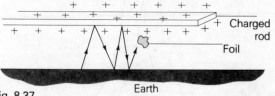

fig. 8.37

down between the rod and earth (fig. 8.37). Why is this?

*17 Photograph 8.d shows a boy standing on insulating blocks, who has become charged by touching a Van de Graaff generator.
   a Why is the boy's hair standing on end?
   b Why does the boy feel a shock when he lets go of the generator and touches the bench?

Boy standing on insulating blocks

Van de Graaff generator

photograph 8.d

***18 Fig. 8.38 shows a light, conducting sphere C hung on an insulating thread between two metal plates A and B. The potential difference V between A and B can be varied.
   a C is initially uncharged and placed midway between A and B before the supply is switched on. Will C move in the electric

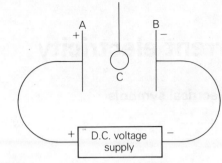

fig. 8.38

field when the supply is switched on?
   b Will it make any difference if C, still uncharged, is initially closer to A than to B? Give a reason for your answer.
   c Write brief notes in explanation of the following observations: i C is given a negative charge. There is a deflection of the sphere which increases as V is gradually made bigger. ii If V is increased so much that C touches one of the plates, C keeps on swinging between the plates, touching them each time. iii While the pendulum is swinging between A and B, the plates are suddenly disconnected from the voltage-supply, leaving the plates charged. The oscillation continues for a while and at first the pendulum makes contact at A and B. When the swing can no longer be detected, the sphere hangs deflected towards one of the plates. It is a long time before C finally hangs midway between the plates.
   d Suggest an optical arrangement for measuring the deflection of C, and give one reason why an optical arrangement is better than mounting a scale close to C. (O. and C.)

***19 A student learning 'A' level physics says 'the leaf of an electroscope rises because it is in an electric field when the electroscope is charged'. What do you think?

9
Current electricity

9.1 Electrical symbols

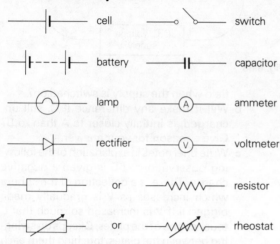

cell   switch

battery   capacitor

lamp   ammeter

rectifier   voltmeter

or   resistor

or   rheostat

9.2 Circuits and circuit diagrams

A lamp cannot be lit just by touching it onto a cell (fig. 9.1a). If a wire is added so that there is a complete loop of circuit then electricity can flow and the lamp will light (fig. 9.1b).

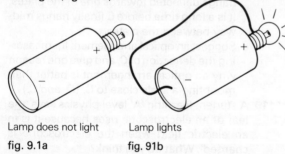

Lamp does not light

fig. 9.1a

Lamp lights

fig. 91b

The way in which a circuit is connected can be shown by a **circuit diagram.** Fig. 9.2 shows two cells connected to a lamp and resistor.

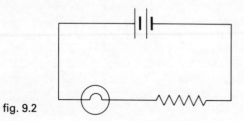

fig. 9.2

9.3 Series and parallel

If lamps are connected in **series** electricity will flow through each of them in turn (fig. 9.3).

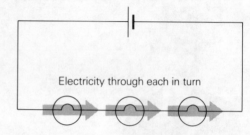

Electricity through each in turn

fig. 9.3 Lamps in series

If lamps are connected in **parallel** electricity from the supply must split up to go through the lamps (fig. 9.4).

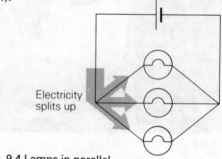

Electricity splits up

fig. 9.4 Lamps in parallel

Fig. 9.5 shows a circuit with one lamp lit to normal brightness by one cell.

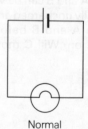

fig. 9.5   Normal

See what happens when extra lamps are added in series (figs. 9.6a and b).

The lamps are dimmer because it is more difficult for the current to flow round the circuit. When extra lamps are added in parallel (figs. 9.7a and b) they each light normally.

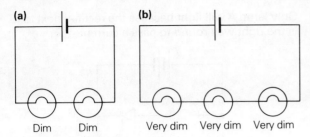

(a)

Dim   Dim

(b)

Very dim   Very dim   Very dim

fig. 9.6 Lamps in series

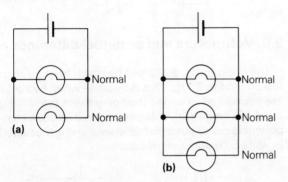

(a)

Normal

Normal

(b)

Normal

Normal

Normal

fig. 9.7 Lamps in parallel

It is as if each lamp had its own separate connections to the cell (figs. 9.8a and b).

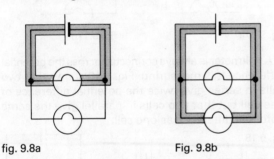

fig. 9.8a   Fig. 9.8b

If any one lamp in parallel is removed or switched off, the others do not change their brightness. This is why house lights are wired in parallel. In fig. 9.9 three lamps are connected to a cell. A and B, which are in series with each other, will be dim.C which is on its own in a loop of the circuit will be lit to normal brightness.

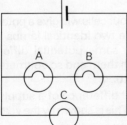

A   B

C

fig. 9.9

9.4 Ammeters and electric current

The brightness of a lamp can be used to judge how much electricity is flowing through it, but to measure the **electric current** accurately in **amperes** an ammeter should be used. Because an ammeter measures the current which flows **through** it, it must be connected in series (fig. 9.10).

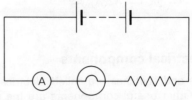

Ammeter in series with lamp and resistor

fig. 9.10

Current is not used up, it just carries electrical energy from the battery to the lamp and resistor and then goes back for more. This means that ammeters anywhere in the circuit will all have the same reading (fig. 9.11).

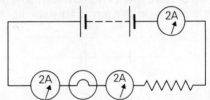

2A

2A   2A

fig. 9.11

Ammeters should be connected with their red terminal nearer the positive side of the battery (fig. 9.12), or the needle will try to go backwards and the ammeter might break.

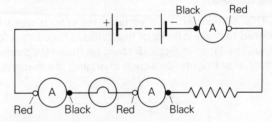

Black   Red

+   −   A

A   A

Red   Black   Red   Black

fig. 9.12

Electric current flows round a circuit like water going through pipes: sometimes it splits up to go through parallel parts, but it comes back together again afterwards. This is shown by the ammeter readings in fig. 9.13.
Notice that in fig. 9.13 if X and Y are identical lamps, then Y will be brightest because it has more current flowing through it.

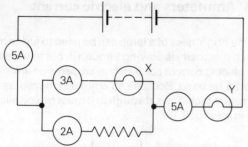

fig. 9.13

9.5 Electrical components

Lamps and switches are called electrical components. Other useful components are the resistor, rheostat and rectifier.

The resistor

This component will control how much current goes round a circuit by making it more difficult for the current to flow. In fig. 9.14 lamp A will be brighter than lamp B. The current in lamp B is smaller because there is a resistor in that loop of the circuit.

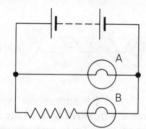

fig. 9.14

The rheostat

This component is a variable resistor. It can be altered to make it more or less difficult for current to flow. The lamp in fig. 9.15 could be made gradually dimmer or brighter by slowly changing the rheostat.

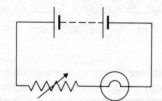

fig. 9.15

The rectifier (or diode)

This component will only let a current flow through it in one direction. Fig. 9.16 shows two lamps in parallel, each with a rectifier in their loop of the circuit.

Only lamp A will light because the rectifier next to it is the right way round to pass a current.

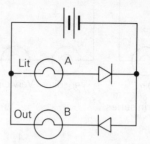

fig. 9.16

9.6 Voltmeters and potential difference

The lamp in fig. 9.17a will be much brighter than the one in fig. 9.17b. This is because when two cells are connected in series they give twice the driving force of a single cell. This driving force across a component is called **potential difference** and is measured in volts by using a voltmeter.

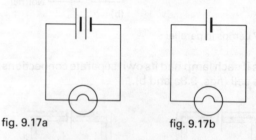

fig. 9.17a   fig. 9.17b

A voltmeter is always connected across the potential difference it is measuring. Fig. 9.18 shows that two cells in series give twice the potential difference of one cell but that two cells in parallel give the same potential difference as one cell.

fig. 9.18

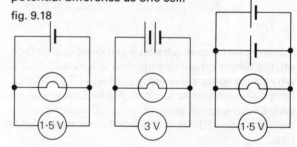

A battery of four cells will give a potential difference of six volts. The two identical lamps in fig. 9.19 will each need the same potential difference to drive current through them and so voltmeters A and B will both read 3 volts.

The potential difference of a supply is shared out round a circuit. This is shown by the voltmeter readings in fig. 9.20.

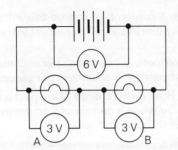

fig. 9.19   A   B

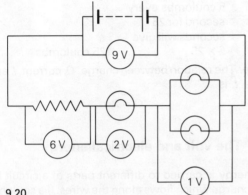

fig. 9.20

Notice that 6 V + 2 V + 1 V = 9 V

9.7 Resistance

The larger the potential difference needed to drive current through part of a circuit the more difficult that part must be for the current to get through. This 'difficulty' is called **resistance**. Notice that in fig. 9.20 the resistor had three times the resistance of the single lamp, because it needed three times the potential difference to drive current through it. Cells are added one by one in series to the circuit in fig. 9.21.

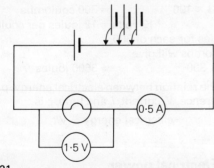

fig. 9.21

A graph of the potential difference and current values is shown in fig. 9.22.

Notice that the graph line is straight. This shows

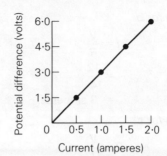

fig. 9.22

that twice the potential difference gives twice the current, three times the potential difference gives three times the current and so on. **The current is proportional to the potential difference.** This rule for resistors is called **Ohm's law.**

Ohm's law gives us the formula

$$V = IR$$

where R is resistance and is measured in **ohms, (Ω)**, V is the potential difference and I is the current. The formula is sometimes drawn in a triangle.

Cover the letter which stands for what you want to find and the other two letters tell you how to calculate it.

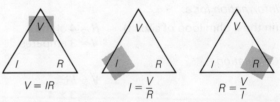

$V = IR$ $I = \dfrac{V}{R}$ $R = \dfrac{V}{I}$

Example: Fig. 9.23 shows three circuits. Calculate the potential difference in **a**, the current in **b** and the resistance in **c**.

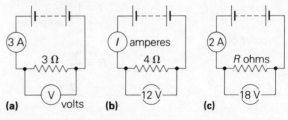

(a)   (b)   (c)

fig. 9.23

Calculation for a

$$V = IR$$
$$= 3 \times 3$$
$$= 9 \text{ volts}$$

71

Calculation for **b**

$$I = \frac{V}{R}$$

$$= \frac{12}{4}$$

$$= 3 \text{ amperes}$$

Calculation for **c**

$$R = \frac{V}{I}$$

$$= \frac{18}{2}$$

$$= 9 \text{ ohms}$$

The Ohm's law equation can also be used for different parts of a circuit.

Example: In fig. 9.24 what is **a** the potential difference of the battery? **b** the resistance of R?

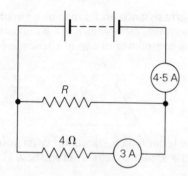
fig. 9.24

Information for **a**
(in the 4 ohm loop of circuit)　　　$R = 4$ ohms
　　　　　　　　　　　　　　　　$I = 3$ amperes

Calculation

$$V = IR$$

$$= 3 \times 4$$

$$= 12 \text{ volts}$$

Information for **b**
(in the R loop of circuit)　　　$V = 12$ volts
　　　　　　　　　　　　　　$I = 4 \cdot 5 - 3$
　　　　　　　　　　　　　　$= 1 \cdot 5$ amperes

Calculation

$$R = \frac{V}{I}$$

$$= \frac{12}{1 \cdot 5}$$

$$= 8 \text{ ohms}$$

9.8　The ampere and electric charge

Electric current is a flow of charge along a wire. Charge is measured in **coulombs** (sections 8.8 and 8.9). When 1 coulomb of charge takes 1 second to flow past a point in a wire, the current in that wire is 1 ampere.

　　　　1 ampere = 1 coulomb per second
　　(4 amperes = 4 coulombs per second)

Example: How much charge flows past a point in a piece of wire when a current of 5 amperes flows for 25 seconds through that wire?

Calculation

　　　　　　　　5 amperes = 5 coulombs per second
∴ 5 coulombs every
　second for 25
　seconds will give
　5×25　　　　　　　= 125 coulombs

Note: The relation between charge, Q, current, I, and time, t, is

$$Q = It$$

9.9　The volt and electrical energy

Energy is carried to different parts of a circuit by the charge which flows along the wires. If a coulomb of charge gives up a joule of energy as it passes through a lamp, the potential difference across that lamp will be 1 volt.

　　　　1 volt = 1 joule per coulomb
　　(6 volts = 6 joules per coulomb)

Example: The potential difference across a heater is 12 volts. How much electrical energy will be turned to heat if its current of 3 amperes flows for 100 seconds?

Calculation

　　　　　　　3 amperes = 3 coulombs per second
3 coulombs every second
　for 100 seconds will
　give 3×100　　　　= 300 coulombs
　　　　　　　　12 volts = 12 joules per coulomb
12 joules for each of 300
　coulombs will give
　12×300　　　　　= 3600 joules

Note: The relation between electrical energy, potential difference, V, current, I, and time, t, is

　　　　electrical energy = Vit

9.10　Electrical power

Power, measured in watts, is the rate at which work is done, or energy changed from one form to another (section 6.10).

1 watt = 1 joule per second
(60 watts = 60 joules per second)

Example: The potential difference across a lamp, carrying a current of 2 amperes, is 12 volts. What is the power of the lamp?

Calculation

12 volts = 12 joules per coulomb
2 amperes = 2 coulombs per second

Therefore, every second the 2 coulombs are each giving 12 joules of electrical energy to the lamp.

∴ total energy per second = 12 × 2
= 24 joules per second
power = 24 watts

Note: The relation between electrical power, potential difference, *V*, and current, *I*, is

electrical power = *VI*
(watts = volts × amperes)

9.11 Electricity and heat

When an electric current flows through a resistance, electrical energy changes to heat energy. This happens in electrical fires, cookers and water heaters, and is why fuses 'blow'. If too much current flows through a fuse it gets so hot that it melts and the circuit is broken.

Another result of this heating effect is that many materials do not seem to obey Ohm's law. In fact, the resistance of most metals increases with heat, as the hot atoms vibrate more and get in the way of the current. Fig. 9.25 is a graph of potential difference against current, for a lamp.

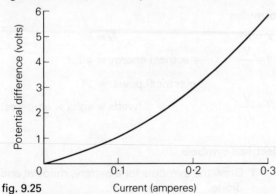

fig. 9.25

The graph line gets steeper, which shows that as more current flows and the filament gets hotter, its resistance increases.

The same effect can be shown by passing a small current through a piece of iron wire then heating the

wire gently in a flame (fig. 9.26). The current falls as the temperature rises showing that the resistance of the wire has increased.

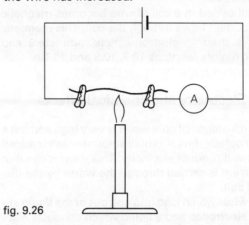

fig. 9.26

The thermistor

If instead of the iron wire in fig. 9.26 a carbon thermistor is used (fig. 9.27) the current rises as the temperature rises. This shows that the hotter a thermistor gets the lower is its resistance.

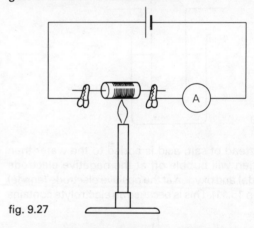

fig. 9.27

9.12 Electricity and magnetism

When current flows through a wire a magnetic

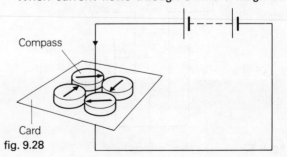

Compass

Card
fig. 9.28

field can be found near to the wire. Compasses show that the direction of this field is circular about the wire (fig. 9.28).

A nail placed in a coil of wire becomes magnetic when current flows through the coil. This magnetic effect is used in electromagnets, ammeters and electric motors (sections 10.7, 10.9 and 10.10).

9.13 Electricity and chemical effects

The resistance of pure water is very high and it is a good insulator, but, if a small amount of salt is added to it, it will conduct electricity. This must mean that the current is carried through the water by the dissolved salt.

The wires which lead into and out of the liquid are called **electrodes** and a liquid which conducts electricity is called an **electrolyte** (fig. 9.29).

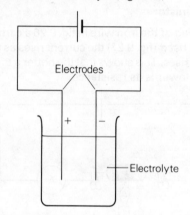

Electrodes

+   −

Electrolyte

fig. 9.29

If instead of salt, acid is added to the water then hydrogen will bubble off at the negative electrode (**cathode**) and oxygen at the positive electrode (**anode**) (section 15.11). This is because an electrolyte contains

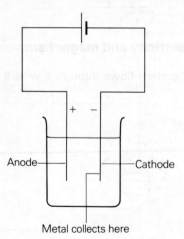

+   −

Anode

Cathode

fig. 9.30   Metal collects here

positive parts which are attracted towards the cathode and negative parts which are attracted towards the anode. These 'parts' are called **positive ions** and **negative ions** and when they move to conduct electricity this is **electrolysis.**

If the electrolyte is a metal salt like copper sulphate dissolved in water, then positive ions of metal move to the cathode and a coating of the metal builds up when a current flows (fig. 9.30).
This discovery led to the electroplating process.

Electric cells

Just as electricity can cause chemical effects, chemical effects can cause electricity. If two different metals such as zinc and copper are put into dilute acid, a potential difference will develop between them which will drive a current round a circuit (fig. 9.31). This is the basis of all electric cells.

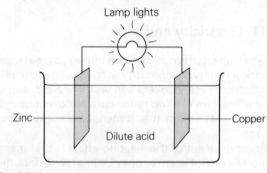

Lamp lights

Zinc   Copper

Dilute acid

fig. 9.31

Revision questions

Formulae

$$V = IR \qquad\qquad Q = It$$

$$I = \frac{V}{R} \qquad \text{electrical energy} = VIt$$

$$\text{electrical power} = VI$$

$$R = \frac{V}{I} \qquad\qquad (\text{watts} = \text{volts} \times \text{amperes})$$

Electrical symbols

* 1 Draw the symbols for a battery, rheostat and diode.
* 2 What do the two symbols shown in fig. 9.32 represent?

(a)   (b)

fig. 9.32

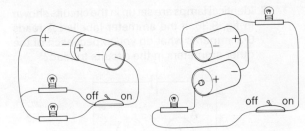

fig. 9.33

Circuits and circuit diagrams

* **3** Draw circuit diagrams for each of the arrangements of cells, lamps and switches shown in fig. 9.33.

Series and parallel

** **4** Which of the identical lamps shown in fig. 9.34 will either not light or else light dimly, normally or brightly? *Hint:* The lamp labelled A lights normally.

* **5** Why do lamps connected to a single cell light more brightly if they are connected in parallel rather than in series?

Ammeters and electric current

* **6** What does an ammeter measure?
* **7** One terminal of each of the ammeters in the circuits in fig. 9.35 has been marked with a *. Which of these marked terminals is red and which black?

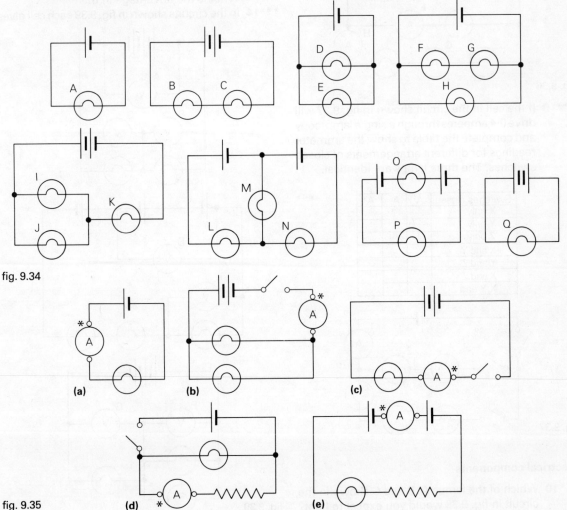

fig. 9.34

fig. 9.35   (a)   (b)   (c)   (d)   (e)

8 Identical lamps are set up in the circuits shown in fig. 9.36. If the ammeter labelled A reads 0·3 amperes what do you expect each of the other ammeters in the circuits to read?

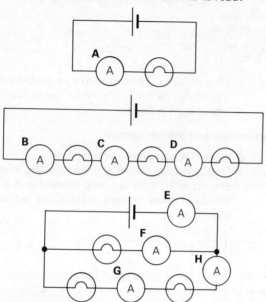

fig. 9.36

9 If the cell in the circuit shown in fig. 9.37 will drive 0·4 amperes through a single lamp, copy and complete the table to show the ammeter readings for different arrangements of closed switches. The three lamps are identical.

Switches closed	A¹	A²	A³
X only			
Y only			
Z only			
X and Y			
Y and Z			
X and Z			
X, Y and Z			

fig. 9.37

Electrical components

*10 Which of the lamps A, B and C shown in the circuit in fig. 9.38 would you expect to light?

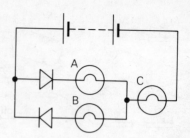

fig. 9.38

11 Draw a circuit using one rheostat in which two lamps can be dimmed down from full brightness while one remains fully bright.

Voltmeters and Potential difference

*12 What is potential difference?

13 Cells used to make up a battery are usually connected in series, but in a heavy lorry there are often two batteries connected in parallel. What is the advantage in this?

***14 In the circuits shown in fig. 9.39 each cell gives

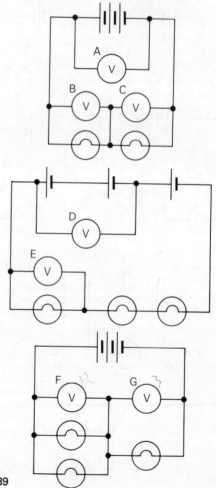

fig. 9.39

76

a potential difference of 1·5 volts and the lamps are identical. What does each voltmeter read?

Resistance

**15 In the circuit shown in fig. 9.40 what are the resistances of R_1 and R_2?

fig. 9.40

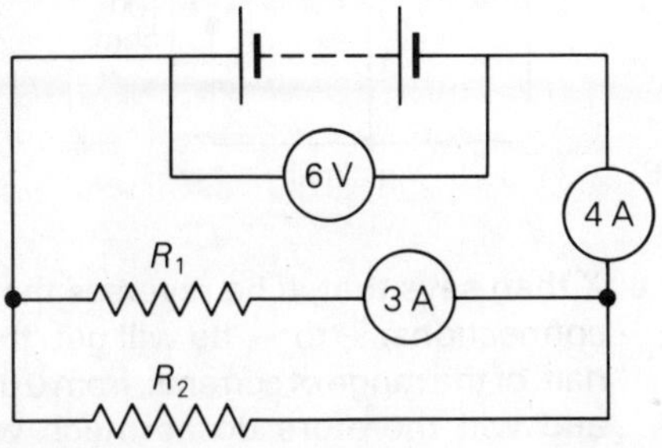

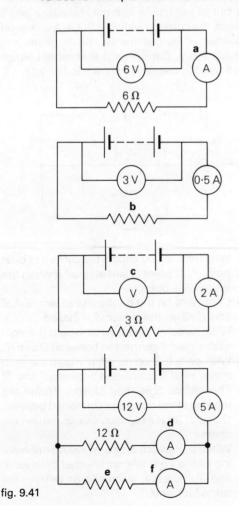

16 In each of the circuits shown in fig. 9.41 find values for the quantities marked **a to **f**.

fig. 9.41

The ampere and electric charge

*17 How many coulombs flow past a point in a wire every second, when the current through that wire is 9 amperes?

**18 If 120 coulombs of charge passed through a heater in 24 seconds, what was the current?

The volt and electrical energy

*19 The potential difference across a lamp is 6 volts. How much electrical energy is given to the lamp by each coulomb of charge that flows through it?

**20 The potential difference across a heater is 24 volts. How much electrical energy will be turned to heat if a current of 5 amperes flows through the heater for 40 seconds?

Electrical power

*21 What amount of power is being used to run the lamp in fig. 9.42?

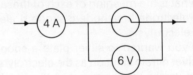

fig. 9.42

**22 If a lamp is marked 240 V, 60 W, what current does it take?

**23 3 amperes flow through a 60 watt heater when it is running normally. What is the potential difference across the heater?

Electricity and heat

**24 The graph in 9.43 was drawn from corresponding values of potential difference and current for a lamp.

Use the formula $R = \dfrac{V}{I}$ to find the resistance

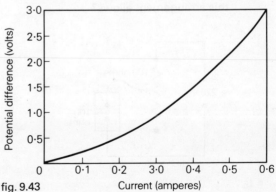

fig. 9.43

of the lamp when it is carrying currents of **a** 0·2 amperes **b** 0·4 amperes **c** 0·6 amperes. Why does the resistance change?

*25 Give one use for a thermistor.

Electricity and magnetism

*26 Draw a diagram to show the pattern which would be formed by iron filings if they were sprinkled on the card shown in fig. 9.44.

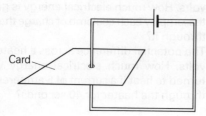

fig. 9.44

Electricity and chemical effects

*27 What is the meaning of each of these words? **a** electrode **b** cathode **c** anode **d** electrolyte **e** electrolysis.

*28 If you wanted to silver plate a spoon using silver nitrate solution as the electrolyte, would you make the spoon act as the anode or the cathode?

Extra questions

***29 Two pupils, X and Y, are each given a piece of electrical apparatus E having a resistance of 100 ohms, and a 100 ohm rheostat. They have an electrical supply of 220 V d.c. They are told to use the rheostat so as to give the biggest possible range of current through the apparatus E.

  a X joins up circuit (i) (fig. 9.45). What is the least and greatest current through E that this arrangement allows?

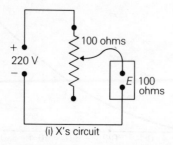

(i) X's circuit

fig. 9.45

b Y joins up circuit (ii) (fig. 9.46). What is his least and greatest current through E?

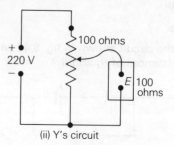

fig. 9.46   (ii) Y's circuit

  c X then says that, if he reverses the source connections, + to −, he will get 'the other half' of the range of currents, from 0 upwards and will therefore do as much with his circuit as Y does with his. Is this so? Give the reason for your answer. (*O. and C.*).

***30 When an ammeter is connected in series with a cell of negligible internal resistance and a lamp, the current reading is 0·2 A. A voltmeter connected across the terminals of the cell reads 1·5 V. Similar cells and similar lamps are used in the circuit shown in fig. 9.47.

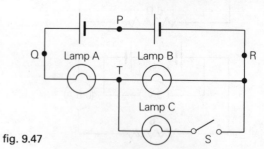

fig. 9.47

  a What would you expect the current to be at point P, at point Q and at point R when the switch S is open?

  b Comment on the brightness of lamps A, B and C when the switch S is closed.

  c With switch S open, what would the voltmeter read if connected between Q and R?

  d With switch S open, what would the voltmeter read if connected between P and T?

  e The switch S is then closed. Would the reading of the voltmeter connected between Q and R increase, decrease or remain the same?

  f When the switch S closes, would the reading of the voltmeter connected between P and T increase, decrease or remain the same? (*O. and C.*)

10
Magnets and Electromagnetism

10.1 North and South seeking poles

Fig. 10.1 shows a bar magnet hanging on a loop of cotton.

fig. 10.1

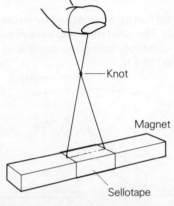

The magnet twists about the knot until it is lined up in a north-south direction. The end which points towards the north is called the **north seeking pole.** The end which points towards the south is called the **south seeking pole** (fig. 10.2).

fig. 10.2

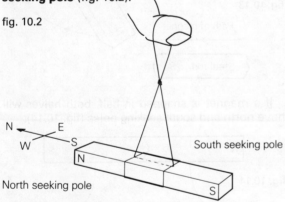

10.2 Like poles repel, unlike poles attract

If two north seeking poles are held together, they are found to push apart (repel).

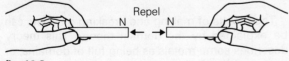

fig. 10.3

Two south seeking poles also repel.

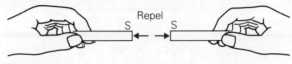

fig. 10.4

A south seeking pole pulls towards (attracts) a north seeking pole.

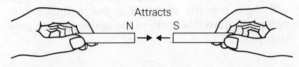

fig. 10.5

These results are summed up in the rule

like poles repel,   unlike poles attract

A compass needle is a small bar magnet balanced at its centre (fig. 10.6).

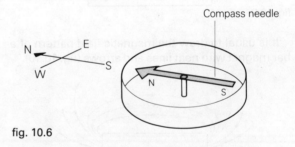

fig. 10.6

Because 'like poles repel', a compass needle will point **away** from the north seeking pole of a magnet (fig. 10.7).

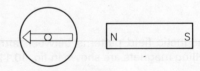

fig. 10.7

10.3 Magnetic field patterns

The magnetic field pattern of a bar magnet can be shown with iron filings (fig. 10.8). The filings are sprinkled thinly onto paper round a magnet.

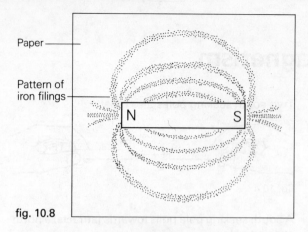

fig. 10.8

Compasses put on the paper instead of iron filings, will show that the direction of the magnetic field pattern is from the north to the south seeking pole (fig. 10.9).

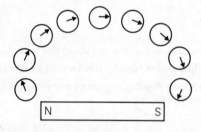

fig. 10.9

It is usual to draw the magnetic field pattern of a bar magnet with neat lines and arrows (fig. 10.10).

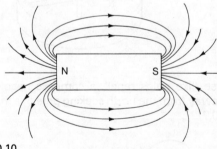

fig. 10.10

The magnetic field patterns between attracting and repelling magnets are shown in fig. 10.11.

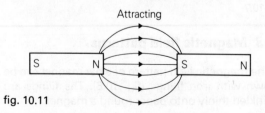

fig. 10.11

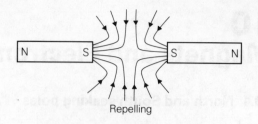

Repelling

10.4 Making and breaking magnets

A steel rod can be magnetised by stroking it with a bar magnet. The steel rod must always be stroked in the same direction, using the same end of the bar magnet (fig. 10.12).

fig. 10.12

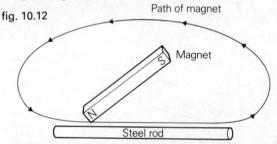

The steel rod drawn in fig. 10.12 will become magnetised with its south seeking pole on the right (fig. 10.13).

fig. 10.13

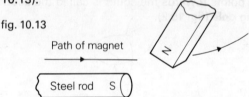

If a magnet is snapped in half, both halves will have north and south seeking poles (fig. 10.14).

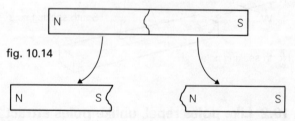

fig. 10.14

10.5 The Domain Theory of magnetism

The results of making and breaking magnets can be explained by the domain theory. This theory describes some metals as being full of domains, or tiny patches of magnetism. In unmagnetised steel

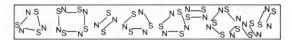

fig. 10.15

these domains are jumbled up, so there is no overall magnetism (fig. 10.15).

In a magnet the domains are lined up so that at one end are the north seeking poles of domains, and at the other end are the south seeking poles (fig. 10.16).

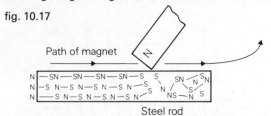

fig. 10.16

Some metals, such as copper and aluminium, cannot be magnetised. These **non-magnetic** metals have no domains to be lined up.

When a steel rod is magnetised by stroking we can imagine the domains being pulled into line by the moving magnet (fig. 10.17).

fig. 10.17

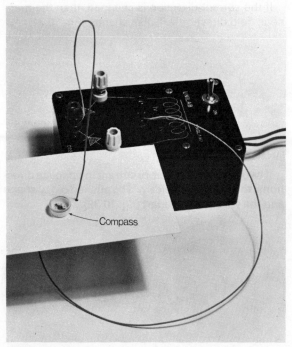

When a magnet is broken, the new ends formed at the break will have one set of domain poles which are south seeking, and one set which are north seeking (fig. 10.18).

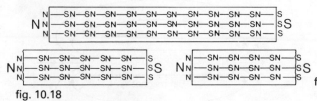

fig. 10.18

10.6 Electromagnetism

Photograph 10.a shows a compass near a wire. When the electricity is switched on, the compass needle will move because the current causes a magnetic field near the wire. Putting the compass in different positions round the wire, shows that the magnetic field pattern is circular (fig. 10.19).

The magnetic field pattern round a wire has been drawn from above in fig. 10.20. The current is coming up 'out of the page'.

Note: Current coming up a wire 'out of the page'

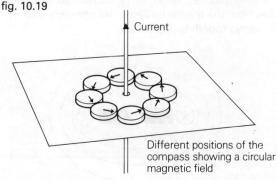

photograph 10.a

fig. 10.19

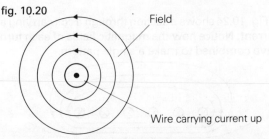

Different positions of the compass showing a circular magnetic field

fig. 10.20

towards you is shown as ⊙ . Current going down a wire 'into the page' away from you is shown as ⊗ . (Imagine the point of a dart coming towards you or the flight feathers of a dart going away from you).

If the current direction is changed, then the magnetic field direction will also change (fig. 10.21).

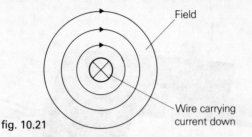

fig. 10.21

If two parallel wires carry current in opposite directions, the magnetic fields will be pushed out of shape and the wires forced apart (fig. 10.22).

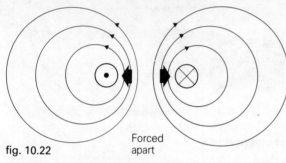

fig. 10.22

If two parallel wires carry current in the same direction, the magnetic fields will combine and pull the wires together (fig. 10.23).

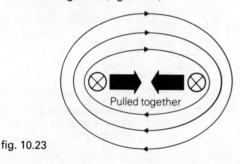

fig. 10.23

Fig. 10.24 shows a section through a coil carrying a current. Notice how the magnetic fields of each turn have combined to make a single pattern.

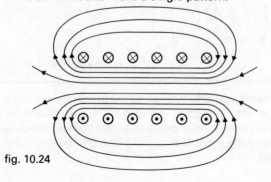

fig. 10.24

If a coil (solenoid) is threaded through a card, then its magnetic field can be investigated with a compass as in fig. 10.25.

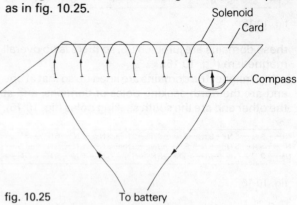

fig. 10.25

10.7 The electromagnet

The magnetic field pattern near a solenoid is like that of a bar magnet (fig. 10.26).

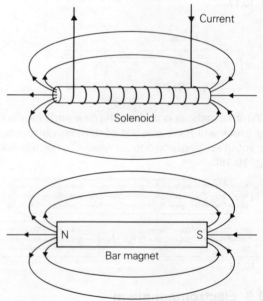

fig. 10.26

Iron filings sprinkled round a small solenoid may not show a very clear pattern when the current is flowing. If an iron nail is put into the solenoid the iron filings will be affected more (fig. 10.27).

The domains of the iron nail have been lined up by the weak magnetic field of the solenoid. The magnetism of the domains now adds to the magnetism of the solenoid to make a much stronger magnetic field. If the current is switched off, the domains 'jumble up'

fig. 10.27

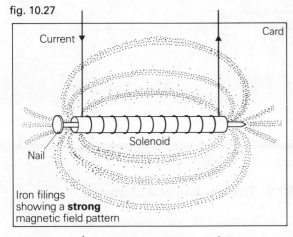

Current

Card

Solenoid

Nail

Iron filings
showing a **strong**
magnetic field pattern

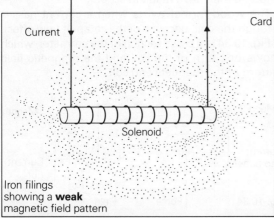

Current

Card

Solenoid

Iron filings
showing a **weak**
magnetic field pattern

photograph 10.b

and the magnetic field gets weaker. This fact is used in a magnetic crane (photograph 10.b). When the current is switched off, the piece of iron will fall.

10.8 The catapult field

Magnadur magnets have poles on their faces (fig. 10.28).

fig. 10.28

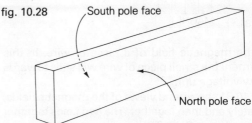

South pole face

North pole face

If two magnets are fitted to an iron yoke so that they attract, the magnetic field pattern between them is like that shown in fig. 10.29.

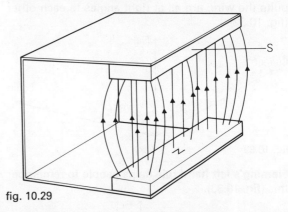

S

fig. 10.29

The apparatus in fig. 10.30 is to show the effect of bringing the magnetic field of magnadur magnets

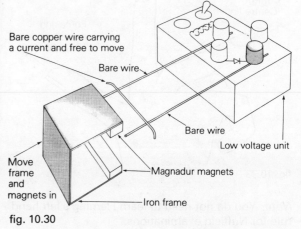

Bare copper wire carrying
a current and free to move

Bare wire

Bare wire

Low voltage unit

Move
frame
and
magnets in

Magnadur magnets

Iron frame

fig. 10.30

83

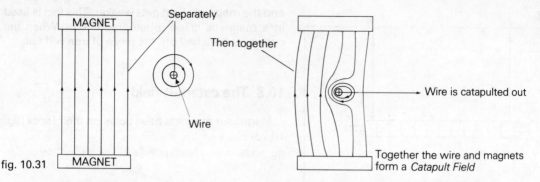

fig. 10.31

Separately

Then together

Wire

Wire is catapulted out

Together the wire and magnets form a *Catapult Field*

near the magnetic field of a piece of wire. In this experiment the small piece of wire will slide towards the low voltage unit.

Fig. 10.31 shows end views of the magnetic fields, separately and then together. The two fields together form a **catapult field**. The wire is **catapulted** to the right as the fields try to get back to their normal shapes.

The magnetic field, current and force which catapults the wire, are all at right angles to each other (fig. 10.32).

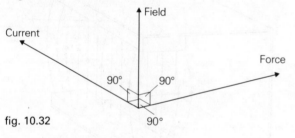

Field

Current

Force

90° 90°

90°

fig. 10.32

Fleming's left hand rule helps people to remember this (fig. 10.33).

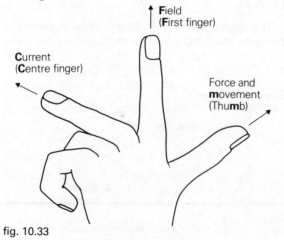

Field
(**F**irst finger)

Current
(**C**entre finger)

Force and
movement
(Thu**m**b)

fig. 10.33

Note: You do not need to learn Fleming's left hand rule for Nuffield examinations.

10.9 The moving coil ammeter

Photograph 10.c is a moving coil ammeter of the kind you may have made in school.

The wood former twists when a current passes through the coil, because of the catapult field effect.

Fig. 10.34 is a cross section of the ammeter, which shows one turn of the coil and the magnetic field pattern of the magnets and coil.

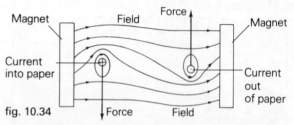

Magnet

Field

Force

Magnet

Current
into paper

Current
out
of paper

fig. 10.34

Force

Field

Because current goes in different directions on opposite sides of the coil, one side is catapulted up and the other side down.

The spirals (photograph 10.c) act as springs. The bigger the current passed through the coil, the further the spirals will twist. When the current is switched off, the spirals will bring the coil back level again.

10.10 The electric motor

The apparatus used as an ammeter in photograph 10.c can be used to make a motor. The spirals must be shortened to make bare wire contacts, and these contacts fixed at the same end of the spindle (fig. 10.35). Sellotape is used to insulate the wires from the spindle.

Bare wire brushes are made to touch the contacts, so that electricity can be passed into the coil (fig. 10.36).

In fig. 10.37 only one turn of the coil is drawn to explain why it turns round and round. One side of the coil has been drawn thicker, to help the explanation.

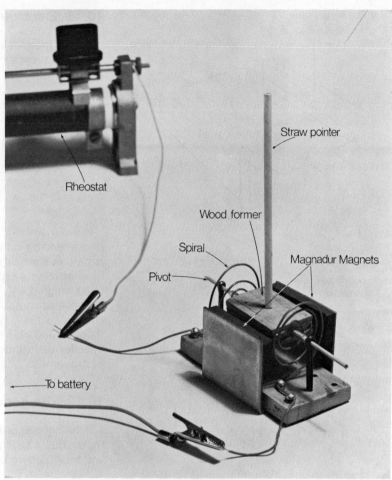

Straw pointer

Rheostat

Wood former

Spiral

Magnadur Magnets

Pivot

To battery

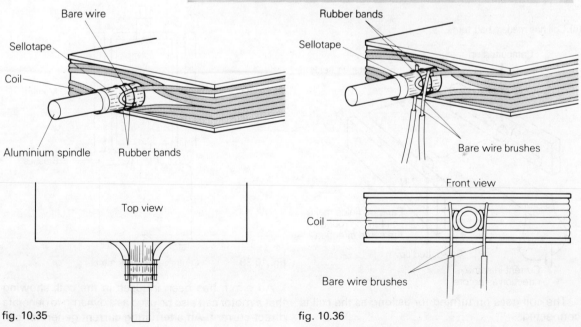

Bare wire

Sellotape

Coil

Aluminium spindle

Rubber bands

Top view

fig. 10.35

Rubber bands

Sellotape

Bare wire brushes

Front view

Coil

Bare wire brushes

fig. 10.36

(a) Coil about to turn

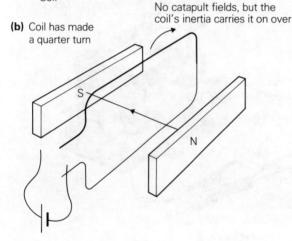

fig. 10.37

Catapulted up

Catapult fields

S

N

Current

Cell

Catapulted down

(b) Coil has made a quarter turn

No catapult fields, but the coil's inertia carries it on over

S

N

(c) Coil has made a half turn

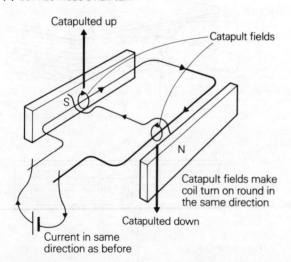

Catapulted up

Catapult fields

S

N

Catapult fields make coil turn on round in the same direction

Catapulted down

Current in same direction as before

The coil goes on turning for as long as the cell is connected.

10.11 Electromagnetic induction

As the magnet in fig. 10.38 is pushed into the coil, the galvanometer needle will move, showing a flow of current.

fig. 10.38

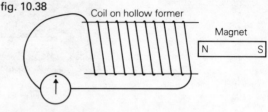

Coil on hollow former

Magnet

N   S

Centre zero galvanometer

If the magnet is pulled out again, the needle will give a reading in the opposite direction. If the magnet is held still inside the coil, there will be no reading. Similar results can be got by pushing a coil over a fixed magnet.

The electromotive force (e.m.f.) which causes a current to flow, is only made (induced) when the magnet and coil move relative to each other. The direction of the induced e.m.f. depends on the direction of movement.

10.12 The generator

If the brushes of a motor are connected to a galvanometer (fig. 10.39) and the coil spun by hand, there will be a reading on the galvanometer.

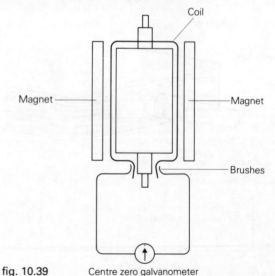

Coil

Magnet

Magnet

Brushes

fig. 10.39   Centre zero galvanometer

An e.m.f. has been induced in the coil, showing that a motor can also be used as a dynamo to generate direct current. An alternating current generator can

fig. 10.40

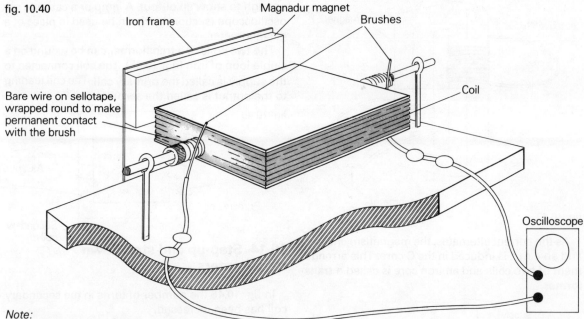

Iron frame

Magnadur magnet

Brushes

Coil

Bare wire on sellotape, wrapped round to make permanent contact with the brush

Oscilloscope

Note:
In order to clarify the diagram a magnet and part of the frame and base have been omitted

be made if the contacts are changed, so there is a brush and contact at each end of the coil (fig. 10.40). An oscilloscope is used to show the alternating output.

10.13 Electromagnetic induction and the transformer

A coil is wound on a C-core and joined to a galvanometer. As a bar magnet is put across the C-core gap (fig. 10.41) the galvanometer needle will give a reading.

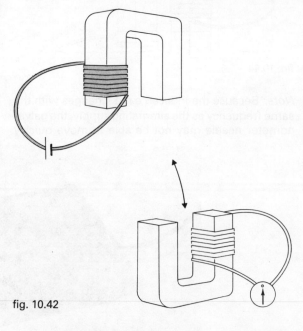

fig. 10.42

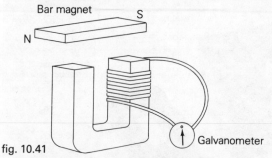

Bar magnet

S

N

Galvanometer

fig. 10.41

If the magnet is pulled off again, the needle will give a reading in the opposite direction. If the magnet is left 'stuck' to the C-core, there will be no reading. An e.m.f. is only induced in the coil when the magnetism in the C-core is being made stronger or weaker.

The same result can be got by using an electromagnet instead of a bar magnet (fig. 10.42).

Instead of moving the electromagnet, it is easier to switch it on and off to change the magnetism in the C-core (fig. 10.43).

Instead of switching the electromagnet on and off, it is easier to run it on an alternating supply (fig. 10.44).

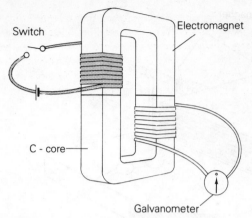

fig. 10.43

As the current alternates, the magnetism changes and an e.m.f. is induced in the C-core. This arrangement of two coils and an iron core is called a **transformer.**

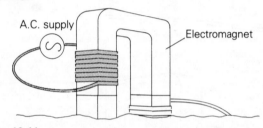

fig. 10.44

Note: Because the induced e.m.f. changes with the same frequency as the alternating supply, the galvanometer needle may not be able to move quickly

enough to show an output. A lamp or a cathode ray oscilloscope (section 11.2) can be used in place of a galvanometer.

The two coils of a transformer can be wound on a single loop of iron (fig. 10.45). The coil connected to the supply is called the **primary coil.** The coil leading to the output is called the **secondary coil.**

fig. 10.45

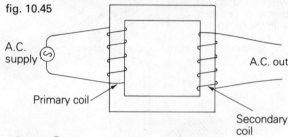

10.14 Step-up and step-down transformers

In fig. 10.46 the number of turns in the secondary coil has been increased.

fig. 10.46

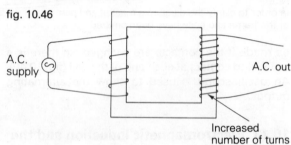

How this affects the output can be tested using the apparatus in photograph 10.d. L_2 is connected to the

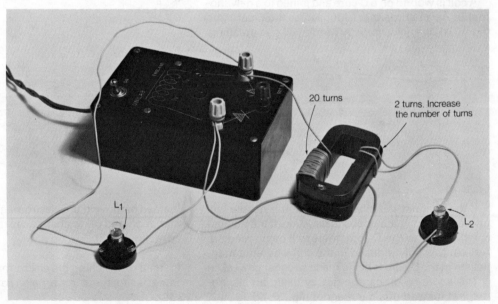

photograph 10.d

output of the transformer, and it will get brighter as the number of turns on the secondary coil is increased. L_1 is used for comparison. It is connected directly to the supply and its brightness does not change.

The experiment in photograph 10.d shows the use of a transformer. It **transforms** (changes) the value of a voltage. If the transformer increases the voltage, it is called a step-up transformer; if it decreases the voltage, it is called a **step-down** transformer.

The circuit shown in fig. 10.47 can be used to compare the voltage and current input and output of a transformer.

The table gives results from such an experiment.

Notice that as the secondary voltage is made bigger, the secondary current gets smaller. This is because the transformer can increase voltage but not power. The table of results shows that the power input and outputs are all roughly the same (about 48 watts). It does not matter if the transformer is stepping the voltage up or down.

10.15 Power lines

The experiment in fig. 10.48 is a model of a power station sending electricity to a village.

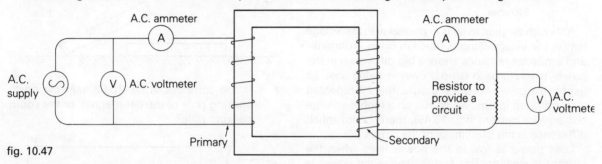

fig. 10.47

Alternating supply voltage i.e. primary voltage (volts)	Primary current (amperes)	Number of turns in primary coil	Number of turns in secondary coil	Secondary voltage (volts)	Secondary current (amperes)
24	2	60	15	6	7·9
24	2	60	30	12	4·0
24	2	60	60	24	2·0
24	2	60	75	30	1·4
24	2	60	120	47	0·9

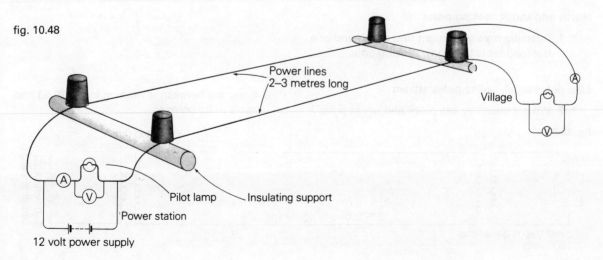

fig. 10.48

fig. 10.49

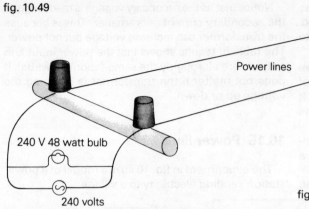

Power lines

240 V 48 watt bulb

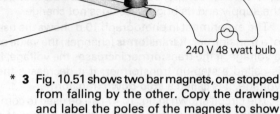

240 V 48 watt bulb

240 volts

Although the pilot lamp is in parallel with the 'village lamp', the village lamp is much dimmer. Voltmeter and ammeter readings show a big difference in the power given to each lamp. Power is being 'lost' as heat in the power lines. If the experiment is repeated with different lamps, which run on a higher voltage but smaller current (fig. 10.49), there is not much difference in the brightness of the lamps.

Less power is lost in the power lines when the current is smaller. This fact is used when power is sent across country through the grid system. A transformer is used to step up the power station voltage to over a quarter of a million volts. This makes the current smaller. The voltage is stepped down again when it reaches a village or town (fig. 10.50).

Revision questions

Formula

electrical power = VI
(watts = volts × amperes)

North and south seeking poles

* **1** Describe how you might find which end of a bar magnet is the north seeking pole.

Like poles repel, unlike poles attract

* **2** What is meant by 'like poles' and 'unlike poles'?

* **3** Fig. 10.51 shows two bar magnets, one stopped from falling by the other. Copy the drawing and label the poles of the magnets to show which might be north seeking and which south seeking.

fig. 10.51

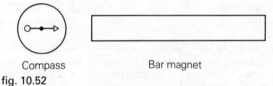

* **4** Is the compass in fig. 10.52 near the north seeking pole of the bar magnet, or the south seeking pole?

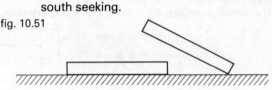

Compass

Bar magnet

fig. 10.52

Magnetic field patterns

* **5** Draw a bar magnet and show the pattern and direction of its magnetic field.

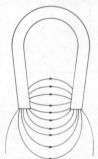

fig. 10.53

* **6** Copy the horseshoe magnet in fig. 10.53 and mark in its poles.

fig. 10.50

Step up transformer

Step down transformer

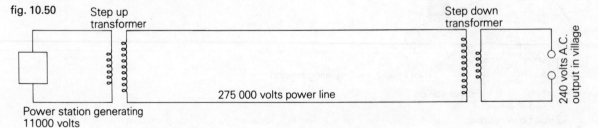

275 000 volts power line

240 volts A.C. output in village

Power station generating 11000 volts

Making and breaking magnets

** **7** Describe how to magnetise a steel rod by stroking it.

* **8** If a bar magnet is snapped in half and the broken ends put together again, will they attract or repel?

The Domain Theory of magnetism

* **9** Does fig. 10.54 show magnetised or unmagnetised steel?

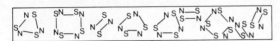

fig. 10.54

** **10** Draw a horseshoe magnet and show how the domains might be arranged.

* **11** What is the basic difference between magnetic and non-magnetic materials?

Electromagnetism

* **12** Fig. 10.55 shows four drawings for the magnetic field pattern near a wire carrying a current. Which one is correct?

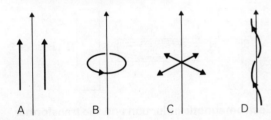

fig. 10.55

* **13** Explain the symbols $\otimes$ and $\odot$.

** **14** In which direction will the three unlabelled compasses point in fig. 10.56? (*Hint:* Remember that the earth's magnetic field is trying to turn each compass needle into a north-south direction).

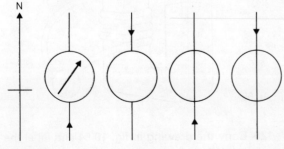

fig. 10.56

** **15** Draw the magnetic field pattern round **a** two parallel wires with currents flowing in the same direction **b** two parallel wires with currents flowing in opposite directions. In each case show whether the wires will push apart or pull together.

* **16** Sketch the magnetic field pattern of a solenoid which is carrying a current.

The electromagnet

** **17** A brass rod inside a solenoid carrying a current will hardly pick up any iron filings. If an iron rod is used instead of a brass one, many iron filings can be picked up. Explain this.

** **18** Why do most of the iron filings picked up by an 'iron nail electromagnet' drop off when the current is switched off?

** **19** Explain what the apparatus in fig. 10.57 will do.

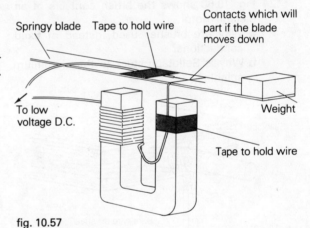

fig. 10.57

The catapult field

** **20** Fig. 10.58 shows the magnetic fields of two magnadur magnets and a piece of wire separately. Sketch how they will combine to make a catapult field, and show in which direction the wire will feel a force.

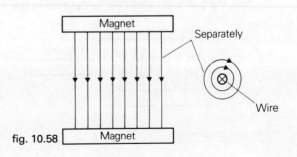

fig. 10.58

*21 Why is the description 'catapult field' used?

**22 Fig. 10.59 is a cross section of a moving coil ammeter, showing one turn of the coil and the magnetic field of the magnets and coil. Use the diagram to explain why the coil twists.

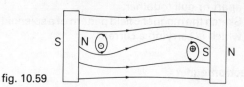

fig. 10.59

***23 Look back at photograph 10.c.
   a What is the purpose of the spirals?
   b Why is a straw fixed to the wooden former?
   c In what ways could the ammeter be made more sensitive to small currents?

The electric motor

**24 Fig. 10.60 shows the brush contacts of an electric motor.
   a Why are brushes used instead of fixed connections?
   b Why is Sellotape stuck to the aluminium spindle?

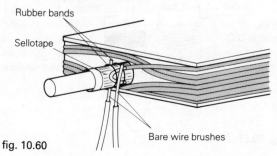

Rubber bands

Sellotape

Bare wire brushes

fig. 10.60

*25 Must the magnadur magnets of a motor be attracting or repelling each other when fixed to the yoke?

Electromagnetic induction

**26 As the magnet in fig. 10.61 is pushed into the coil, the galvanometer needle deflects to the

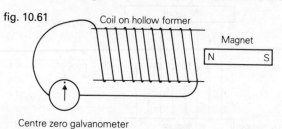

fig. 10.61

Coil on hollow former

Magnet

Centre zero galvanometer

left. Which way would the needle deflect if the magnet was held still and the coil pushed over it?

The generator

**27 Part of the generator which was drawn in fig. 10.39 is shown again in fig. 10.62. Describe and explain how the induced e.m.f. changes in size and direction as the coil moves through positions 1, 2 and 3.

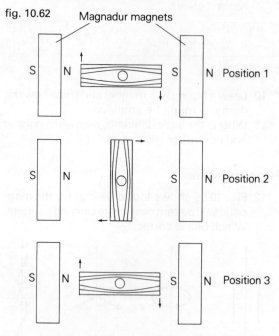

fig. 10.62   Magnadur magnets

Position 1

Position 2

Position 3

Electromagnetic induction and the transformer

**28 What would you expect to see on the galvanometer in fig. 10.63, if the magnet were spun round and round?

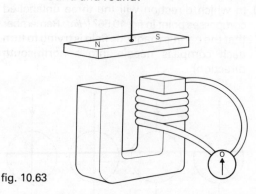

fig. 10.63

*29 Copy the drawing in fig. 10.64 and label the primary and secondary coils.

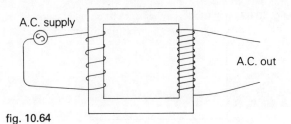

fig. 10.64

Step-up and step-down transformers

*30 Is the transformer shown in fig. 10.64, a step-up or step-down type?

**31 A 12 volt alternating supply is connected to the 50 turn primary coil of a transformer. What voltage might you expect from the 200 turn secondary coil?

**32 Suppose the transformer in question 31 is used to step down voltage. What value would it change the 12 volt alternating supply to?

**33 What output can be expected from the 1000 turn secondary coil of a transformer when a 6 volt battery is left connected to the 200 turn primary coil?

***34 1800 watts are transformed from an alternating 60 volt supply, to be delivered at 6000 volts.
  a What value of alternating current is supplied to the transformer?
  b What is the output current from the transformer?

Power lines

**35 Why are step-up transformers useful in the transmission of electrical power?

Extra questions

***36 Fig. 10. 65 shows two coils. The inner coil is connected to a battery, the outer coil to a galvanometer. Explain why the galvanometer gives a reading whenever a piece of iron is moved in or out of the inner coil.

**37 Fig. 10.66 shows a wire AB pointing due north and south. An electric current flows in the direction AB. The north pole of a compass needle, which is placed below the wire is deflected towards the west with a large deflection.

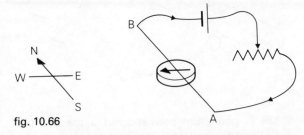

fig. 10.66

  a State two ways in which you could make the needle deflect to the east.
  b State two ways in which you could make the deflection of the needle smaller.
  c Describe briefly a practical application of the magnetic effect of an electric current. (M.R.E.B.)

**38 In fig. 10.67 a d.c. supply, switch and variable resistor are connected to the primary coil of a transformer. A centre zero galvanometer is connected to the secondary coil. The switch is closed and the reading on the galvanometer is zero. When the switch is opened so that the current ceases to flow in the primary circuit the galvanometer deflects to the right and then returns to zero.

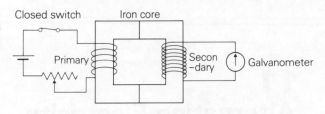

fig. 10.67

  a Explain why this happens.
  in each of the following, state what is likely to happen.
  b The switch is closed so that current flows in the primary circuit.
  c When the primary current is flowing the resistance in the circuit is suddenly increased by altering the variable resistor. (M.R.E.B.)

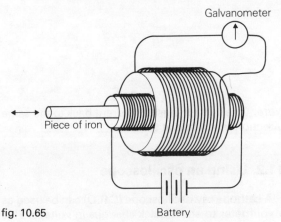

fig. 10.65   Battery

fig. 10.68

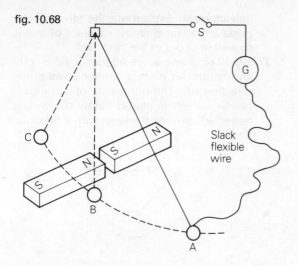

fig. 10.69

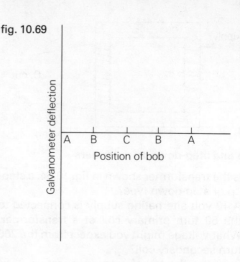

***39 A pendulum consisting of a massive bob on the end of a long copper wire swings between the poles of two magnets as shown in fig. 10.68. A slack, flexible wire which does not impede the swing of the pendulum is connected to the bottom of the copper wire. A circuit is completed through a sensitive centre-zero galvanometer, a switch and a wire to the top of the pendulum.

a The switch is closed. The pendulum is allowed to swing. At what point in the swing will the reading of the galvanometer be greatest? Explain your answer.

b When the current flows in this circuit energy is being converted from electrical energy to heat. Where does the electrical energy come from?

c With the switch open, the pendulum swings take longer to die away than they do when the switch is closed. Explain this.

d The switch is closed. Copy the set of axes shown in fig. 10.69 and sketch a graph of the galvanometer deflection against the position of the bob.

e What is the effect of the galvanometer deflection of (i) using a pair of stronger magnets, (ii) reversing the direction of the magnetic field?

f (i) If the pendulum is released from the same point each time, increasing the mass of the bob has little effect on the galvanometer deflections. Why? (ii) When the mass is increased as in f(i), the time taken for the pendulum swings to die away is longer. Why is this? (*O. and C.*)

11
Alternating Electricity

11.1 The difference between direct and alternating current

The electricity in direct current (d.c.) always moves in the same direction. In alternating current (a.c.) the direction changes regularly. Cells and batteries make d.c.. The mains supply is a.c., alternating at 50 cycles per second (50 hertz).

Note: One cycle brings the current back to the same direction that it had at the start.

11.2 Using an oscilloscope

A cathode ray oscilloscope (C.R.O) can be used as a voltmeter to show quick changes in voltage. This makes it useful for measuring alternating electricity. (For an explanation of how an oscilloscope works, see section 15.6).

Fig. 11.1 shows an oscilloscope with its time base off and with no voltage across its terminals.

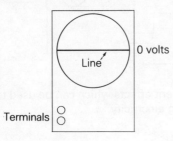

fig. 11.1

The time base can be switched on to make the dot move slowly across the screen. The spot can be speeded up until it makes a line (fig. 11.2).

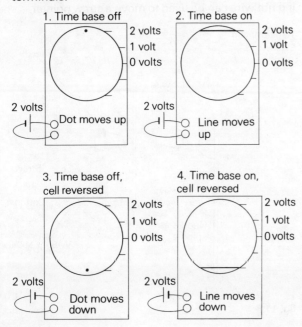

fig. 11.2

Fig. 11.3 shows traces which can be made by connecting a direct voltage across the oscilloscope terminals.

fig. 11.3

Fig. 11.4 shows traces which could be made by connecting an alternating voltage, with a peak (maximum) of 2 volts.

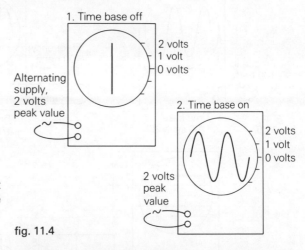

fig. 11.4

With the time base on, the spot moves up and down as it goes across. This gives the familiar wave graph of voltage against time.

The number of waves on the oscilloscope screen depends on the frequency of the supply and the speed of the time base. The trace in fig. 11.4 could have been made with a supply frequency of 50 hertz and a time base which took the spot across the screen in $\frac{1}{25}$ second. (50 hertz would mean that each cycle took $\frac{1}{50}$ second, and in $\frac{1}{25}$ second there are 2 cycles.)

Fig. 11.5 shows two other possible traces.

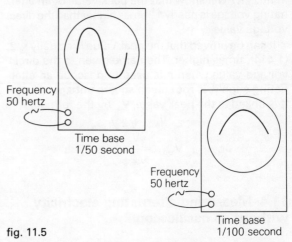

fig. 11.5

If a rectifier (section 11.4) is connected with an alternating supply across the terminals of an oscilloscope, the trace may change in one of two ways. The change will depend on the direction in which the rectifier passes current (fig. 11.6).

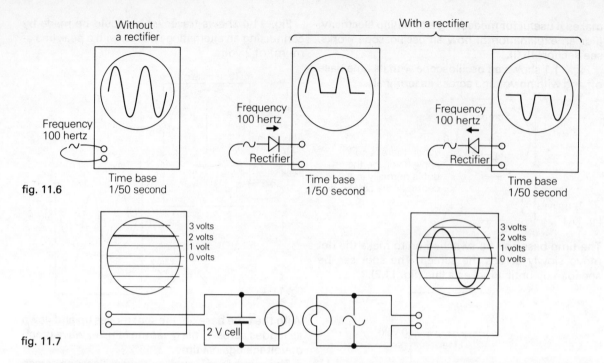

Frequency
100 hertz

Time base
1/50 second

fig. 11.6

With a rectifier

Frequency
100 hertz

Rectifier

Time base
1/50 second

Frequency
100 hertz

Rectifier

Time base
1/50 second

3 volts
2 volts
1 volt
0 volts

3 volts
2 volts
1 volts
0 volts

2 V cell

fig. 11.7

11.3 The link between direct and alternating voltage

The alternating voltage lighting a lamp is **not** measured at its peak, but is given the same value as the direct voltage which will light an identical lamp to the same brightness. An experiment like the one in fig. 11.7 will show that the peak value of an alternating voltage is nearly $1\frac{1}{2}$ times higher than the direct voltage value.

It can be proved that the peak value is actually $\sqrt{2}$, (1·414), times higher. The name given to the direct voltage value when it is used to describe an alternating supply, is **root mean square voltage**, ($V_{r.m.s.}$). It is linked to the peak value, V_o, by the formula

$$V_o = \sqrt{2}\, V_{r.m.s.}$$

or,
$$V_{r.m.s.} = \frac{V_o}{\sqrt{2}}$$

11.4 Measuring alternating electricity without an oscilloscope

If an alternating supply is connected to a meter which is meant to measure direct current or voltage, the needle will probably quiver but still point to zero. The inertia of the meter parts (section 1.5) does not let the needle move far in any one direction before it is pushed back again. The following sections show four different effects which can be used to measure alternating electricity.

Heating effect

When alternating current flows through a resistance wire it gets hot. Fig. 11.8 shows how an expanding hot wire can be used to move a straw pointer.

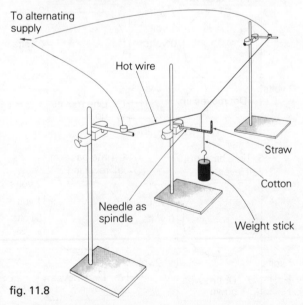

To alternating supply

Hot wire

Straw

Cotton

Needle as spindle

Weight stick

fig. 11.8

A **hot wire ammeter** is based on this effect.

Magnetic attraction effect

An iron key is attracted towards a coil which has an alternating current flowing through it (fig. 11.9).

fig. 11.9

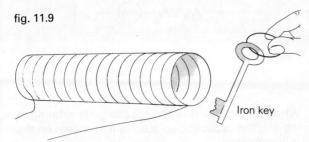

Iron key

The **attraction type moving iron meter** is based on this effect.

Magnetic repulsion effect

Two iron bars through a coil carrying alternating current, will be magnetised so that their north seeking ends are always together and will repel. Fig. 11.10 shows how this repulsion can be used to move a straw pointer when an alternating current flows.

fig. 11.10

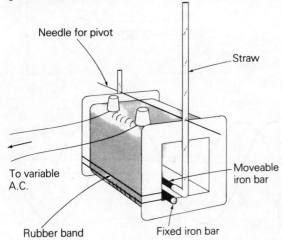

Needle for pivot

Straw

To variable A.C.

Moveable iron bar

Rubber band

Fixed iron bar

The **repulsion type moving iron meter** is based on this effect.

Electrostatic effect

If an alternating voltage is connected between the top plate and case of a gold leaf electroscope, the leaf will always have a charge which is opposite in sign to that of the case, and will be attracted towards it. Fig. 11.11 shows how this effect can be used to show changes in alternating supply.

The **electrostatic voltmeter** is based on this effect.
Note: A rectifier is often used to change a d.c. meter into an a.c. meter. The rectifier only lets current pass in one direction and so the meter needle is kept pushed to one side by a series of d.c. pulses (fig. 11.12).

fig. 11.12

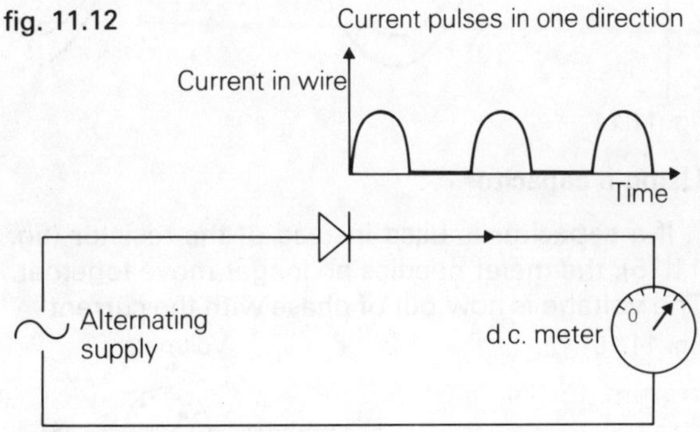

Current pulses in one direction

Current in wire

Time

Alternating supply

d.c. meter

11.5 a.c. circuits

Using a resistor

When slow alternating voltage is connected to a resistor, voltmeter and milliammeter as shown in fig. 11.13, the needles of both meters move together. This shows that the voltage and current are **in phase**.

A graph showing the change of voltage and current with time is drawn in fig. 11.14.

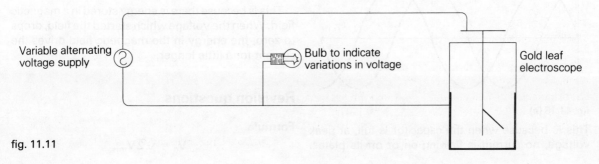

Variable alternating voltage supply

Bulb to indicate variations in voltage

Gold leaf electroscope

fig. 11.11

fig. 11.13

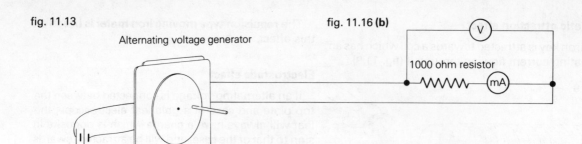

Alternating voltage generator

fig. 11.16 (b)

1000 ohm resistor

Battery

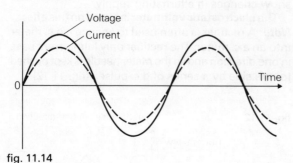

fig. 11.14

Using a capacitor

If a **capacitor** is used instead of the resistor (fig. 11.15), the meter needles no longer move together. The voltage is now out of phase with the current.

fig. 11.15

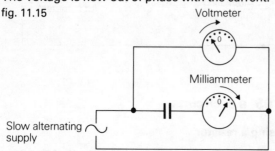

Voltmeter

Milliammeter

Slow alternating supply

A graph showing change of voltage and current with time shows that for a **capacitor** the current is 90° ($\frac{1}{4}$ cycle) ahead of the voltage (fig. 11.16(a)).

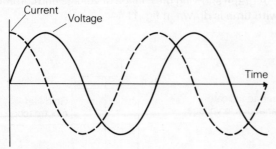

Current   Voltage

Time

fig. 11.16 (a)

This is because when the capacitor is full, at peak voltage, no current is flowing on or off its plates.

When the voltage is changing, charge is entering or leaving the capacitor, so a current is shown on the milliammeter.

Using an inductor

If the capacitor is now replaced by an **inductor** (fig. 11.17), (the coil of an electromagnet can be used), the voltage is found to be 90° ($\frac{1}{4}$ cycle) ahead of the current (fig. 11.18).

fig. 11.17

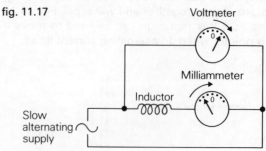

Voltmeter

Milliammeter

Inductor

Slow alternating supply

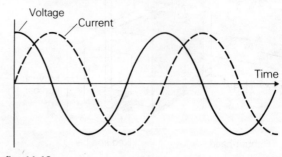

Voltage   Current

Time

fig. 11.18

This is because there is energy stored in a magnetic field. When the voltage which started the field, drops to zero, the energy in the magnetic field drives the current for a little longer.

Revision questions

Formula

$$V_o = \sqrt{2}\, V_{rms}$$

or $V_{rms} = \dfrac{V_o}{\sqrt{2}}$

take $\sqrt{2}$ as 1·4

The difference between direct and alternating current

** **1** Explain simply the difference between direct and alternating current.

* **2** Does a torch cell provide direct or alternating current?

Using an oscilloscope

*** **3** Fig. 11.19 shows a 6 volt battery connected to an oscilloscope whose time base is switched off. Sketch the appearance of the screen if the 6 volt battery is replaced by **a** an alternating 50 hertz voltage with a peak value of 6 volts; the time base still switched off. **b** an alternating 50 hertz voltage with a peak value of 6 volts; the time base switched on to give a sweep time of $\frac{1}{50}$ second. **c** an alternating 100 hertz voltage with a peak value of 4 volts; the time base switched on to give a sweep time of $\frac{1}{200}$ second. **d** an alternating 100 hertz voltage with a peak value of 3 volts; the time base switched on to give a sweep time of $\frac{1}{50}$ second. **e** as in **d** but with a rectifier in series with the alternating supply. **f** a 4 volt battery, the time base switched on to give a sweep time of $\frac{1}{100}$ second.

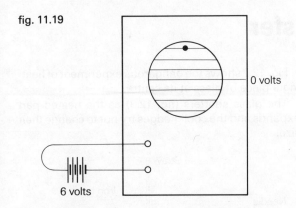

fig. 11.19

0 volts

6 volts

The link between direct and alternating voltage

* **4** What do the letters r.m.s. stand for?

* **5** How would the brightness of two identical lamps compare if one was run on a 6 volt direct supply and the other a $6V_{r.m.s.}$ supply?

** **6** The peak value of an alternating supply is 70 volts. Calculate the r.m.s. value of the supply.

** **7** Mains voltage is supplied at $240V_{r.m.s.}$. What is the peak value of the supply?

Measuring alternating electricity without an oscilloscope

** **8** Design a simple ammeter which depends on the heating effect of an electric current.

** **9** An alternating current fed into a d.c. meter (such as the moving coil ammeter, section 10.9) makes the pointer vibrate on zero.
  a Why doesn't it give a proper reading?
  b How could you convert it to an a.c. meter?

a.c. circuits

* **10** What does it mean to say that the current and voltage are **in phase** when a resistor is connected to an alternating supply?

*** **11** When a capacitor is connected to an alternating supply, the current is out of phase with the voltage, leading it by 90°.
  a What does this mean?
  b Why does it happen?

** **12** A voltmeter, milliammeter and inductor are connected to a slow alternating supply as shown in fig. 11.20. Describe how the needles of the meters will move when the switch is closed and sketch a graph to show how the current and voltage change with time.

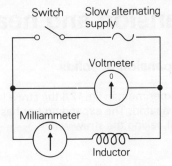

Switch   Slow alternating supply

Voltmeter

Milliammeter

Inductor

fig. 11.20

Extra question

*** **13** An oscilloscope is adjusted so that when a 2 volt d.c. supply is connected across the input terminals there is a deflection of 1 cm. The grid on the tube represents 1 cm spacings.
  a The time base is switched off. What was connected across the input terminals so as to produce the traces shown in fig. 11.21?

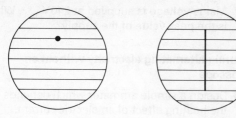

fig. 11.21

b Four similar lamps are connected in series with a 12 volt d.c. supply and an ammeter (fig. 11.22). The internal resistance of the supply and the resistance of the ammeter are negligible.

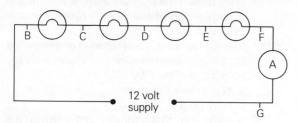

12 volt supply

fig. 11.22

What would the trace on the oscilloscope be like if the input terminals were connected (i) between B and C, (ii) between E and F, (iii) between B and D, (iv), between F and G?

c The time-base is now switched on and the spot sweeps across the screen in 0·001 second. A signal generator is connected across the input terminals and the trace produced is shown in fig. 11.23.

fig. 11.23

(i) What is the frequency of the signal? (ii) What would the trace look like if the signal generator was adjusted to give a frequency of 2000 hertz at the same voltage? (iii) What would the trace look like if a rectifier was placed in series with the signal generator (frequency 2000 hertz)?

12
Expansion and heat transfer

12.1 Expansion of solids

In the experiment in fig. 12.1 the straw turns when the bar is heated. The expanding bar has made the needle roll, taking the straw with it.

Fig. 12.2 shows the dangerous experiment of heating a piece of glass at its centre.

The glass shatters (fig. 12.3) as the heated part expands and the cooler edges try not to change their size.

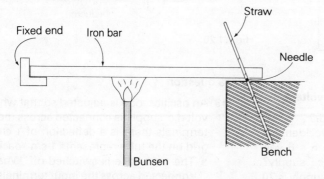

fig. 12.1 SIDE VIEW

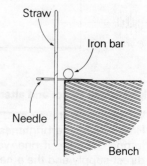

END VIEW

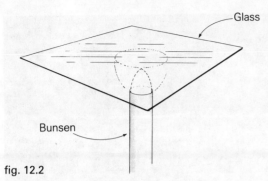

fig. 12.2

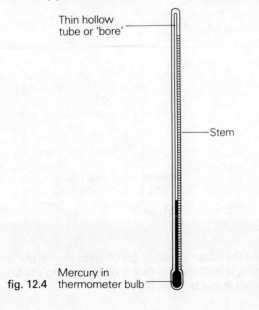

fig. 12.3

12.2 Expansion of liquids

A mercury thermometer gives an example of how a liquid expands when it is heated. Mercury in the thermometer bulb (fig. 12.4) expands slightly when the thermometer is put into hot water. This small expansion is noticed because the hollow tube inside the thermometer stem is so thin. A small amount of mercury pushed into the stem moves up a long way.

Thin hollow
tube or 'bore'

Stem

Mercury in
fig. 12.4   thermometer bulb

12.3 Expansion of gases

Fig. 12.5 shows a gas (air) being gently heated in a flask. The water indictator moves quickly up the glass tube. It has been pushed up by the expanding air.

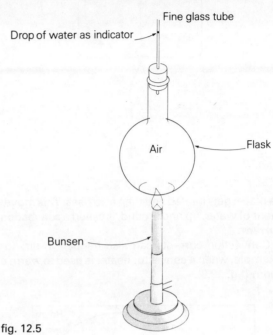

Fine glass tube

Drop of water as indicator

Air

Flask

Bunsen

fig. 12.5

12.4 Convection

In fig. 12.6 a small crystal of potassium permanganate has been dropped to the bottom of a beaker of cold water. A small flame is used to heat the water near the crystal.

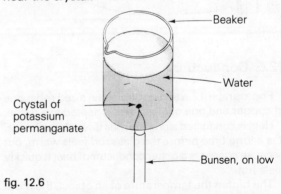

Beaker

Water

Crystal of
potassium
permanganate

Bunsen, on low

fig. 12.6

A purple stain from the crystal shows that the warm water first rises to the surface and then circulates back down again (fig. 12.7).

Because warm water expands and is less dense than cold water, it floats upwards. Cold water takes

101

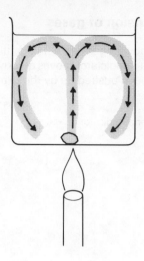

fig. 12.7

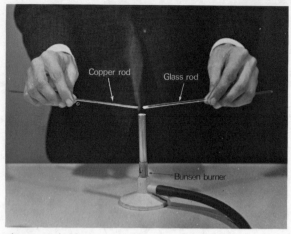

photograph 12.a

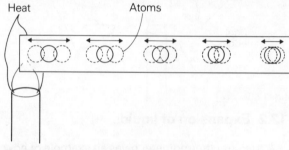

fig. 12.9

its place, gets heated and then also rises. This movement of water, up and around, is called a **convection current**.

Convection currents can also happen in air; for example, when a convector heater is used to warm a room (fig. 12.8).

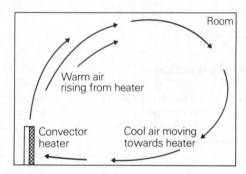

fig. 12.8

12.5 Conduction

Photograph 12.a shows two equal sized rods, one of copper and one of glass, being heated in a flame.

Heat is conducted along the rods towards the hands. It is a long time before the glass rod feels warm, but because copper is a better conductor of heat it quickly feels hot.

The higher the temperature of an object, the more its atoms are vibrating. When one end of a rod is heated, the atoms in that end vibrate more. Each atom affects the one next to it and so the vibrations pass along the rod (fig. 12.9). Soon the temperature at the other end of the rod starts to rise. This is how heat is conducted.

Water: a bad conductor of heat

Fig. 12.10 shows a small piece of ice trapped under wire gauze at the bottom of a test tube of water.

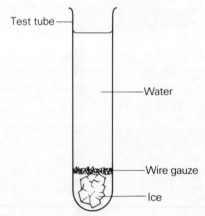

fig. 12.10

When the water is heated gently near the top of the test tube, it isn't long before it boils, leaving the ice unmelted at the bottom (fig. 12.11).

Because warmed water does not sink, the ice cannot be melted by convected heat. Heat must **conduct**

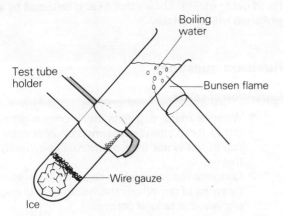

fig. 12.11

down through the water to melt the ice. It takes a long time for this to happen. This shows that water is a bad conductor of heat.

Air: a bad conductor of heat

Air is also a bad conductor of heat. This property is made use of in double glazing. A thin layer of still air, trapped between two windows, will stop heat escaping from a room as quickly as it would through a single pane of glass (fig. 12.12).

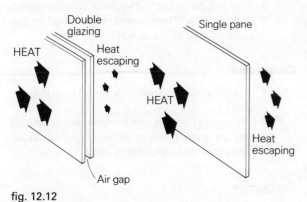

fig. 12.12

12.6 Radiation

Although we cannot always see when an object is hot, we can often feel the heat 'shining' out of it. When this happens, the heat is travelling to us by radiation (fig. 12.13).

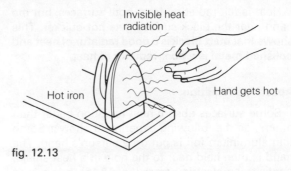

fig. 12.13

Some surfaces are better heat radiators than others, as the following experiment shows: Bunsen burners are used to heat a thick copper slab (fig. 12.14). One side of the slab is polished and the other is painted a dull (matt) black.

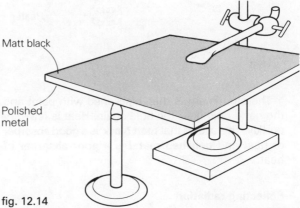

fig. 12.14

The slab is turned onto its side and a person holds his hands about 5 centimetres from each surface (fig. 12.15).

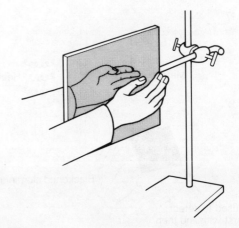

fig. 12.15

Heat is felt radiating from both surfaces, but the hand near the black surface gets hot quicker. This shows that **matt black** is a **good radiator** of heat and **polished metal** is a **poor radiator** of heat.

Absorbing radiation

Some surfaces absorb heat radiation better than others, as the following experiment shows: Some thin aluminium foil is put on a person's hand. The hand is then held near to the hole in a heat shield, opposite an electric heater (fig. 12.16). It is a long time before any heat is felt.

fig. 12.16

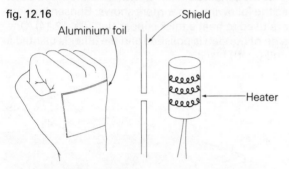

Aluminium foil

Shield

Heater

The aluminium is then blackened with paint and the hand held near the hole again. Heat is felt very quickly. This shows that **matt black** is a **good absorber** of heat and **polished metal** is a **poor absorber** of heat.

Reflecting radiation

What happened to the heat which was not absorbed by the shiny aluminium surface in fig. 12.16?—Perhaps it was reflected?

Fig. 12.17 shows an experiment to see if heat can be reflected. A polished metal mirror is held at an

fig. 12.17

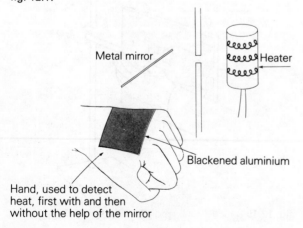

Metal mirror

Heater

Blackened aluminium

Hand, used to detect heat, first with and then without the help of the mirror

angle which might reflect heat down onto the hand which is coated with blackened aluminium. Without the mirror no heat is felt. With the mirror in place the hand gets hot. This shows that **heat is reflected by a polished metal surface.**

Revision questions

Expansion of solids

* **1** When a metal cap gets stuck onto a glass bottle, it can often be loosened by dipping the cap in hot water for a moment. Explain why this works.
* **2** Concrete roads are laid in sections, separated by strips of tar. Why is this better than laying a continous strip of concrete?

Expansion of liquids

* **3** If a car radiator is filled to the top when the engine is cold, explain why some water will spill over when the car is being driven.
* **4** Milk is measured from a cup into a saucepan where it is heated up to make coffee. When the hot milk is poured into the cup there is some left over. Why?

Expansion of gases

** **5** A fountain pen sometimes makes blots when it is being used nearly empty. Explain this.
** **6** Why is it a mistake to check the tyre pressures of a car which has been standing half in the sun and half in the shade?

Convection

** **7** In what way is convection linked with expansion?
* **8** Christmas decorations hanging in the ceiling can be seen moving above the hot water pipes in the room. Why is this?

Conduction

** **9** Explain conduction in terms of atoms vibrating.
* **10** Why is it unusual for saucepans to have metal handles?
** **11** Why does polystyrene which is at room temperature, feel warm to the touch?
** **12** In fig. 12.18 a test tube of water is held near its top and heated gently at the bottom. In fig.

12.19 a test tube of water is held at the bottom and heated gently near the top. Explain what is felt in each case and what will happen to the water level in fig. 12.18.

fig. 12.18

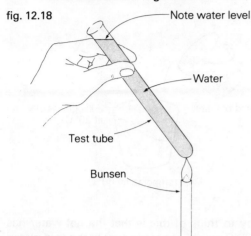

Note water level

Water

Test tube

Bunsen

fig. 12.19

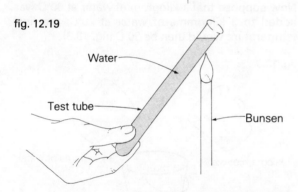

Water

Test tube

Bunsen

13 Tramps sometimes keep layers of old newspaper under their clothing. Why is this?

14 Why does double glazing stop heat loss from a room?

Radiation

15 Why is it more sensible to use a shiny teapot than one which is dull and dirty on the outside?

16 Snow can be made to melt more quickly on a sunny day by sprinkling it with soot. Why is this?

17 Two hollow metal cubes of equal size are connected by a hollow tube containing water as shown in fig. 12.20.
  a Explain what will happen to the water levels as soon as a lighted bunsen is held half way between the cubes.
  b Explain what would happen if instead of a bunsen flame, 'dry ice' was put there.

fig. 12.20

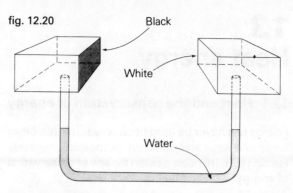

Black

White

Water

Extra questions

18 Why is it a mistake to put cold water into the cooling system of an engine that has just boiled dry?

19 A thermometer bulb is dipped into hot water. The mercury level is seen to drop slightly before moving up. Explain this.

20 Explain the expansion of **a** solids, **b** liquids, **c** gases, in terms of atoms or molecules.

21 The temperature of the sea changes very little from night to day, but the temperature of the land changes a lot. Why do breezes blow from the sea to the land by day and from the land to the sea by night?

22 One thick and one thin copper rod, are held with one end in a bunsen flame. Both rods are 20 centimetres long and are held at the end furthest from the flame. Explain if any difference will be noticed in how quickly heat is felt.

23 Water in the hot water tank shown in fig. 12.21 was heated by an electrical immersion heater.

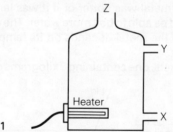

Z

Y

Heater

X

fig. 12.21

  a Explain why the immersion heater is placed at the bottom of the tank.
  b To which point, X, Y or Z, is each of the following connected: (i) the cold water supply, (ii) the hot taps, (iii) the overflow pipe?
  c What would you do to reduce the heat loss from the hot water tank? Explain why this would be a good idea. (*O. and C.*)

13
Heat energy

13.1 Heat and the conservation of energy

Energy can never be used up, it only turns into other kinds of energy and does not disappear completely (section 6.7). This idea is called the **law of conservation of energy**. It means that

the total energy put into = the total energy got out
    a machine   of the machine

An object which is hot is able to do things it would not be able to do if it were cold. For instance, a large hot block of metal could be dropped into some water. The water would boil, and the steam used to drive a piston to wind up a crane (fig. 13.1).

It is the heat in the block which works the crane. Clearly then, heat is a form of energy, which in this case changes into gravitational potential energy of the load which the crane lifts.

Often heat is produced when other sorts of energy are used up. As a car stops, the kinetic energy of the car changes to heat first in the brake drums and then in the atmosphere. Heat energy which is wasted into the atmosphere is no longer useful because it has become so spread out that we cannot use it to drive a machine.

13.2 Measuring heat energy

The crane in section 13.1 would run for longer if the piece of metal was hotter or if it was larger, for then it would be able to boil more water. The amount of energy in the metal depends on its temperature and its mass.

If two buckets, one containing 3 kilograms of water

at 60°C and the other 3 kilograms of water at 20°C, were poured together, the final temperature of the mixture would be 40°C; half way between 60°C and 20°C (fig. 13.2).

fig. 13.2

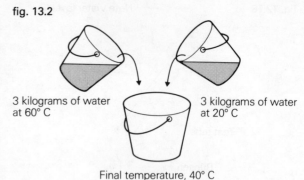

3 kilograms of water at 60° C

3 kilograms of water at 20° C

Final temperature, 40° C

The way to think of this is that the hot water has given '20°C worth' of heat energy to the cold water. Now suppose that 1 kilogram of water at 60°C was added to 3 kilograms of water at 20°C; the final temperature would then be 30°C (fig. 13.3).

fig. 13.3

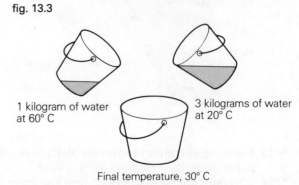

1 kilogram of water at 60° C

3 kilograms of water at 20° C

Final temperature, 30° C

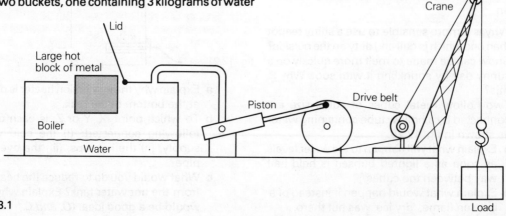

fig. 13.1

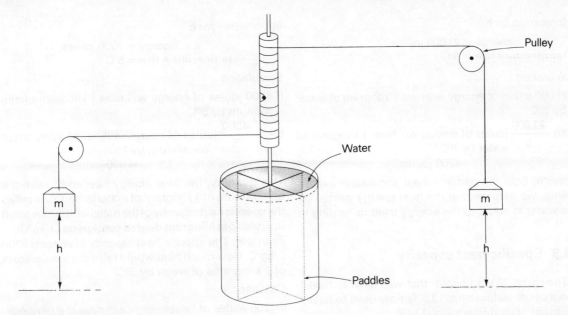

fig. 13.4 James Joule's experiment

The 3 kilograms of cold water is warmed through 10°C, by heat from the 1 kilogram of hot water cooling through 30°C. The amount of heat transferred depends on the mass of the water and the temperature change. 1 kilogram cooling through 30°C gives enough heat energy to warm 3 kilograms by 10°C. Because heat is a form of energy it is measured in **joules**.

In the apparatus shown in fig. 13.4, the falling masses drive paddle wheels round in the water and potential energy is changed into heat energy in the water. In an experiment like this in 1842, James Joule found that it takes about 4200 joules to heat 1 kilogram of water by 1°C.

Example: Two 100 kilogram masses fall 4 metres to heat 1 kilogram of water by 1·9°C (fig. 13.4). Assuming care has been taken not to lose any heat to the atmosphere, calculate how many joules of energy will heat 1 kilogram of water by 1°C.

Information

total falling mass, m = 200 kilograms
height, h = 4 metres
gravitational field = 10 newtons per kilogram
strength, g
mass of water = 1 kilogram
temperature rise of = 1·9°C
water

Calculation

potential energy = mgh (section 6.4)
= 200 × 10 × 4
= 8000 joules

If 8000 joules of energy will heat 1 kilogram of water by 1·9°C

then $\dfrac{8000}{1\cdot9}$ joules of energy will heat 1 kilogram of

water by 1°C = (approximately) 4200 joules

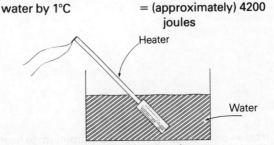

fig. 13.5 An electrical heating experiment

Using the apparatus shown in fig. 13.5, electrical energy can be changed into heat.

Example: When a 30 watt heater is used to heat 1 kilogram of water for 700 seconds the temperature rises by 5°C.

a How much electrical energy is changed into heat?
b How much energy would be needed to heat 1 kilogram of water by 1°C?

Information for **a**

power = 30 watts
time = 700 seconds

Calculation

electrical energy = VIt (section 9.9)
= power × time (section 9.10)
= 30 × 700
= 21 000 joules

Information for **b**

energy = 21000 joules
temperature rise = 5°C

Calculation

If 21000 joules of energy will heat 1 kilogram of water by 5°C

then $\dfrac{21000}{5}$ joules of energy will heat 1 kilogram of water by 1°C

= 4200 joules

Note: In both the paddle wheel and heater experiments, we assume that the heat energy gained by the water is equal to the energy used in heating it.

13.3 Specific heat capacity

The same 30 watt heater that was used to heat 1 kilogram of water in fig. 13.5, is now used to heat 1 kilogram of aluminium (fig. 13.6).

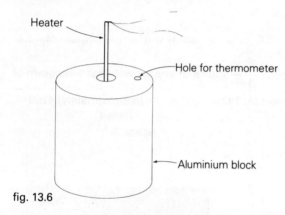

Heater

Hole for thermometer

Aluminium block

fig. 13.6

It takes only 150 seconds for the aluminium to heat up by 5°C, instead of the 700 seconds it took the water. This means that aluminium does not hold so much energy as water does when its temperature rises by 5°C.

Example: Given that a 30 watt electrical heater will heat 1 kilogram of aluminium by 5°C in 150 seconds, **a** what is the electrical energy used? **b** How much energy would be needed to heat 1 kilogram of aluminium by 1°C?

Information for **a**

power = 30 watts
time = 150 seconds

Calculation

electrical energy = power × time
= 30 × 150
= 4500 joules

Information for **b**

energy = 4500 joules
temperature rise = 5°C

Calculation

If 4500 joules of energy will heat 1 kilogram of aluminium by 5°C

then $\dfrac{4500}{5}$ joules of energy will heat 1 kilogram of aluminium by 1°C

= 900 joules

This quantity, the heat energy needed to raise the temperature of 1 kilogram of material by 1°C, is called the **specific heat capacity** of the material. It is measured in **joules per kilogram degree centigrade** (J/kg°C).

Example: The specific heat capacity of water is 4200 J/kg°C. How much heat would raise the temperature of 2 kilograms of water by 3°C?

Calculation

If 4200 joules of heat energy will raise the temperature of 1 kilogram by 1°C

then 2 × 4200 joules of heat energy will raise the temperature of 2 kilograms by 1°C

and 2 × 4200 × 3 joules of heat energy will raise the temperature of 2 kilograms by 3°C

= 25200 joules

Note: The answer to this question was got by multiplying together **mass, specific heat capacity** and **temperature change.** Such calculations can be done using the formula

heat energy = mass × specific heat capacity × temperature change

A lead bullet fired into a wall will rise in temperature because its kinetic energy is changed into heat (fig. 13.7).

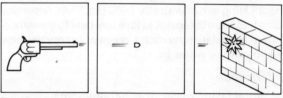

fig. 13.7

Example: Calculate the temperature change of a 1 gram (0·001 kilogram) lead bullet travelling at 200 metres per second when it hits a brick wall and stops. Take the specific heat capacity of lead to be 125 J/kg°C and assume that all the kinetic energy is changed into heat energy in the bullet.

Information

m = 0·001 kilogram
v = 200 metres per second

Information

$$m = 0.001 \text{ kilogram}$$
$$v = 200 \text{ metres per second}$$
$$\text{specific heat capacity} = 125 \text{ J/kg°C}$$

Calculation

$$\text{kinetic energy} = \tfrac{1}{2}mv^2$$
$$= \tfrac{1}{2} \times 0.001 \times 200 \times 200$$
$$= 20 \text{ joules (which becomes heat energy)}$$

$$\text{since heat energy} = \text{mass} \times \text{specific heat capacity} \times \text{temperature change}$$

$$20 = 0.001 \times 125 \times \text{temperature change}$$
$$20 = 0.125 \times \text{temperature change}$$
$$\therefore \text{temperature change} = \frac{20}{0.125}$$
$$= 160°C$$

Revision questions

Formulae

$$\text{kinetic energy} = \tfrac{1}{2}mv^2$$
$$\text{gravitational potential energy} = mgh$$
$$\text{electrical power} = VI$$
$$\text{electrical energy} = VIt$$
$$\text{heat energy} = \text{mass} \times \text{specific heat capacity} \times \text{temperature change}$$

Heat and the conservation of energy

* **1** Each of the items in the following list changes one kind of energy into one or more other kinds of energy. Describe the energy changes involved in each case:
  a Light bulb
  b Bicycle
  c Microphone
  d Clockwork mouse

** **2** A perpetual motion machine is one which will run for ever without wasting energy. Why is it impossible to make such a machine, when the law of conservation of energy says that energy is never destroyed?

Measuring heat energy

** **3** Water from the two buckets shown in fig. 13.8 is mixed together and stirred.

1 kilogram of water at 50° C   2 kilograms of water at 20° C

fig. 13.8

  a Calculate the final temperature of the mixture.
  b Why is it important that the mixture is stirred?
  c Why would the calculated result be higher than a result found by experiment?

*** **4** A 70 watt immersion heater is used to heat 2 kilograms of water. When it is left on for 10 minutes (600 seconds) the water temperature rises by 5°C.
  a How much electrical energy is used in 10 minutes?
  b What energy would be needed to raise the temperature of 1 kilogram of water by 1°C?

*** **5** When setting up the experiment shown in fig. 13.5, one group of pupils decide to leave the experiment running for a long time, (15 minutes), and another group choose a short time, (5 minutes).
  a Which group would you expect to get the most accurate results?
  b Would better results be obtained by using a larger mass of water? Explain your answer.

Specific heat capacity

* **6** Using a 30 watt heater to heat 0.5 kilograms of oil it is found that it takes 600 seconds to raise the temperature by 10°C. What is the specific heat capacity of the oil?

** **7** Through what height has a 40 kilogram block of metal (specific heat capacity 500 J/kg°C) fallen if its temperature rises by 0.5°C on impact? (Assume that all the heat generated from the gravitational potential energy is turned into heat in the metal.) (Take g as 10 newtons per kilogram.)

** **8** A bullet of mass 0.005 kilograms and specific heat capacity 600 joules per kilogram per degree centigrade is moving at 240 metres per second. What will be the temperature rise of the bullet if it is stopped by hitting a wall?

109

Extra questions

*** 9 A cardboard tube 0·5 metres long and sealed at both ends contains 1 kilogram of lead shot (fig. 13.9). The tube is turned upside down so that the lead falls through 0·5 metres. This is done a total of 100 times and the lead warms up by 2·5°C. (Take *g* as 10 newtons per kilogram.)

   a Calculate the specific heat capacity of lead.
   b What temperature rise would you expect if 0·5 kilogram of lead shot had been used?
   c Compare the result you have obtained for the specific heat capacity of lead with the more accurate one of 130 J/kg°C. Why are they different?

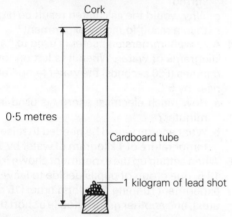

Cork

0·5 metres

Cardboard tube

1 kilogram of lead shot

fig. 13.9

***10 An immersion heater rated at 30 watt is used to heat a solid aluminium block of mass 1 kg. The temperatures are recorded at different times after switching on the heater.

Time (min)

0	4	8	12	16	20	24	28

Temp. °C

10·0	17·0	22·5	25·0	26·0	26·5	26·5	26·5

   a Plot a graph of temperature against time.
   b What is the heat lost per second from the block when it is at 26·5°C?
   c If a 25 watt heater is substituted, show as a rough sketch on the same graph paper what difference this would make.

The 30 watt heater is then used to heat 1 kg of water in a thin plastic container. The temperature and times taken are now as follows.

Time (min)

0	4	8	12	16	20	24	28

Temp. °C

10·0	11·6	13·3	15·0	16·7	18·4	19·7	20·6

   d Plot the graph of these readings on the same sheet of graph paper.
   e Use either the graphs or the data to compare the specific heat capacities of the aluminium and the water.
   f If the aluminium block were painted with carbon black and the experiment repeated what differences in the results would you expect?
   g A boy notices that in bright sunshine, after a shower of rain, a dark car dries more quickly than a white one. What physical explanation can you offer for this? (*O. and C.*).

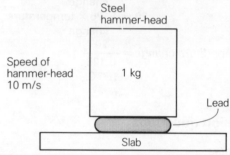

Steel hammer-head

Speed of hammer-head 10 m/s

1 kg

Lead

Slab

fig. 13.10

***11 Fig. 13.10 shows a lump of lead, mass 0·6 kilograms, being hit by a steel hammer-head, mass 1 kilogram moving at 10 metres per second. When, in an attempt to determine the specific heat capacity of lead, the hitting process is done 15 times, the temperature of the lead rises 7·5°C.

   a What is the kinetic energy of the hammer head just before each hit?
   b What is the total kinetic energy lost by the hammer-head during the experiment?
   c Assuming that all this kinetic energy is changed to heat in the lead calculate the specific heat capacity of lead.
   d In performing the experiment why is it better to have the hammer-head made of steel rather than of lead?
   e The slab on which the hitting is done might be made of wood or steel. What would be the advantages and disadvantages of each of these materials? (*O. and C.*).

14
Circular motion

14.1 Satellites in orbit

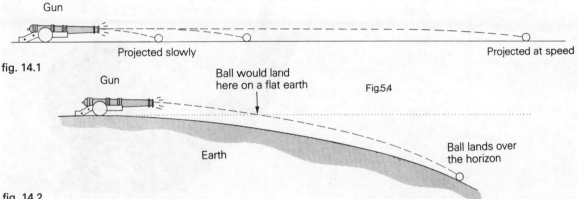

Gun

Projected slowly   Projected at speed

fig. 14.1

Gun

Ball would land
here on a flat earth

Fig.54

Earth

Ball lands over
the horizon

fig. 14.2

Newton explained satellites nearly 300 years before the Russians launched their first Sputnik. His explanation went like this: cannon balls fired at different speeds will curve down to hit the ground at different distances from the gun (fig. 14.1).

Because the earth is curved and not flat, the ball might go over the horizon before it lands (fig. 14.2).

The faster the ball is fired, the further it will go round the earth before landing (fig. 14.3). If it is fired fast enough, the ball will orbit the earth.

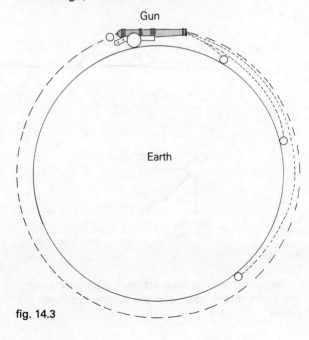

Gun

Earth

fig. 14.3

14.2 Centripetal force

Newton, in his first law (section 5.8), said that unless a moving object feels a force it will keep going at a constant velocity in a straight line. A satellite in orbit feels the force of gravity pulling it towards the earth, so it does not move in a straight line.

Any object moving in a circle needs an inward or **centripetal** force to pull it into a curved path. Photograph 14.a shows a bung being swung round on a string. The person feels the bung trying to move away, so to keep it moving in a circle he has to pull inwards on the string all the time.

If the person lets go of the string (fig. 14.4), the bung will keep going in the direction it is pointing at the time, and move off at a tangent to the circle.

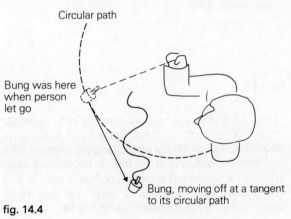

Circular path

Bung was here
when person
let go

Bung, moving off at a tangent
to its circular path

fig. 14.4

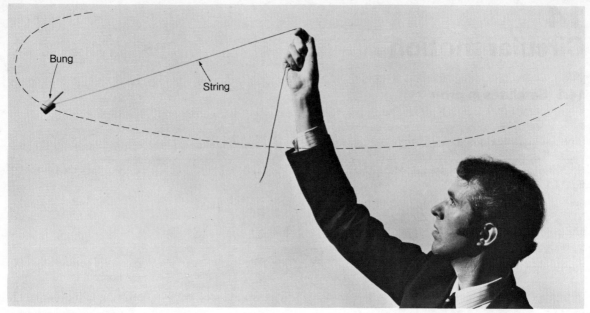

photograph 14.a

14.3 Centripetal acceleration

In section 5.10 we saw that trolleys accelerate in the direction they are pulled. In the same way, a centripetal force will make an inward or **centripetal** acceleration (fig. 14.5).

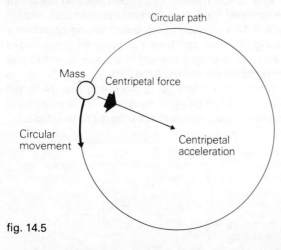

Circular path

Mass

Centripetal force

Circular movement

Centripetal acceleration

fig. 14.5

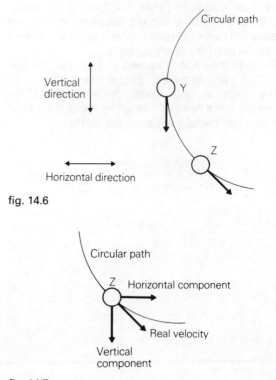

Circular path

Vertical direction

Y

Z

Horizontal direction

fig. 14.6

Circular path

Z   Horizontal component

Real velocity

Vertical component

fig. 14.7

Fig. 14.6 shows an object moving with constant speed along a circular track. Because its direction is changing, its velocity is also changing (section 5.1).

When the object is at Y it has no movement sideways, in a horizontal direction. When it gets to Z, a component of its velocity is horizontal (fig. 14.7). (see 'component velocities', section 5.14).

Because there has been a change of velocity towards the right, there has been an acceleration **into** the circle.

14.4 Formulae for circular motion

It can be proved by geometry that

$$\text{centripetal acceleration, } a = \frac{v^2}{R}$$

where v is the speed round the circular path and R is the radius of the circle.

because **force = mass × acceleration**
centripetal force = mass of object × its centripetal acceleration

therefore $F = \dfrac{mv^2}{R}$

14.5 A test for $F = \dfrac{mv^2}{R}$

The turntable in fig. 14.8 is turned faster and faster, until the truck moves out to an average distance R from the centre, and just touches the wooden stop.

The circular speed, v, of the truck is calculated using $v = \dfrac{\text{distance}}{\text{time}}$, where **distance** is the average circumference of the truck's path $2\pi R$, and **time** is the time of one revolution. The mass, m, of the truck is found using a balance.

The centripetal force, F, made by the spring is now calculated using the formula $F = \dfrac{mv^2}{R}$.

The turntable is then stopped and a newton balance used to pull the truck out to the wooden stop. The real force made by the spring can be measured with the balance and compared with the calculated value. Both values should be about the same.

Revision questions

Formulae

$$\text{centripetal acceleration, } a = \frac{v^2}{R}$$

$$\text{centripetal force, } F = \frac{mv^2}{R}$$

gravitational field strength, g = 10 newtons per kilogram

Satellites in orbit

* **1** Jane says, 'When a satellite is in orbit, the earth curves away from it as fast as the satellite curves towards the earth'. Explain, with the help of a sketch, what she means.

** **2** Newton's explanation of orbits (section 4.1) would not work if the cannon ball was fired inside the earth's atmosphere. Why not?

Centripetal force

* **3** Fig. 14.9 is an overhead view of a bung moving round in a circular path.

fig. 14.9

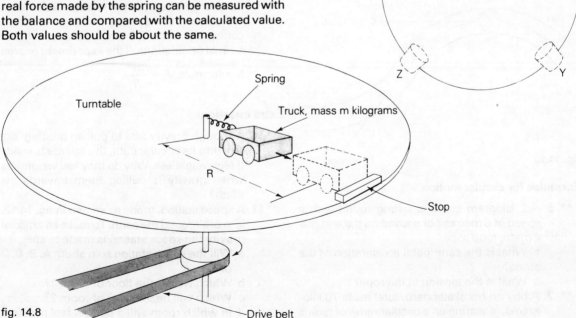

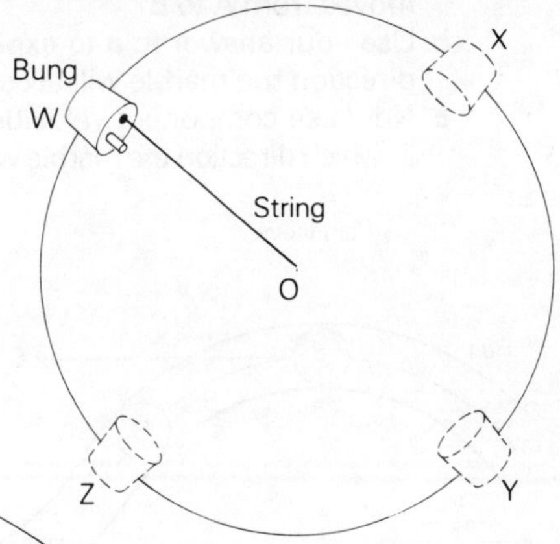

fig. 14.8

a What are the directions of the force on the bung in positions W, X, Y and Z?

b If the string breaks when the bung is at X, in which direction (seen from above) would the bung move?

** **4** A penny is placed on a record turning at $33\frac{1}{3}$ revolutions per minute (r.p.m.). The penny does not slide off until the rate of revolution is increased to 78 r.p.m.. A small piece of plasticine stuck on the record next to the penny will stop the coin sliding off.

a Draw the positions of the plasticine and penny on the record.

b In which direction does the plasticine make a force on the penny?

c What provided this force when the record was turning at $33\frac{1}{3}$ r.p.m.?

Centripetal acceleration

*** **5** Fig. 14.10 is a plan view of a marble rolling along a curtain rail at constant speed.

a Which side of the rail, the outside or inside curve, will make a force on the marble as it moves from A to B?

b Use your answer to **a** to explain in which direction the marble will accelerate.

c Now use component velocities to explain in which direction the marble will accelerate.

Plan view

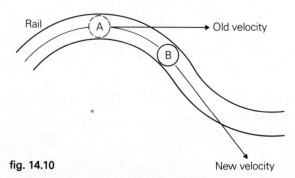

fig. 14.10   New velocity

Formulae for circular motion

** **6** A 2 kilogram stone is swung round with a speed of 6 metres per second on the end of a 4 metre long rope.

a What is the centripetal acceleration of the stone?

b What is the tension in the rope?

** **7** A boy on his skateboard, total mass 70 kilograms, is skating on a circular ramp of radius

2 metres (fig. 14.11). He passes the lowest point with a speed of 6 metres per second. What is the force between the skateboard and the ramp at this point? (*Hint:* Don't forget gravity).

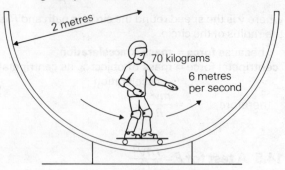

fig. 14.11

** **8** A satellite orbits the earth in a circular path of radius 6430 kilometres, (100 miles above the earth's surface). Take the downward acceleration of the satellite to be 10 metres per second per second and calculate **a** its orbital speed, **b** its time of orbit.

A test for $F = \dfrac{mv^2}{R}$

*** **9** In the experiment described in section 14.5, fig. 14.7, the truck had a mass of 0·4 kilograms and moved in a circle of radius 0·25 metres, eight times every ten seconds. When the turntable was stopped and a newton balance used to pull the truck out to the wooden stop, it showed that the spring had been making a centripetal force of 2 newtons. Say, with the help of calculations, if the experiment proved the formula, $F = \dfrac{mv^2}{R}$.

Extra questions

* **10** Although gravity acts to pull an orbiting 'sky lab' into its circular path, the scientists inside it feel weightless. Why do they feel weightless when gravity is pulling them towards the earth?

** **11** A space station, made as shown in fig. 14.12, is in orbit round the earth. To make an artificial gravity the space station is made to spin.

a Will the space station spin about A, B, C, D or E?

b Which will be the floor of room 1?

c Which will be the floor of room 2?

d In which room will a person feel heavier?

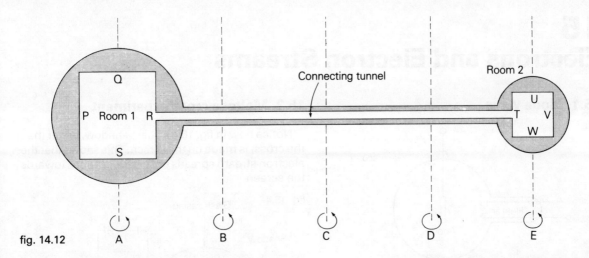

fig. 14.12 A   B   C   D   E

e If a person moves from room 1 to room 2, what changes in artificial gravity will he feel?

***12 a** A centripetal force is required for a body to move in a circular path. What provides the centripetal force for the object in each of the following examples? (i) The moon going round the earth. (ii) A car going round a corner. (iii) A rubber bung attached to a piece of string and whirled in a horizontal circle.

b Fig. 14.13 shows the path taken by a hammer which is being whirled in a horizontal circle.

fig. 14.13

(i) Copy and mark on the diagram the direction of the forces which act on the hammer when it is in position P. (ii) When the hammer reaches position Q, the thrower lets go. Mark on the diagram the initial direction in which the hammer moves. (iii) The axis of rotation of the thrower is 2 metres from the hammer. The speed of the hammer is 10 metres per second. Calculate the centripetal acceleration of the hammer. (iv) The mass of the hammer is 7 kilograms. Calculate the centripetal force which the thrower exerts on the hammer.

c Fig. 14.14 shows a 'hot-wheels' track in the form of a loop. Explain how it is possible for the car to 'loop the loop'. (M.R.E.B.)

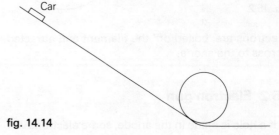

fig. 14.14

115

15
Electrons and Electron Streams

15.1 Diode valve

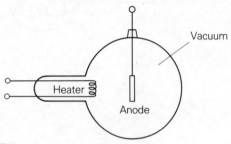

fig. 15.1

Fig. 15.1 shows a simple diode valve. It will conduct electricity when the filament is hot and is made more negative than the anode (fig. 15.2).

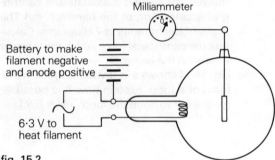

fig. 15.2

Electrons are 'boiled off' the filament and attracted across to the anode.

15.2 Electron gun

If a hole is made in the anode, some electrons will go through and come out in a stream on the other side (fig. 15.3).

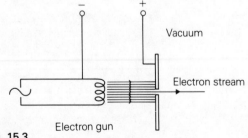

fig. 15.3

15.3 Maltese cross experiment

Notice how in fig. 15.4 a sharp shadow, larger than the cross, is made on the screen. This shows that the electron stream spreads out in straight lines towards the screen.

fig. 15.4

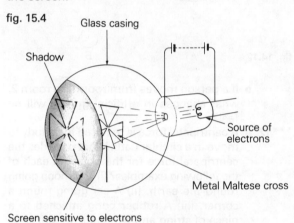

If magnets are held at the top and bottom of the tube, the shadow of the cross will move to the side.

A stream (or beam) of electrons is catapulted out of a magnetic field (fig. 15.5) as if it is a wire carrying a current (section 10.8).

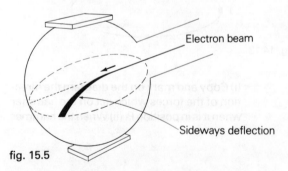

fig. 15.5

This is evidence that an electron stream is a current of moving charge.

15.4 Perrin tube experiment

In a Perrin tube is a metal can called a Faraday cylinder. The electron stream is deflected into the cylinder by the magnetic field of two coils. If the

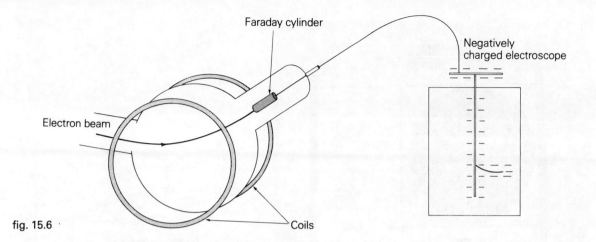

fig. 15.6

cylinder is connected to a negatively charged electroscope (fig. 15.6) the leaf stays up. If the electroscope has first been charged positively, its leaf will fall and then go up again. This shows that the electron stream has a negative charge.

15.5 Deflection tube

If a potential difference is made across A and B so that A is positive, the electron beam is seen to curve

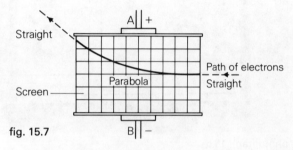

fig. 15.7

up in a parabola towards A (fig. 15.7). This is more proof that a stream of electrons has a negative charge.

The electrons can also be deflected upwards by magnets put on each side of the tube. The difference is that the curve will be part of a circle and not a parabola (fig. 15.8).

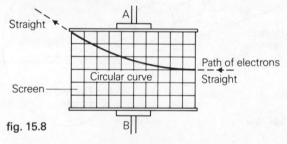

fig. 15.8

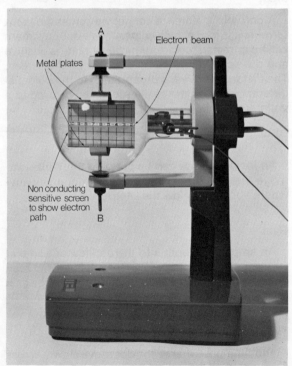

photograph 15.a (Deflection tube)

15.6 Cathode ray oscilloscope (C.R.O.)

Photograph 15.b shows a cathode ray oscilloscope. Fig. 15.9 is a simplified diagram of the tube inside.

Cathode rays

The **heated cathode** gives off electrons which are attracted towards the **accelerating anode,** then travel in a stream or 'ray' towards the screen. Hence, 'cathode rays'.

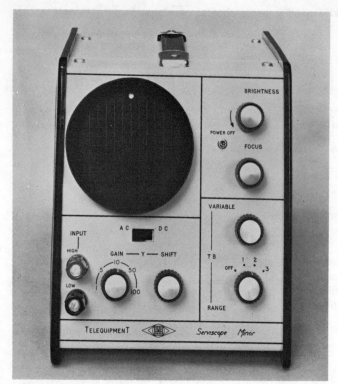

photograph 15.b

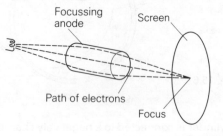

Focussing anode

Screen

Path of electrons

Focus

fig. 15.10

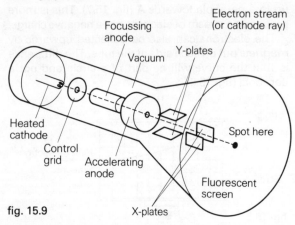

Focussing anode

Electron stream (or cathode ray)

Vacuum

Y-plates

Heated cathode

Control grid

Accelerating anode

Spot here

Fluorescent screen

fig. 15.9

X-plates

Brightness

The **brightness knob** is connected to the **control grid**. The more negative the grid is made the less electrons will get through to the screen and so the dimmer the spot will be.

Focus

Electrons can be focussed at the screen by making the **focussing anode** more, or less, positive (fig. 15.10). This is controlled by the **focus knob**.

Input

A potential difference connected across the **input terminals** is led to the **Y-plates**. The electron stream will be attracted towards whichever plate is positive and the spot will move up or down on the screen. The distance moved is proportional to the potential difference and so the oscilloscope can be used as a voltmeter.

Shift

An inside voltage can be put onto the **Y-plates** to move the spot up or down, to a starting point anywhere above or below the centre.

Gain

An amplifier is built into the oscilloscope so that very small input voltages can be amplified and seen on the screen. Amplification is controlled by the **gain knob**.

Time base (T.B.)

The time base makes the dot move slowly across the screen and fly back to sweep slowly across again. This is done by a circuit which makes a steadily in-

118

creasing voltage between the **X-plates** to attract the electron stream to one side. It then switches back to start all over again. The sweep time can be changed in steps using the **range knob,** or more gradually by using the **variable knob.**

A.C.—D.C.

Switched to the A.C. position, the oscilloscope spot will only be moved by an alternating input voltage. Switched to the D.C. position, the spot will be moved by both direct or alternating input voltages. The switch is used most in the D.C. position.

15.7 Millikan and the charge of one electron

Before looking at Millikan's experiment, it will help to work through a simple maths problem.
Problem: Five bags contain different numbers of tennis balls. The bags weigh 14·5, 22, 6·5, 30 and 54 newtons. What is the most likely weight of one ball?
Answer: Because the weight of one ball must fit into the weights of each bag-full exactly, the most likely weight of one ball is 0·5 newtons. (Notice that this weight was found without weighing just one ball.)

Millikan's experiment

Charge in an electric field feels a force (section 8.7). By balancing the electric force on a charged oil drop against its weight (fig. 15.11), Millikan was able to calculate the size of the charge.

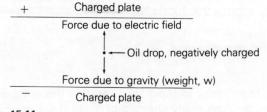

fig. 15.11

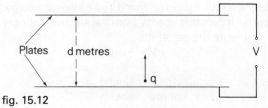

fig. 15.12

If the plates are d metres apart and V volts are connected across them (fig. 15.12), it can be proved that the electric force on a charge of q coulombs is $\dfrac{Vq}{d}$ newtons.

When the electric force, $\dfrac{Vq}{d}$, is balanced by the weight of the drop, W,

$$\frac{Vq}{d} = W$$

Changing this equation round gives

$$q = \frac{Wd}{V}$$

so that charge can be calculated.

Millikan did many experiments to get different values of q. Just as the different weights of the bag-fulls of tennis balls could be used to find the weight of one ball, Millikan found that there was one small value of charge that fitted into all his results for q exactly. This value, $1·6 \times 10^{-19}$ coulombs, came to be known as the charge, e, of one electron. Millikan had shown that electricity came in 'lumps' of definite size.

$$e = 1·6 \times 10^{-19} \text{ coulombs}$$

15.8 The energy of a moving electron

An electron moving across the potential difference between the filament and anode of an electron gun gains energy (fig. 15.13). For an electron charge of e coulombs and a potential difference of V volts, the electron will gain eV joules of energy from the electrical supply.

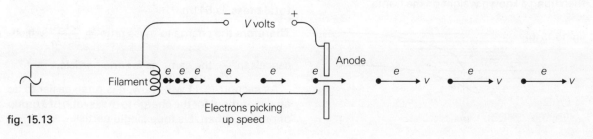

fig. 15.13

As the electron picks up speed it gains kinetic energy. Because it gets this energy from the electrical supply we can write the equation

$$eV = \tfrac{1}{2}mv^2$$

electrical kinetic
energy energy

Where m is the mass of the electron and v is its final velocity.

15.9 'Weighing' a magnetic field

If a current, I, flows along a wire length, L, at right angles to a magnetic field, B, there will be a 'catapult field' force of F (fig. 15.14).

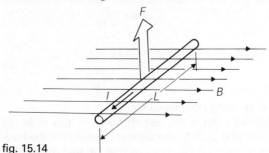

fig. 15.14

F depends on the sizes of B, I and L, and the relation linking them is

$$F = BIL$$

This equation can be rewritten as

$$B = \frac{F}{IL}$$

The method shown in fig. 15.15 can be used to find the size of a magnetic field, B.

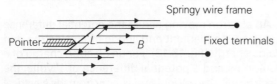

fig. 15.15 **(a)**

Make a springy wire frame level with a pointer and then hang a known weight on the frame.

fig. 15.15 **(b)**

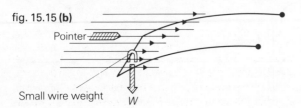

Connect the frame to a variable power supply and adjust the current until the frame is level with the pointer again.

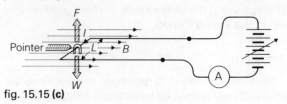

fig. 15.15 **(c)**

Since $F = W$, and L and I can be measured, then B is easily calculated using

$$B = \frac{F}{IL}$$

Note: Because the magnetic field has been found by a method of balancing we say it has been 'weighed'.

15.10 $\dfrac{e}{m}$ and m of an electron

Photograph 15.c shows a working fine beam tube. Electrons from an electron gun are made to move in a circle by the magnetism of two coils. Low pressure gas in the tube glows when it is hit by electrons, so the circular path can be seen.

Using results from this apparatus and the equations mentioned in sections 15.8 and 15.9, it is possible to calculate the **charge to mass ratio**, $\dfrac{e}{m}$, of an electron.

Next, using Millikan's value for e, $1\cdot6 \times 10^{-19}$ coulombs, the **mass, m,** of an electron can be found.

$$\frac{e}{m} = 1\cdot8 \times 10^{11} \text{ coulombs per kilogram}$$

$$m = 9 \times 10^{-31} \text{ kilograms}$$

The importance of $\dfrac{e}{m}$

The charge to mass ratio remains the same, no matter how many charged particles there are. For example, if there are 541 particles, each of charge e and mass m, then the **total charge** is 541e and the **total mass** is 541m.

Therefore the charge to mass ratio $= \dfrac{541e}{541m}$, which cancels to $\dfrac{e}{m}$, the same as for one particle.

As section 15.11 will show, it is often easier to do an experiment for the charge to mass ratio of a group of particles than it is for a single particle.

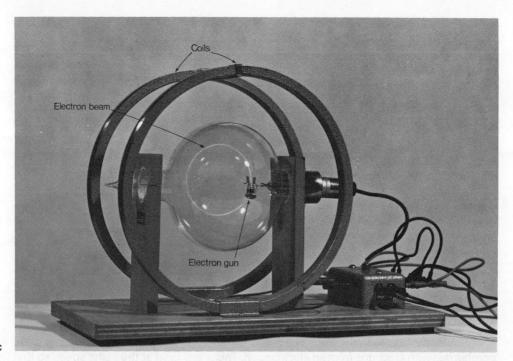

photograph 15.c

15.11 $\dfrac{e}{M}$ and M of a hydrogen ion

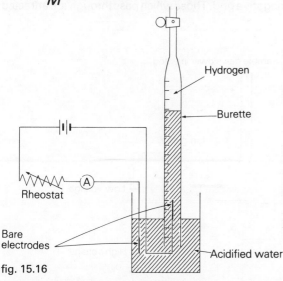

fig. 15.16

In fig. 15.16 a current of 1 ampere is passed through acidified water for 20 minutes (1200 seconds) and hydrogen gas is collected in a burette. The total charge carried by the hydrogen ions in the water before they bubble off as a gas is 1200 coulombs. (1 coulomb per second for 1200 seconds).

The total mass of hydrogen collected can be calculated by measuring the volume of hydrogen and

knowing that its density is 0·1 kilograms per cubic metre. (Mass = density × volume; see section 2.2).

Knowing the total charge and total mass then the **charge to mass ratio,** $\dfrac{e}{M}$, for a hydrogen ion can be calculated, to give

$$\frac{e}{M} = 9·6 \times 10^7 \text{ coulombs per kilogram}$$

A hydrogen ion is a hydrogen atom which has lost an electron, so the charge of a hydrogen ion is the same as the charge of an electron, only positive.

Knowing e and $\dfrac{e}{M}$, the mass M of a hydrogen ion can be calculated, to give

$$M = 1·67 \times 10^{-27} \text{ kilograms}$$

This is about 1840 times bigger than the mass of an electron.

15.12 To find $\dfrac{e}{M}$ and M by mass spectrometer

In section 15.10 $\dfrac{e}{m}$ and m of an electron were found by swinging electrons round in a magnetic field. In the mass spectrometer, other charged particles (ions) are swung round in a magnetic field. This helps us calculate their **charge to mass ratio** and their **mass.**

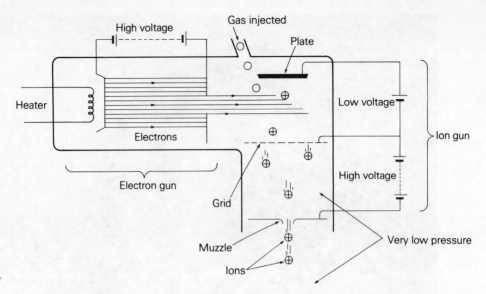

fig. 15.17

Ion gun

Atoms or molecules in the form of a gas, are first bombarded with electrons from an electron gun. This knocks electrons off some of the atoms and turns them into positive ions. The ions are then fired from an ion gun (fig. 15.17) into a magnetic field.

It is important that all ions of the same substance are fired at the same speed so that they travel in the same size circles. From where they are made in the ion gun, ions drift different distances towards a slightly negative grid. Those which pass through are attracted

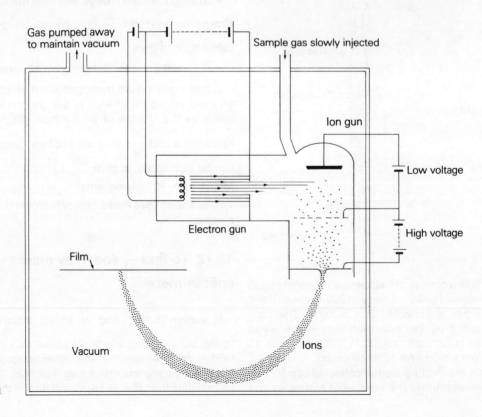

fig. 15.18

very strongly towards a very negative muzzle. In this way the ions pick up most of their speed between the grid and the muzzle, so ions of the same charge and mass move as fast as each other. Without a grid these ions would be attracted across different distances and end up with different speeds.

Dempster's mass spectrometer

Fig. 15.18 is a diagram of Dempster's mass spectrometer. Notice how the ions are made to travel in a semi-circle before they hit a film. This has the effect of focussing the ions which spread out as they leave the muzzle. It is called 180° focussing.

To see why the ions focus, try this test. Mark a dot on a piece of paper. Put a coin flat on the piece of paper with its edge touching the dot and draw round the coin. Move the coin slightly but keep its edge touching the dot. Draw round the coin again (fig. 15.19). Notice that all the circles cross (or focus) after a semi-circle (fig. 15.20).

fig. 15.19

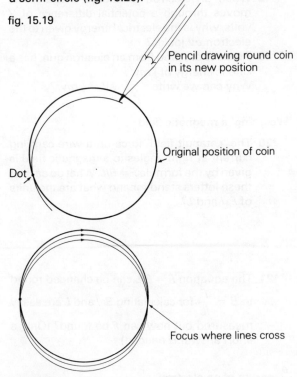

Pencil drawing round coin in its new position

Original position of coin

Dot

Focus where lines cross

fig. 15.20

After finding the place where the ions hit the film, the radius of their circular path can be worked out. Next, by the same method as was used for an electron in section 15.10, $\dfrac{e}{M}$ and M can be calculated for the ion.

15.13 Other uses of the mass spectrometer

Identifying isotopes

Sometimes an element is made of atoms which are chemically the same but which have different masses. These 'different' types of atoms are **isotopes** of the element (section 17.11).

Chlorine seems to have an atomic weight of 35·5 atomic mass units, but when the gas is tested in a mass spectrometer two lines are found on the film. One line is for 35 and the other for 37 atomic mass units (fig. 15.21). Chlorine is a mixture of two isotopes.

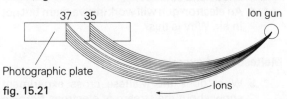

37 35   Ion gun

Photographic plate

fig. 15.21   Ions

Analysing compounds

If a vaporised compound is bombarded with very fast electrons, not only are ions of the compound made, but the compound is broken down and a number of smaller ions made. In this way a compound will give several lines on a spectrometer film which help to identify the elements it is made of.

Testing for impurities

A mass spectrometer photograph will show faint lines for any impurities in a substance which should be pure.

Testing Einstein's equation, $E = mc^2$

Einstein said that mass can be changed into energy and that a mass, m, will give an energy, E, where

$$E = mc^2$$

c being the velocity of light

The energy got from certain atomic reactions can be calculated, and using a mass spectrometer the mass of particles before the reaction can be compared with the mass after the reaction. When this is done, the results are found to fit the equation, $E = mc^2$, where E is the energy gained and m is the mass lost.

Revision questions

Diode valve

** **1** A working diode valve only conducts electricity when the anode is positive. Why is it more likely that negative charge is moving from the cathode to the anode, than positive charge is moving from the anode to the cathode?

Electron gun

* **2** Sketch and label a diagram of an electron gun.
** **3** What will be the effect on an electron stream of **a** increasing the voltage between the anode and cathode, **b** increasing the voltage to the filament, **c** reversing the voltage between the anode and cathode?
* **4** An electron gun will work in a vacuum but not in air. Why is this?

Maltese cross experiment

* **5** What does the Maltese cross experiment show about the stream of electrons from an electron gun?
* **6** Ralph says, 'The shadow of the cross is made by light from the filament and is nothing to do with electron streams'. How could you test to see if he is right?

Perrin tube experiment

** **7** The Faraday cylinder of a Perrin tube is connected to a positively charged gold leaf electroscope. **Explain** what will happen to the gold leaf when the Perrin tube is switched on and the electron stream deflected into the Faraday cylinder.

Deflection tube

* **8** Explain how the deflection tube gives evidence that an electron stream has a negative charge.
** **9** What would be seen on the screen of a deflection tube if the positive and negative plates were replaced by north and south seeking magnetic poles?
* **10** Sketch the different shapes of curve which an electron stream will follow **a** in an electric field, **b** in a magnetic field.

Cathode ray oscilloscope (C.R.O.)

* **11** Why is an oscilloscope called a 'cathode ray' oscilloscope?
* **12** Why can a C.R.O. be used as a voltmeter?
* **13** When might the **gain** on an oscilloscope need to be turned full up?

** **14** To show the wave shape of a very high frequency alternating voltage clearly, would the **sweep time** of the **time base** need to be long or short?

Millikan and the charge of one electron

* **15** In Millikan's experiment a charged oil drop is held stationary between two metal plates by balancing two forces. Which two forces are balanced?
** **16** Although an oil drop may never have just one electron charge it is possible to reason out that such a charge exists. How can this be done from a set of different results for charge?
* **17** What did Millikan's experiment show about electric charge?

The energy of a moving electron

** **18** When an electron of charge e coulombs, moves through a potential difference of V volts, why is the electrical energy given to the electron eV joules?
** **19** An electron, fired from an electron gun, has a kinetic energy of $\frac{1}{2}mv^2$.
Why can we write $eV = \frac{1}{2}mv^2$?

'Weighing' a magnetic field

* **20** The 'catapult field' force on a wire carrying current at right angles to a magnetic field is given by the formula $F = BIL$. What do each of these letters stand for and what are the units of F, I and L?

** **21** The equation $F = BIL$ can be changed round to $B = \dfrac{F}{IL}$ for calculating B. I and L are easily measured but how can F be found? (Only a short answer is needed).

$\dfrac{e}{m}$ and m of an electron

* **22** Why is some gas at low pressure left inside a fine beam tube?
** **23** Given that $\dfrac{e}{m} = 1 \cdot 8 \times 10^{11}$ coulombs per kilogram and $e = 1 \cdot 6 \times 10^{-19}$ coulombs, calculate the mass of an electron.

124

$\dfrac{e}{M}$ and M of a hydrogen ion

***24** For the experiment described in section 15.11, when a current of 1 ampere was passed through acidified water for 20 minutes calculate **a** the total charge passed, **b** the charge to mass ratio of a hydrogen ion, **c** the mass of a hydrogen ion.
(Density of hydrogen = 0·1 kilograms per cubic metre, 60 cubic centimetres of hydrogen are collected, and charge, $e = 1·6 \times 10^{-19}$ coulombs.)

*25** Why does the charge of a hydrogen ion have the same size as the charge of an electron?

$\dfrac{e}{M}$ and M by mass spectrometer

*26** Fig. 15.22 is a diagram of a simple ion gun. Must the muzzle be made positive or negative for the gun to work?

fig. 15.22

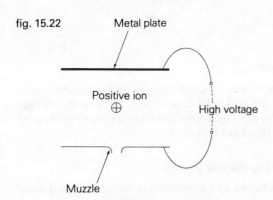

27 Compare the 'firing speeds' of the ion in fig. 15.22 if **a** it moves from the position shown to the muzzle, **b** it moves from near the metal plate to the muzzle.
28 Why is a grid included in the ion gun of a Dempster's mass spectrometer?
*29** Why must ions, fired from the muzzle of an ion gun, be focussed?

Other uses of the mass spectrometer

*30** A scientist believes that he has discovered a completely new element. How can he prove that this element really is 'new'?
31 Michael asks, 'If the ions in an ion gun are made by bombarding a **gas** with electrons, how can a mass spectrometer be used to test a solid?' Answer Michael's question.

Extra questions

*32** Natural uranium is a mixture of isotopes, one of which is more useful to atomic scientists than the others. How can the useful isotope be separated out?
***33** The velocity selector in fig. 15.23 only allows ions of the same velocity to pass through S. After passing through S, the ions enter a uniform magnetic field and travel in a circular path.

fig. 15.23   X

a Copy fig. 15.23 and mark on it, at X, the direction of the force exerted on the ions.
b In which direction is the magnetic field, AA, BB or CC?
c The force on a moving charge in a magnetic field = Bqv. The centripetal force on a body moving in a circle = $\dfrac{mv^2}{r}$

Why is $Bqv = \dfrac{mv^2}{r}$?

d The radius of the above circle is 3 cm. Calculate the radius of the circular path taken by a beam of ions of the **same** charge but having **twice** the mass. (*M.R.E.B.*)

***34** A manufacturer makes an electron 'deflection tube' which consists of an evacuated glass bulb with some electrodes in it. He states that the tube works best if a 6 V supply is connected between A and B and a 3 kV supply between A and C. The electrode at C has a small hole in

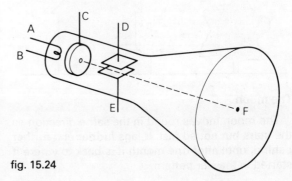

fig. 15.24

125

it, and just beyond the hole there are two parallel metal plates with a connection to each of them (fig. 15.24).

a What is the purpose of having a potential difference between A and B?

b Which terminal of the 3 kV supply should be connected to C?

c Explain the purpose of the high voltage.

d Why is the tube 'evacuated'?

When the manufacturer's instructions are followed, a spot of green light appears at F on a special coating on the inside of this deflection tube.

e When a p.d. of 100 V is applied between D and E (D positive) the spot moves away from F. Draw a diagram to show the direction in which the spot moves.

f Explain why the spot moves in **e**.

g How could you make the spot move further from F?

h If the spot is not very bright, what **two** separate changes might you make to increase the brightness?

i An alternating voltage of frequency 50 Hz is applied across the plates D and E. Describe what you would now see on the screen.

j The tube shown in fig. 15.24 could **not** be used to display an alternating voltage as a wavy line, as an oscilloscope does. What could be done to achieve this result? (*O. and C.*)

16
Astronomy

16.1 Movement in the sky

The stars

The stars appear to be 'stuck' on the inside of a great 'celestial' sphere, turning slowly around the earth. The star pattern rotates anticlockwise about a fixed point in the sky near the pole star (fig. 16.1). In 24 hours the stars turn through 361°, making slightly more than one revolution.

fig. 16.1

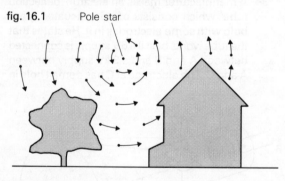

Pole star

The moon

The moon moves round in the same direction as the stars but not so fast. It lags further and further behind, until after one month it is back to where it started in the star pattern.

The sun

The sun also moves round in the same direction as the stars and it too lags behind. Because it only lags behind by 1° a day, the sun takes a whole year to drop back to where it started.

Freezing the star pattern

Centuries ago astronomers found it helped them to draw the star pattern as if it did not move, and then to plot the paths of the moon, sun and planets across this 'frozen' pattern.

The ecliptic

The sun does not move through the star pattern along the **celestial equator** (directly above the earth's equator) but along a path called the **ecliptic**. The ecliptic makes an angle of $23\frac{1}{2}°$ with the celestial equator and crosses it in two places (fig. 16.2).

The path of the moon through the stars is very close to that of the sun: it is, in fact, at about 5° to the ecliptic.

Equinox

An equinox is a time of year when day and night have the same length. This happens when the sun is

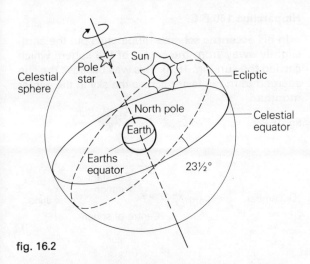

fig. 16.2

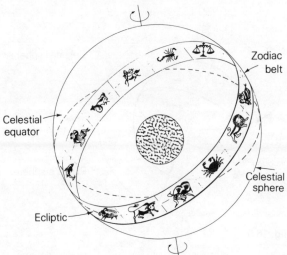

fig. 16.4

directly above the earth's equator. There is a spring and an autumn equinox every year, because the ecliptic crosses the celestial equator in two places as fig. 16.2 showed.

The planets

The word **planet** comes from the Greek word for **wanderer**. Planets look like stars but they 'wander' through the frozen star pattern. Instead of travelling in one direction like the sun or moon, they sometimes move backwards and their path shows a series of loops; one loop for every earth year (fig. 16.3).

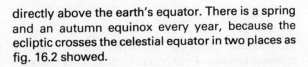

Path of planet

fig. 16.3

The backward movement of a planet on a loop is called **retrograde motion**.

The zodiac

The zodiac is a belt of stars centred on the ecliptic, through which the sun, moon and planets move. The zodiac is divided up into twelve sections and each is named after a group, or constellation, of stars in that section (fig. 16.4).

16.2 Some early Greek models

Thales 600 B.C.

Thales's model of the universe showed the stars

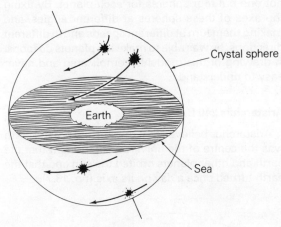

fig. 16.5

fixed to a crystal sphere which rotated once a day round a flat earth (fig. 16.5).

The sun and moon slid backwards along the inside surface of the sphere, and the sea stretched from the shores of the flat earth out to the sphere.

Pythagoras 530 B.C.

In the model by Pythagoras, a round earth was in the centre of the crystal sphere. The sun, moon and planets were each fixed to separate spheres. Each sphere rotated on a different axis and in the opposite direction to the stars. The sphere of one planet is shown in fig. 16.6.

127

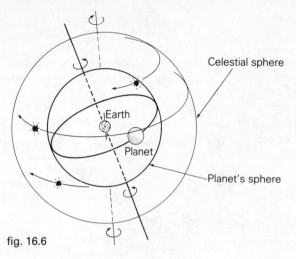

fig. 16.6

Eudoxus 370 B.C.

Eudoxus improved Pythagoras's model by having not one but **four** spheres for **each** planet. By fixing the axes of these spheres at different angles, and making them turn at different speeds and in different directions, he was able to make the planets do loops. A drawing of this model is complicated and never easy to understand.

Aristarchus 240 B.C.

Aristarchus believed that the sun and not the earth was the centre of the universe. He thought that the earth and other planets orbited the sun and that the earth turned once a day on its axis (fig. 16.7).

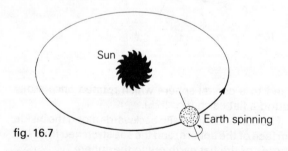

fig. 16.7

This theory was turned down for the following reasons.

a Man was too important not to be at the centre of the universe.

b There would be a terrific wind if the earth was moving round the sun.

c Everybody would be thrown off the earth if it was spinning.

d The stars would seem to alter their positions slightly as the earth moved round its orbit.

Hipparchus 140 B.C.

In his **eccentric scheme** Hipparchus put the earth slightly away from the centre of the sphere which carried the sun (fig. 16.8). This was because the sun seemed to move faster across the sky in the winter months.

fig. 16.8

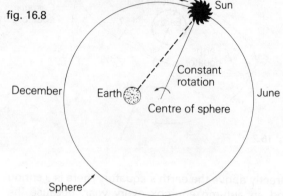

To explain the loops of the planets he used an **epicycle scheme**. Each planet rotated on a small epicycle sphere as it moved in orbit round the earth along the deferent sphere (fig. 16.9).

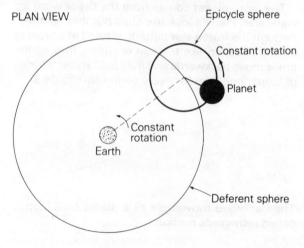

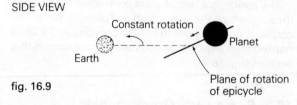

fig. 16.9

Ptolemy 120 A.D.

To make the Hipparchus model more accurate, Ptolemy used the **equant** Q in fig. 16.10. From it an

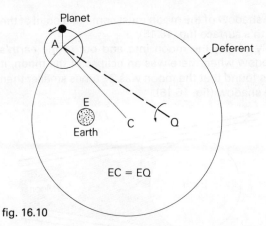

fig. 16.10

imaginary line QA swept round at a constant rate. The actual centre of orbit is C in the diagram, and the earth is the same distance from C as Q is on the other side.

Ptolemy's scheme proved very reliable for predicting the positions of the sun, moon and planets. Its details were used for over a thousand years by astronomers, priests, sailors—all those who needed to know about the pattern of the skies.

Note: The models described in this section are worked out to imitate the movement of the sun, moon and planets, so that their future positions can be predicted and such events as eclipses foretold. What the models do not do is explain **why** things move as they do. The driving force and mechanism of the heavens is left to the gods!

16.3 Evidence for a round earth

By the time Pythagoras thought out his model of the universe in 530 B.C., the earth was thought to be

fig. 16.11

round. There were three main bits of evidence for this.

1 Ships dropped down over the horizon (fig. 16.11).
2 The angle a person needs to look up at to see the pole star, changes from place to place on earth (fig. 16.12).

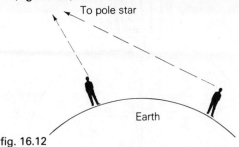

fig. 16.12

3 In an eclipse of the moon, a flat disc shaped earth would make a thin shadow on the moon. A spherical earth, would, and does, make a circular shadow (fig. 16.13).

fig. 16.13

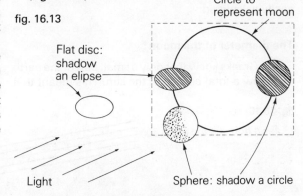

16.4 Greek measurements

The circumference and radius of the earth

Eratosthenes 240 B.C. knew that on a certain day in a place called Syene, the sun's reflection could be seen in the water at the bottom of a deep well. This meant that the sun was directly overhead. On the same day in Alexandria, 500 miles due south of Syene, the sun made a shadow with an angle of $7\frac{1}{2}°$ at the top of tall objects.

These facts, shown in fig. 16.14, were used by Eratosthenes to calculate the circumference of the earth.

He reasoned that the well and a tall object would make an angle of $7\frac{1}{2}°$ at the centre of the earth. If $7\frac{1}{2}°$ took you 500 miles round the earth, 360° would take you 48 times further.

$$48 \times 500 = 24\,000$$

fig. 16.14

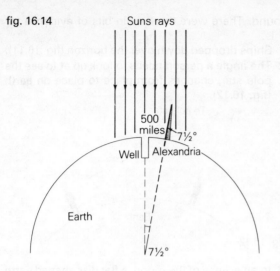

Suns rays

500 miles

Well · Alexandria

7½°

Earth

7½°

Therefore the circumference of the earth is 24 000 miles.

Since $24\,000 = 2\pi R$, the radius of the earth was then easily calculated.

The diameter of the moon

The Greeks knew that only a small part of the earth ever saw a total eclipse of the sun. This meant that

the shadow of the moon must come to a point at the earth's surface (fig. 16.15).

By timing the moon into and out of the earth's shadow when there was an eclipse of the moon, it was found that the moon was $2\frac{1}{2}$ times smaller than the shadow (fig. 16.16).

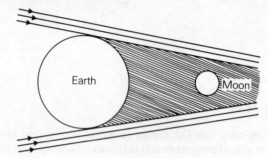

Earth

Moon

fig. 16.16

But just as the moon's shadow gets narrower (fig. 16.15), the earth's shadow must also get narrower and by the same amount; that is, by one moon diameter.

This means that the moon has a diameter, not $2\frac{1}{2}$, but $3\frac{1}{2}$ times smaller than the earth's. If the diameter of the earth is known it is easy to calculate the size of the moon.

fig. 16.15

Rays from the top of the sun

Shadow, narrowed to a point

Moon

Earth

Rays from the bottom of the sun

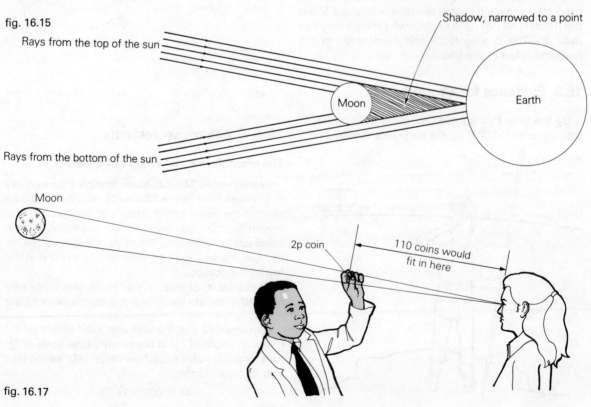

Moon

2p coin

110 coins would fit in here

fig. 16.17

Distance from the earth to the moon

It is possible to exactly blot out the moon by holding up a 2p coin. To do this the 2p has to be held 110 'coin diameters' away from the eye (fig. 16.17).

This means there is a triangle between the coin and the eye, of base 1 coin and height 110 coins. The Greeks realised that there must also be a triangle between the moon and the eye of base 1 moon and height 110 moons. The known value for the diameter of the moon was multiplied by 110 to give the distance from the earth to the moon.

Distance from the earth to the sun

Knowing the distance from the earth to the moon, the Greeks used geometry to work out how far away the sun was. When the moon was half in shadow (fig. 16.18) they realised that the angle between the sun, moon and earth was 90°.

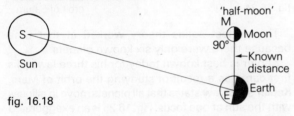

fig. 16.18

By measuring the angle between the sun, earth and moon, SEM (fig. 16.19), enough facts were known about the triangle to calculate ES, the distance from the earth to the sun.

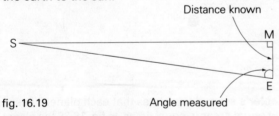

fig. 16.19

16.5 The sun is at the centre

Copernicus 1473–1543

Copernicus thought that Ptolemy's model was too complicated to show how God's universe really worked. He took up the earlier idea of Aristarchus that the planets and a spinning earth orbited the sun. Unlike Aristarchus, he was able to give evidence to support his idea.

It was noticed that Venus never moved more than 46° from the sun. This he explained by drawing Venus in a smaller orbit than the earth (fig. 16.20).

It was an illusion that planets did loops. The thick lines on fig. 16.21 show that although Jupiter moves

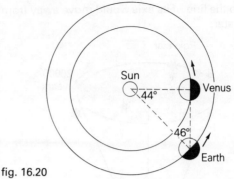

fig. 16.20

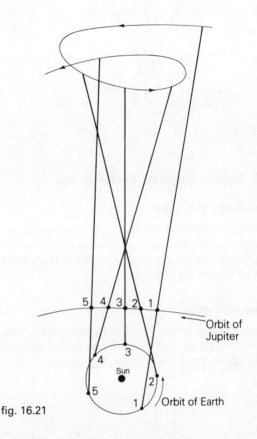

fig. 16.21

forward all the time, sometimes it **seems** to have gone backward in a loop.

Records showed that although the stars seemed to revolve about the pole star, this had not always been so. The centre of revolution had gradually changed over the years. Only for a short time every 26 000 years would the centre be back near the pole star.

Copernicus suggested that at that moment the earth was spinning with its axis pointing up at the pole star. The earth was slowly wobbling on its axis though, doing one 'wobble' every 26 000 years (fig.

131

16.22), so the line of its axis would move away from the pole star.

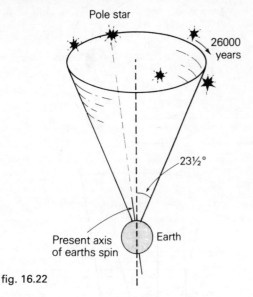

fig. 16.22

16.6 Kepler, pupil of Tycho Brahe

Tycho Brahe 1546–1601

Brahe was a Danish nobleman who devoted his life to making very accurate measurements of the stars and planets. His work played an important part in the work of Kepler, his pupil.

Kepler 1571–1630

Kepler was a brilliant mathematician. One of his first theories was that the solar system had been based on the five perfect solids (fig. 16.23).

fig. 16.23

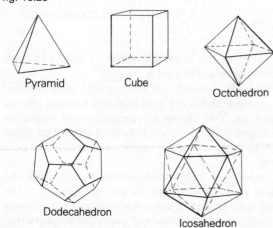

His idea was that the sphere of each planet's orbit fitted into a perfect solid, the next orbital sphere fitted round that solid, and so on. Fig. 16.24 gives the idea by showing the spheres of Saturn, Jupiter and Mars.

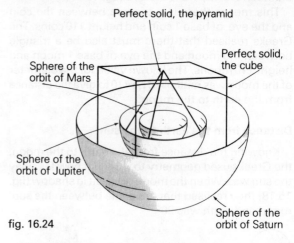

fig. 16.24

The perfect solids theory worked at that time because there were only six known planets.

Kepler is best known today for his three laws. His first came as a result of studying the orbit of Mars. **Kepler's first law** states that all planets move in ellipses with the sun at one focus. Fig. 16.25 is an exaggerated drawing of the elliptical orbit of Mars.

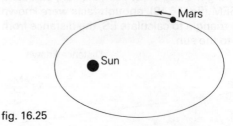

fig. 16.25

Kepler's second law states that each planet sweeps out equal areas in equal times. In fig. 16.26 the planet has moved faster when nearer to the sun, so that each of the areas between the dotted lines is equal.

fig. 16.26

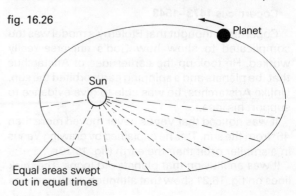

Equal areas swept out in equal times

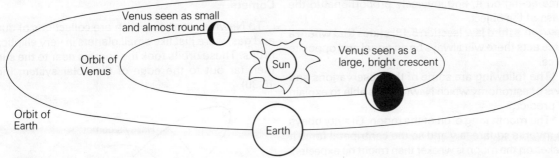

fig. 16.27

Kepler's third law states that $\dfrac{R^3}{T^2}$ = a constant for all orbits about the sun, where R is the radius of the orbit and T is the time for one complete orbit.
Note: The three findings of Kepler are all called laws and not theories. They state facts but do not **explain** the motion of the planets.

16.7 Galileo 1564–1642

Using his telescope (a Dutch invention) Galileo found evidence to support the 'sun in centre' theory of Copernicus. He noticed that Venus changed in size and sometimes had a crescent shape like the moon. This supported the view that the orbit of Venus was closer to the sun than the orbit of the earth (fig. 16.27).

Galileo noticed that the star pattern close to Jupiter kept changing. Fig. 16.28 shows what he saw on different nights.

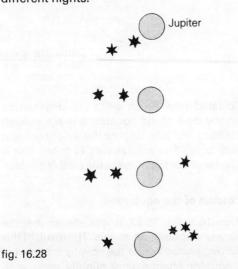

fig. 16.28

He decided that these 'stars' were in fact moons in orbit round Jupiter. The earth was not the centre for **these** orbits.

Galileo saw that the sun and moon were not perfectly smooth, bright objects put in the sky to light the earth. The sun had sun-spots and there were mountains and craters on the moon.

All this was valuable scientific evidence but it got Galileo into a lot of trouble with the Church, which still believed that the earth must be the centre of the universe.

16.8 Newton 1642–1726

Newton had a theory that all movement in the solar system could be explained by his law of gravitation. This law said that where there are two masses m_1 and m_2 with their centres a distance d apart (fig. 16.29), the force of attraction between them is given by

$$F = G\,\frac{m_1 m_2}{d^2}$$

where G is the universal gravitational constant.

fig. 16.29

With his law of gravitation, the formula for centripetal force, $F = \dfrac{mv^2}{R}$ (section 14.4), and his three laws of motion, Newton was able to explain and even predict astronomical observations.

Here is a reminder of Newton's three laws of motion:
Newton's first law (section 5.8) states that when a body is moving with a constant velocity or else not moving at all, either there are no forces acting on it or the forces which do act balance one another.
Newtons second law (section 5.10) states that the acceleration of an object is directly proportional to the

133

force acting on it, and inversely proportional to the mass of the object.

Newton's third law (section 5.13) states that where a force acts there will always be an equal and opposite force.

*The following are some of the observations and laws of astronomy which Newton was able to explain or predict:

*The month long orbit of the moon. Gravity obeys an inverse square law and so the centripetal force it makes on the moon is weaker than might be expected.

*Kepler's three laws. These could be explained mathematically using Newton's law of gravitation and his laws of motion.

*Comets. These could be explained as being matter moving in very elliptical orbits.

*The mass of a planet. This could be calculated if that planet had a satellite or moon.

*The bulged shape of the earth. This was shown to be needed to provide a centripetal force when the earth was in molten form.

*Small differences in acceleration due to gravity at different places on the earth. These could be explained as being due to the earth's spin and shape.

*Tides. These were shown to be due to the gravitational attraction of the moon, with the sun having a small effect.

*The mass of the moon. This was calculated using the earth's tides as a satellite of the moon.

*The precession of the equinoxes. This was shown to be due to the earth's bulge. The 26 000 year period was roughly predicted.

*Changes in the speed of the moon. These were shown to be due to the gravitational pull of the sun.

*Changes in the speeds of planets. These were shown to be due to the gravitational pull of other planets.

*The discovery of Neptune. This was predicted because of changes in the speed of Uranus. Both prediction and discovery, which depended on Newton's law of gravitation, were made after the death of Newton.

A good theory should

1 stand up to being tested,
2 be able to explain what is seen,
3 be able to predict what has not yet been seen.

In this way Newton's theory that the solar system was governed by the laws of gravitation and motion was a good theory.

16.10 Some explanations and predictions

Here are a few explanations and predictions of Newton's theory described in more detail.

Comets

To Newton, comets, which are collections of dust and gas, were just like small planets in very elliptical orbits. These orbits took the comets near to the sun, then far out to the edge of the solar system (fig. 16.30).

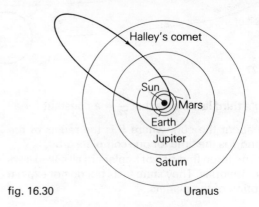

fig. 16.30

The bulge of the earth

Newton imagined two pipes of liquid from the centre of the earth, one to the equator and one to a pole (fig. 16.31).

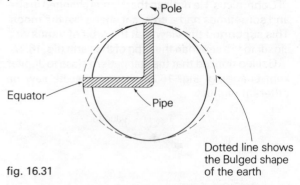

fig. 16.31

He calculated how much extra liquid would be needed in the pipe to the equator to make enough centripetal force and also balance the weight of liquid in the 'polar pipe'. The answer was 14 miles. This is roughly the height of the bulge at the earth's equator.

The precession of the equinoxes

In section 16.5, fig. 16.22, it was shown that the earth is slowly wobbling on its axis. The result of this is that the two places where the ecliptic crosses the celestial equator change very slightly each year. Because these places fix the times of the Spring and Autumn equinoxes, (section 16.1), then the equinoxes are also changing, or **precessing.**

Newton imagined the spinning earth to be like a huge, tilted gyroscope. Just as a gyroscope will wobble when a force tries to twist it over (fig. 16.32), the earth wobbles because it feels a twisting force.

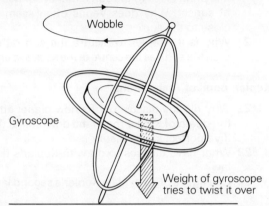

fig. 16.32

The twisting force on the earth is due to the sun's gravitational pull on the bulge of the earth (fig. 16.33).

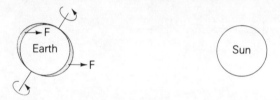

fig. 16.33

The part of the bulge which is nearer the sun feels a larger force than the part which is further away (fig. 16.34). The result is, a twisting force trying to turn the earth up straight.

fig. 16.34

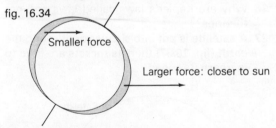

The discovery of Neptune

After Newton's death it was discovered that Uranus was not keeping to the orbit predicted by Newton's theory. The planet was speeding up then slowing down, as if attracted by an unknown planet in a larger orbit. Fig. 16.35 shows how this unknown planet might have attracted Uranus. The closer the planets, the larger the gravitational force between them. This is shown by the size of arrows on the diagram.

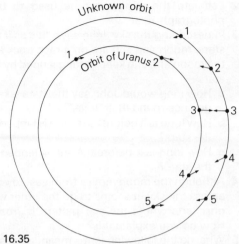

fig. 16.35

Because of the behaviour of Uranus, a new planet was looked for in the predicted position. This is how Neptune was discovered.

Revision questions

Movement in the sky

* **1** Photograph 16.a of the night sky was taken by a Trowbridge schoolboy. What does it show? (The straight white lines are telephone wires.)

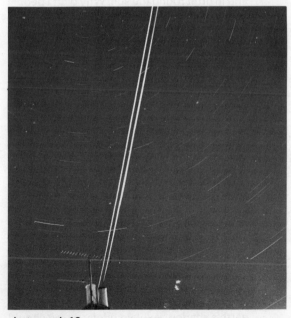

photograph 16.a
(by Martin Cooper)

** **2** Estimate the exposure time used to take photograph 16.a.

** **3** In describing the sky John says, 'It's as if the stars, moon and sun are on a race track and the moon and sun keep getting lapped by the stars'.
  a How long would John say the stars take to go once round their 'track'?
  b How long is it before the moon is lapped by the stars?
  c How long is it before the sun is lapped by the stars?

** **4** Although the moon moves from east to west across the sky, it seems to go the other way on charts where the star pattern is frozen. How do you explain this?

* **5** What do the following terms mean: **a** celestial sphere, **b** ecliptic?

* **6** What is special about an equinox?

* **7** One song starts, 'I was born under a wandering star'. What is a 'wandering star'?

* **8** What is the zodiac?

Some early Greek models

* **9** Sketch Thale's model of the universe.

*10 Say how an astronomical model can be useful, and also what it does not do.

*11 Why did Eudoxus need four spheres to show the movement of each planet?

*12 Aristarchus said that the earth was spinning and in orbit round the sun. Why didn't people believe him?

***13 Why, in the side view of Hipparchus's epicycle scheme (fig. 16.9) is the 'plane of rotation of the epicycle' at an angle?

***14 How would Hipparchus explain retrograde motion?

*15 What use was Ptolemy's astronomical model?

Evidence for a round earth

*16 How does an eclipse of the moon give evidence in favour of a round earth?

*17 Give two pieces of evidence, one old and one new, that the earth is round.

Greek measurements

***18 Read how Eratosthenes set about finding the circumference of the earth. Explain his method in your own words and use the value given to calculate the earth's radius.

**19 If the moon is $2\frac{1}{2}$ times smaller than the earth's shadow, explain briefly why it should be $3\frac{1}{2}$ times smaller than the earth itself.

The sun is at the centre

**20 Venus is sometimes called the morning star and sometimes called the evening star because it is often close to the sun either at sunrise or at sunset. Why does Venus often seem so close to the sun?

**21 Why is it simpler to picture the sun rather than the earth as the centre of the solar system?

Kepler, pupil of Tycho Brahe

**22 Why did the discovery of a new planet after the death of Kepler mean the downfall of the 'five perfect solids theory'?

*23 What have ellipses to do with Kepler's first law?

**24 Use fig. 16.36 to explain Kepler's second law.

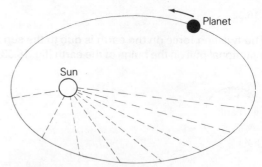

fig. 16.36

**25 Use the fraction $\dfrac{R^3}{T^2}$ and a sketch to explain Kepler's third law.

**26 Why are Kepler's laws called laws and not theories?

***27 A satellite is put into circular orbit round the earth (fig. 16.37) then its rockets are fired to increase its speed.

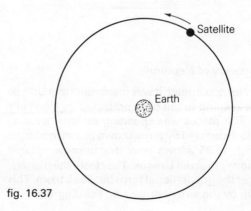

fig. 16.37

Its new orbit is an ellipse. Sketch the new orbit and mark the position where the rockets were fired.

Galileo 1564–1642

**28 Explain the statement, 'Venus has phases like the moon'.

***29 In what ways did the surface flaws of the sun and moon, the changing star pattern round Jupiter and the phases of Venus support Copernicus's Theory?

Newton 1642–1726

*30 Newton's law of gravitation can be written as the equation

$$F = G\frac{m_1 m_2}{d^2}$$

What do the symbols stand for?

**31 Experiments have shown that the value of G, universal gravitational constant, is $6 \cdot 7 \times 10^{-11}$ newton metres squared per kilogram squared.

Use this value in the equation $F = G\dfrac{m_1 m_2}{d^2}$

to calculate the force of attraction between the sun and the earth. The mass of the sun is 2×10^{30} kilograms, the mass of the earth is 6×10^{24} kilograms and their distance apart is 15×10^{10} metres.

**32 Why was Newton's theory a good theory?

Some explanations and predictions

**33 Explain the following statement: to the Greeks comets were something to be feared, but to Newton comets were no more than planets.

**34 How can the bulged shape of the earth be explained by the fact that the earth was once in molten form?

**35 Photograph 16.b shows a bicycle wheel gyroscope. Without the rubber band in place the wheel will spin at a fixed angle. Explain what will happen to the spinning wheel if the rubber band is fixed on.

***36 In what way are the bulges of the earth responsible for the precession of the equinoxes?

**37 What sort of evidence might point to the existence of an undiscovered planet?

Extra questions

***38 Explain how the spin and bulge of the earth both act to affect the weight of a person standing on the equator.

Rubber band, to try to turn the wheel upright

Wheel to be spun

photograph 16.b

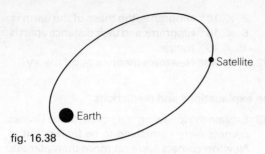

fig. 16.38

***39 a** Fig. 16.38 shows the path of an artificial satellite in orbit about the earth.
(i) The earth exerts a force on the satellite. What effect has this force? (ii) The satellite exerts a force on the earth. Copy fig. 16.38 and mark the direction of this force on the diagram. (iii) What effect does this last force have?

b (i) Kepler's second law applied to the satellite is that equal areas are swept out in equal times. Use a diagram to explain the meaning of this law. (ii) How does the speed of the satellite change during one complete orbit?

c State **three** features which any good theory should have. Illustrate your answer by referring to the theory of gravitation. (*M.R.E.B.*)

***40** Explain each of the following seven statements in the light of our model of the solar system. Draw diagrams if this makes your explanation clearer.

a There is an unchanging pattern of stars, revolving daily round an axis through the pole star.

b It is known that the sun shares this daily motion, but drifts at a rate of about 1° in a day in the opposite direction to the star pattern.

c The moon also drifts through the star pattern, but at the faster rate of about 90° in a week.

d The paths of these motions fall in a narrow band of the star pattern.

e The planet Jupiter makes reverse loops (one for each of our years) as it moves through the star pattern.

f The interval between successive tides at a certain place is approximately 12½ hours, so that the morning tide, say, occurs about an hour later than it did the day before.

g The planet Venus, as seen through a telescope, can look like the moon when half-full. (*O. and C.*)

***41** At midnight on a certain day the constellation of the Plough appeared as shown in fig. 16.39. Three hours later the Plough had moved.

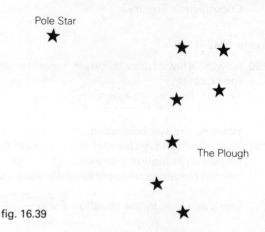

fig. 16.39

a Draw a rough sketch to show the original and the new positions of the constellation.

b Calculate the angle that the Plough moves through in the 3 hours.

c Would a planet ever be seen in the constellation of the Plough? Give a reason for your answer.

d How would the ancient Greek astronomers have explained the movement of the constellations?

e (i) What is the modern explanation of the movement of the constellations? (ii) What evidence is there in support of this modern explanation?

f Draw a sketch to show the path that Jupiter appears to follow when moving across the sky in the course of 1 year.

g How was the way we see Jupiter move explained on Ptolemy's system of epicycles?

h What is the explanation of the motion of Jupiter which we accept today? (*O. and C.*)

17
Radioactivity

17.1 Ionising air

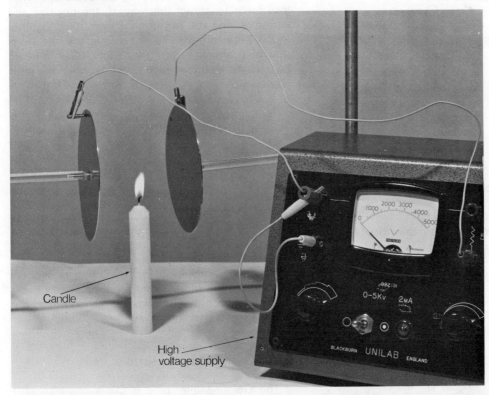

photograph 17.a

Photograph 17.a shows a candle burning between two metal plates. When a high voltage is switched on across the plates the flame spreads out (fig. 17.1).

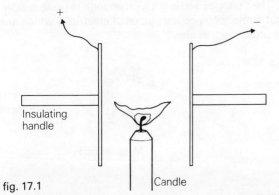

fig. 17.1

Heat energy has ionised the gas in the flame. Positive ions have been attracted towards the negative plate and negative ions towards the positive plate.

A burning match held near the top plate of a charged gold leaf electroscope makes the leaf go down. The charge on the plate attracts oppositely charged ions from the flame and the two types of charge cancel (fig. 17.2).

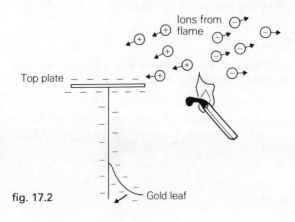

fig. 17.2

A radioactive source held near to a charged electroscope will also make the leaf go down. Radiation ionises the air and some of the ions cancel the charge on the electroscope (fig. 17.3).

fig. 17.3

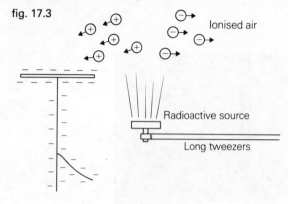

Ionised air

Radioactive source

Long tweezers

17.2 The match counter

The two metal spheres in fig. 17.4 are just too far apart for a spark to cross the gap without help.

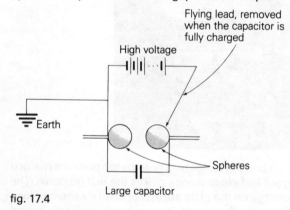

Flying lead, removed when the capacitor is fully charged

High voltage

Earth

Spheres

Large capacitor

fig. 17.4

When a match is struck under the gap a spark is made between the spheres. The spark is triggered off by the ions in the match flame.

Sparks

Imagine just one pair of ions between the two charged spheres (fig. 17.5).

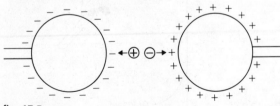

fig. 17.5

These ions accelerate towards the spheres, knocking into molecules of air and ionising them. The new ions then accelerate and make even more ions. Soon there is a whole avalanche of positive ions going one way and negative ions going the other way.

When ions reach the spheres they cancel some of the charge which is attracting the avalanche. With less force to attract them apart, the positive and negative ions still in the gap come back together again. It is as the positive ions recover their electrons that heat and light are given out. Noise is heard because of a sudden high pressure when the air is heated.

17.3 The spark counter

Instead of the two spheres of a match counter, the **spark counter** in photograph 17.b has a thin wire and a gauze.

The power supply is adjusted so that a spark will not cross the gap without help. When radium, a radioactive source, is held closer than about 6 centimetres from the gauze, sparks are seen and heard at random between the gauze and wire. Sparks happen where radioactive particles ionise the air. This experiment shows that the radiation causing the sparks has a range of about 6 centimetres in air and **does not** come out of the radium at regular intervals.

17.4 Geiger-Müller tube

The Geiger-Müller tube is like a spark counter, except that the gauze is replaced by a cylindrical metal electrode and the gas between the wire and cylinder is at low pressure (fig. 17.6).

The voltage used is not high enough to make sparks, but avalanches cause pulses of electricity which are counted by a scaler.

fig. 17.6

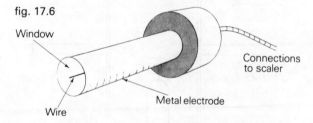

Window

Connections to scaler

Metal electrode

Wire

17.5 Alpha, beta and gamma radiation

The Geiger-Müller tube helps to identify 3 different types of radiation. When radiation from radium is

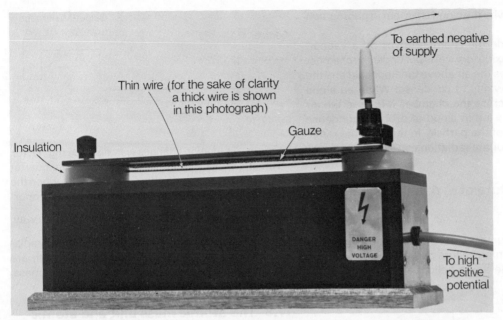

photograph 17.b

passed between charged plates some of it bends towards the negative, some towards the positive and some is not deflected at all. These three types of radiation are called **alpha** (α), **beta** (β) and **gamma** (γ), see fig. 17.7.

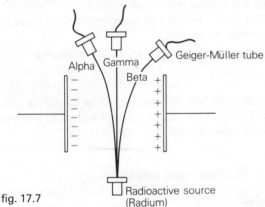

fig. 17.7

The alpha radiation has a positive charge and a range of about 6 centimetres in air. Beta radiation has a negative charge and a range of about 1·5 metres, although this varies with the type of source used. Gamma radiation has no charge and is not stopped by air.

To find what materials are needed to stop α, β and γ radiations the experiment in fig. 17.8 is set up.

It is found that a piece of paper will stop the alpha particles from reaching the Geiger-Müller tube. Beta radiation will pass through paper but be stopped by a thin sheet of aluminium, and gamma radiation can only be stopped by thick lead.

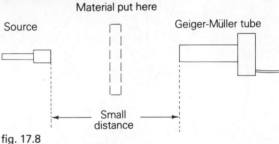

fig. 17.8

17.6 The cloud chamber

When a vapour is cooled it will condense.—Dew forms on grass on a cold morning, and clouds made of millions of water droplets form in cold air.

If a cold vapour is ionised it will condense more

photograph 17.c

quickly. This is why the cloud chamber in photograph 17.c works.

Meths inside the chamber gives off a vapour. Solid carbon dioxide (dry ice) is put under the chamber floor. This makes the air above the floor cold and the meths vapour wants to condense. When an alpha particle goes across the chamber it ionises the air and vapour and a thin cloud of droplets condense along the path of the particle. In this way the range and behaviour of the radiation can be seen.

17.7 The nature of α, β and γ radiation

Alpha

If an alpha source is placed at the centre of a cloud chamber containing helium gas, a collision between an alpha particle and a helium atom is sometimes seen (fig. 17.9).

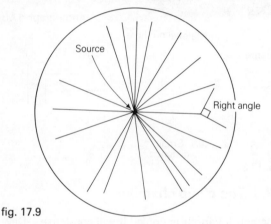

fig. 17.9

With no other gas is the angle after collison a right angle.

Experiments with colliding magnetic pucks or marbles show that only when an object is hit elastically by something with the same mass will the angle between them after collision be 90°. This and other evidence led scientists to believe that an alpha particle is like a **helium ion** (or helium atom which has lost its electrons).

Beta

Experiments to test the size of charge and mass show a beta particle to be the same as an **electron**.

Gamma

A gamma source can be moved further and further away from a Geiger-Müller tube to see how the

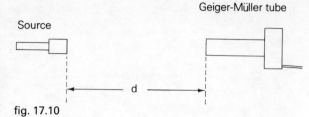

fig. 17.10

strength of radiation changes with distance (fig. 17.10).

Results show that the strength drops to a quarter when the distance is doubled and to a ninth when the distance is trebled. Therefore the strength is proportional to $\dfrac{1}{\text{distance}^2}$. Light behaves in the same way. This and other experiments show that gamma radiation belongs to the same family as light; both are **electromagnetic waves** and have no charge or mass.

17.8 The atomic mass unit and atomic weight

The mass of an atom is very small; for example, an atom of nitrogen is about $2\cdot3 \times 10^{-26}$ kilograms. Rather than have such small numbers, a new unit is used, the **atomic mass unit** (a.m.u.).

Oxygen is taken as a standard which has a mass of 16 atomic mass units.

$$\therefore 1 \text{ atomic mass unit} = \tfrac{1}{16}\text{th the mass of an oxygen atom}$$
$$1 \text{ a.m.u.} = 1\cdot66 \times 10^{-27} \text{ kilograms}$$

On this scale one nitrogen atom has 14·0075 a.m.u. and this number is sometimes called its **atomic weight** (even though it is really a mass).

17.9 Protons and neutrons

Protons

Atoms have no overall charge, so for each of their negative electrons they must also have a positive charge. The particles which have this positive charge are called **protons**. A proton has an atomic weight of about 1 a.m.u..

Neutrons

Only about half the atomic weight of an atom is made up of protons. For example nitrogen has 7 protons and an atomic weight of about 14 a.m.u.. The difference in 'weight' is made up by neutrons which also have a mass of about 1 a.m.u. but which have no charge. Nitrogen has 7 protons and 7 neutrons.

Note: An electron has a mass of about $\frac{1}{1840}$ a.m.u. and so has little effect on the atomic weight of an atom.

17.10 Atomic number and mass number

Atomic number (Z)

This is the number of **protons** an atom has. Nitrogen has an atomic number of 7 and this is written $_7$N.

Mass number (A)

This is the number of **protons** PLUS **neutrons** an atom has. Nitrogen has a mass number of 14 and this is written ^{14}N.

To show both the atomic number and the mass number of nitrogen we write $^{14}_{7}$N.

17.11 Isotopes

Atoms of the same element will do the same chemical reactions. The way an atom reacts depends on its number of protons, or **atomic number**. If the atomic number changes then the atom will react differently and will be a different element. If the number of neutrons changes this will not affect the way an atom reacts and it will stay the same element.

Atoms with different numbers of neutrons but the same number of protons are called **isotopes** of the same element. For example carbon may have 6 or 8 neutrons. $^{12}_{6}$C and $^{14}_{6}$C are both isotopes of carbon.

Chlorine may have 18 or 20 neutrons. $^{35}_{17}$Cl and $^{37}_{17}$Cl are both isotopes of chlorine.

17.12 Element changes

The effect of emitting alpha radiation

Helium has an atomic number of 2 and a mass number of 4. Because an alpha particle is like a helium ion we can write $^{4}_{2}\alpha$

When a radioactive atom gives off an alpha particle, the atom's atomic number and mass number will change and a new element will be made. For example, neptunium loses an alpha particle to become proto-actinium

$$^{237}_{93}\text{Np} \xrightarrow{\quad \nearrow ^{4}_{2}\alpha \quad} {}^{233}_{91}\text{Pa}$$

The effect of emitting beta radiation

A beta particle is the fast electron that is made when a neutron turns into a proton (fig. 17.11).

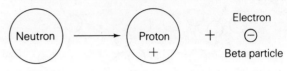

fig. 17.11

Beta particles have such a small mass compared to a proton or neutron that the mass number of an atom does not change when a beta particle leaves. Because a beta particle leaves behind an extra proton the atomic number of the atom goes up and it becomes a different element. A beta particle can be written as $^{0}_{-1}\beta$

An example of an atom becoming a different element by losing a beta particle is when carbon-14 turns to nitrogen.

$$^{14}_{6}\text{C} \xrightarrow{\quad \nearrow ^{0}_{-1}\beta \quad} {}^{14}_{7}\text{N}$$

The effect of emitting gamma radiation

When an alpha or beta particle is shot out, the inside of an atom may have more energy than it needs. It gives out this extra energy in the form of a gamma ray. Because a gamma ray has no mass or charge, it has *no* effect on the atomic number or mass number, so the element does not change.

17.13 Radioactive decay series

Often one radioactive element will decay into another element which is also radioactive. This new element will then itself decay and sometimes a whole series of decays happens. Radon changes to polonium and lead before becoming bismuth.

$$^{220}_{86}\text{Rn} \xrightarrow{\nearrow ^{4}_{2}\alpha} {}^{216}_{84}\text{Po} \xrightarrow{\nearrow ^{4}_{2}\alpha} {}^{212}_{82}\text{Pb} \xrightarrow{\nearrow ^{0}_{-1}\beta} {}^{212}_{83}\text{Bi}$$

17.4 Exponential decay

Imagine a group of 20 radioactive atoms (fig. 17.12).

fig. 17.12

Each atom is likely to decay, giving out an alpha or beta particle and changing to another element. Suppose in 3 seconds 6 atoms decay as shown in fig. 17.13

fig. 17.13

Because there are now only 14 radioactive atoms left, **less** than 6 atoms are likely to decay in the next 3 seconds. Perhaps only 4 atoms will decay. This is shown in fig. 17.14 where those already decayed are marked with a cross.

fig. 17.14

Although radioactive atoms decay at random as was shown by the spark counter (section 17.3), there is a pattern to the rate at which they decay. The rate is fast to begin with when there are lots of radioactive atoms, and gets slower as there are less radioactive atoms left.

If a Geiger-counter is used to find how a radioactive substance decays, a graph of the results will have the shape shown in fig. 17.15. This shows an **exponential decay**.

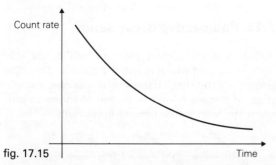

fig. 17.15

A radioactive element goes on decaying at a slower and slower rate for a long time. Because it is not possible to say how long it will go on for, the idea of **half-life** is used.

Half-life

This is the time it takes for half the atoms of a radioactive sample to decay. In the example in fig. 17.12 there were 20 radioactive atoms to start with. It

took 6 seconds for there to be only 10 left so that the half-life was 6 seconds.

A graph of the decay of the radioactive substance can be used to find its half-life. In fig. 17.16 the half-life is one hour. After a time of 3 hours the count rate will have dropped to 1500; half what it was an hour before.

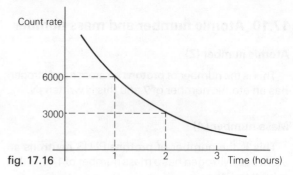

fig. 17.16

17.15 Models of the atom

The billiard ball model

A solid positive atom of protons and neutrons, with small negative electrons stuck all over the surface (fig. 17.17).

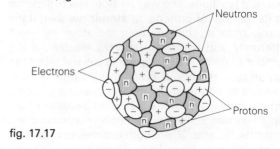

fig. 17.17

This model explained ionisation as electrons getting knocked off the surface. It could **not** explain how radiation could pass through the closely packed atoms in metal foil.

The plum pudding model

Electrons are the 'plums' mixed in a soft dough of protons and neutrons (fig. 17.18).

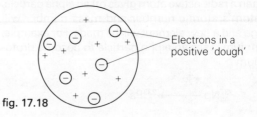

fig. 17.18

144

This model explained how radioactive particles could seem to go straight through thin foil. The even mixture of positives and negatives would not attract or repel a charged particle strongly enough to put it much off course. This is like the magnetic experiment in fig. 17.19.

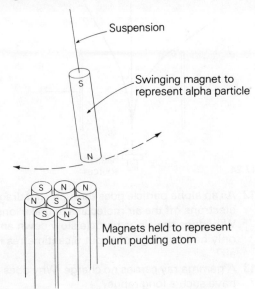

fig. 17.19

The swinging magnet is hardly affected by the mixture of north and south seeking poles.

Although the plum pudding model can explain the straight alpha tracks in a cloud chamber it does not account for the collisions which are sometimes seen (fig. 17.20).

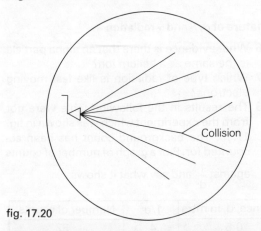

fig. 17.20

To be knocked off course an alpha particle must hit an object which has a large mass and positive charge. The object must also be very small in size or else collisions would happen more often.

The hollow atom model

A positively charged nucleus of large mass and small size surrounded by negative electrons. The space taken up by the atom is mostly empty (fig. 17.21).

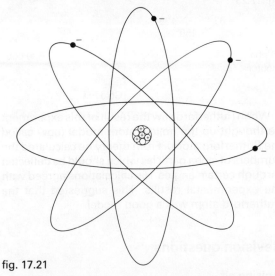

fig. 17.21

This model can explain both the straight alpha tracks and the rare collisions in a cloud chamber. The empty space and the small mass of the electrons will not put an alpha particle off course. The small width of the nucleus will mean that collisions do not happen very often.

17.16 Rutherford's alpha scattering experiment

Rutherford suggested the experiment of firing alpha particles into thin gold foil to see if any were reflected back (fig. 17.22).

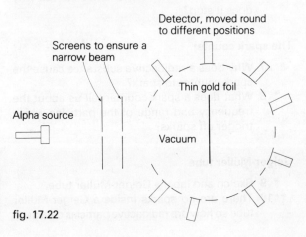

fig. 17.22

A detector was moved round and allowed to count for some time in different positions. The angles and approximate counts on one side, are shown in fig. 17.23.

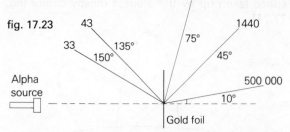

fig. 17.23

When Rutherford saw the result of this experiment he thought up the hollow atom model (now called the Rutherford atom). From theory he calculated the numbers of alpha particles which should be deflected through certain angles. His calculations agreed with the experimental results. This suggested that the Rutherford atom was a good model.

Revision questions

Ionising air

* 1 Where does the energy come from to ionise the gas in a flame?
** 2 Why does a flame contain both positive and negative ions and not just one type?
* 3 Why is it possible for positive radiation to discharge a positively charged gold leaf electroscope?

The match counter

* 4 Why does striking a match beneath the gap of a match counter trigger off a spark?
** 5 Explain how a spark is caused.
** 6 Once an avalanche of ions has started why does it stop?

The spark counter

** 7 Why does a radioactive substance cause the spark counter to spark?
* 8 What does a spark counter tell us about the frequency and range of the particles which trigger off sparks?

Geiger-Müller tube

* 9 Sketch and label a Geiger-Müller tube.
**10 There are no sparks inside a Geiger-Müller tube so how are radioactive particles detected?

Alpha, beta and gamma radiation

*11 Fig. 17.24 shows the behaviour of the three types of radiation in an electric field. Copy the drawing, label which type goes with which path and give its charge.

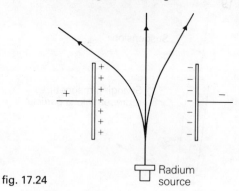

fig. 17.24

**12 As an alpha particle goes through air it drags electrons off the air molecules to make ions. Why does the alpha particle slow down and only have a range of about 6 centimetres in air?
**13 A gamma ray carries no charge. Why does it have such a long range?

The cloud chamber

*14 What is the purpose of the dry ice under the floor of a cloud chamber?
*15 When Michael says, 'I can see alpha particles going across the cloud chamber', what does he really mean?

The nature of α, β and γ radiation

*16 What evidence is there that an alpha particle is the same as a helium ion?
*17 Which type of radiation is like fast moving electrons?
**18 The results in the following table were got from the experiment which was shown in fig. 17.10. The background count has been accounted for. Plot a graph of number of counts against $\frac{1}{d^2}$ and say what it shows.

Distance, d, in mtrs	$1/d^2$	Number of counts
0·5	4	82
0·4	6·25	120
0·3	11·1	240
0·2	25	500
0·1	100	2012

The atomic mass unit and atomic weight

*19 Why is the mass of an atom usually given in atomic mass units and not in kilograms?

*20 What is the link between oxygen and the atomic mass unit?

*21 What is the atomic weight of oxygen?

Protons and neutrons

*22 How does the charge of a proton compare with the charge of an electron?

*23 What is the approximate atomic weight of **a** a proton, **b** a neutron?

*24 What is the basic difference between a proton and a neutron?

*25 Why do electrons have little effect on the atomic weight of an atom?

Atomic number and mass number

*26 What does the atomic number tell you about an atom?

*27 What does the mass number tell you about an atom?

**28 Lithium can be written $^{7}_{3}$Li. How many protons, neutrons and electrons are there in a neutral atom of lithium?

*29 Berylium (Be) contains 4 protons and 5 neutrons. Write the correct atomic and mass numbers by its symbol.

Isotopes

*30 What decides the way an element will react; atomic number or mass number?

*31 What does it mean to say that $^{238}_{92}$U and $^{239}_{92}$U are both isotopes of uranium?

*32 Which two of the following list are isotopes of the same element?

$^{59}_{21}$W $^{59}_{22}$X $^{61}_{21}$Y $^{61}_{20}$Z

Element changes

*33 Write atomic numbers and mass numbers beside the symbols for alpha and beta particles.

*34 Radon shoots out an alpha particle and becomes polonium.

$$^{220}_{86}\text{Rn} \xrightarrow{\quad^{4}_{2}\alpha\quad} {}^{?}_{?}\text{Po}$$

What are the atomic number and mass number of polonium?

*35 Fill in the missing numbers in the following equation.

$$^{14}_{6}\text{C} \xrightarrow{\quad\beta\quad} {}^{?}_{?}\text{N}$$

*36 What effect does giving off a gamma ray have on the atomic number and mass number of an atom?

Radioactive decay series

**37 The equation shows part of an imaginary radioactive decay series. Copy it and fill in the blank spaces.

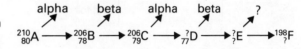

$$^{210}_{80}\text{A} \longrightarrow {}^{206}_{78}\text{B} \longrightarrow {}^{206}_{79}\text{C} \longrightarrow {}^{?}_{77}\text{D} \longrightarrow {}^{?}_{?}\text{E} \longrightarrow {}^{198}_{?}\text{F}$$

*38 Two substances from the equation in question 37 could not be separated chemically if mixed. Which ones?

Exponential decay

*39 Explain simply why the rate at which a radioactive substance decays gets slower and slower as time goes on.

*40 Sketch a graph to show how a radioactive element decays.

*41 What does it mean to say that the half-life of radon-219 is 4 seconds?

**42 A radioactive substance which has a half-life of one hour gives a count rate of 1200 at 12 o'clock. What will the count rate be after 1 hour and what will the count rate be at 4 o'clock?

**43 If a box of radioactive material with a half-life of 20 minutes and emitting β particles weighs 6 newtons at 2 o'clock, what will the box weigh at 3 o'clock?

**44 If the radioactive part of a sample had a mass of 8 kilograms and a half-life of 1 year, after how many years would the radioactive part have a mass of 1 kilogram?

Models of the atom

**45 What is the disadvantage of picturing atoms to be solid, like billiard balls?

**46 Most alpha particles can pass straight through gold leaf without changing direction. How does the 'plum pudding model' explain this?

**47 What evidence do cloud chamber tracks give against the 'plum pudding model'?

*48 What is meant by the 'hollow atom model'?

Rutherford's alpha scattering experiment

**49 Why, in the diagram of the experiment suggested by Rutherford (fig. 17.25), was it necessary to have the apparatus in a vacuum?

fig. 17.25

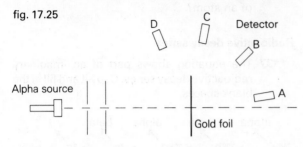

**50 How would the number of alpha particles arriving at A, B, C and D in fig. 17.25 vary? Which model of the atom explains these results best? Why?

Extra questions

**51 Explain what would happen to the length of alpha tracks in a cloud chamber if the pressure was increased above atmospheric pressure.

***52 Explain whether the strength of radiation from an alpha source in a vacuum would show an inverse square relation with distance?

**53 A radioactive decay series is shown below. Copy it and fill in the missing words and numbers.

$$_{80}^{210}A \xrightarrow{?} {}_{78}^{?}B \xrightarrow{?} {}^{206}_{?}C \xrightarrow{alpha} {}^{?}_{?}D \xrightarrow{beta} {}^{?}_{?}E \xrightarrow{?} {}^{198}_{?}F$$

***54 A pupil is given a radioactive source. He is told that it emits one kind of radiation only and he is asked to identify the kind of radiation. He sets up a counting instrument, connects a G.M. tube with a thin end-window to it, and applies the correct voltage to the G.M. tube. Holding the source with a pair of long tweezers in front of the end-window, he finds the count-rate is high.

  a Describe what experiments he might do to determine the nature of the radiation emitted.

  b Why was it wise to use long tweezers?

  c The pupil knows that radioactive sources get weaker as time goes by, so he measures the number of counts per minute one morning and repeats the measurement one day later, only to find the number of counts recorded is actually a little greater. Explain

this and suggest what should be tried in order to test whether this source gets weaker as time goes by.

  d When 1 mg of some radioactive strontium was analysed, it was found to contain 0.96 mg of strontium (atomic number 38) and 0·04 mg of a stable element called yttrium (atomic number 39). Assuming it was pure strontium initially, how do you explain the presence of yttrium? The half-life of this strontium isotope is about 7½ weeks. If another 1 mg sample of the source is analysed 15 weeks after the first analysis, what would the analysis figures be? (*O. and C.*)

**55 The 'radiation' emitted by a radioactive source is invisible and therefore it has to be detected by the effects that it produces. One of these is the ionisation of a gas.

  a A gold leaf electroscope is positively charged. A radioactive source which emits alpha particles is brought near to the top of the electroscope (fig. 17.26).

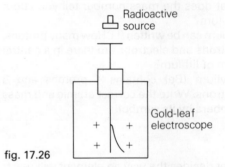

fig. 17.26

(i) What is observed? (ii) Give the reasons for your answer.

  b The same radioactive source is now brought near to a spark counter which is correctly adjusted (fig. 17.27) and sparks are seen and heard in a random sequence.

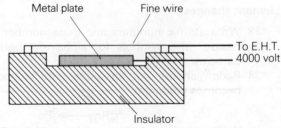

fig. 17.27

(i) What does this tell us about the way in which alpha particles are emitted from the source? (ii) Explain why sparks are not produced across the gap when the potential difference is too small. (iii) A thin sheet of paper is placed between the source and the spark counter and the sparks stop. Why is this? (iv) State one other way in which you could alter the conditions of the experiment so that the sparks stop. (*M.R.E.B.*)

18
Oscillations and Waves

18.1 Simple harmonic motion (S.H.M.)

The following figures and photographs show six kinds of oscillations that have something in common.

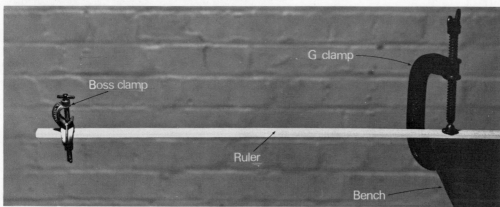

photograph 18.a A boss clamp vibrating up and down on a clamped ruler

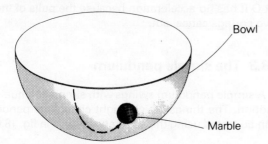

fig. 18.1 A marble rolling in a round bowl

fig. 18.2 A vibrating tuning fork

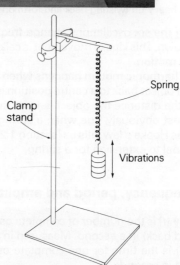

fig. 18.3 A mass vibrating up and down on a spring

149

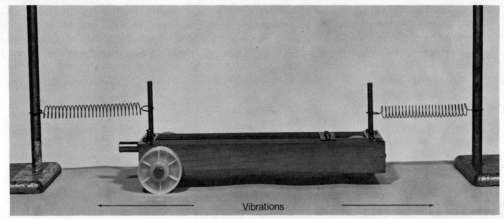

photograph 18.b A trolley vibrating between two springs

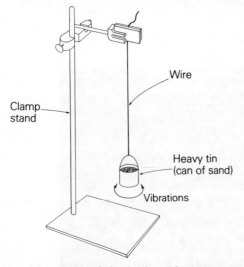

fig. 18.4 A heavy tin twisting back and forth on a wire

None of the six oscillations change frequency as they die down. This kind of movement is called **simple harmonic motion.**

Simple harmonic motion happens when the force pulling an object back to a centre position is proportional to the distance the object is from the centre. This is most obviously true when a spring is used, because as Hooke's law tells us (section 1.2), force is proportional to extension for a spring.

18.2 Frequency, period and amplitude

Frequency (f) is the number of complete oscillations (there and back) in a second. Measured in **hertz**.
Period (T) is the time for one complete oscillation. Measured in **seconds**.
Amplitude (a) is the furthest an oscillating object

moves from the centre of its vibration. Measured in **metres**.

The amplitude of a mass oscillating between two springs is shown in fig. 18.5. The centre of vibration is O and the furthest points the object reaches are Y and Z.

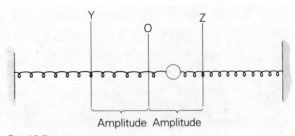

fig. 18.5

At Y and Z the object has no speed.
At O its speed is greatest.
At Y and Z the object will have greatest acceleration because the force of the springs is greatest here.
The object always accelerates towards O because the springs always pull towards O.
At O it has no acceleration because the pulls of the two springs cancel out.

18.3 The simple pendulum

A simple pendulum swings with simple harmonic motion. The things which might change its period can be tested using the apparatus shown in fig. 18.6

Amplitude of swing

For small swings there is no noticeable change in period as the amplitude dies down. For wide swings the time gets slightly less as the amplitude gets less. This shows that a simple pendulum only moves with simple harmonic motion when its amplitude is small.

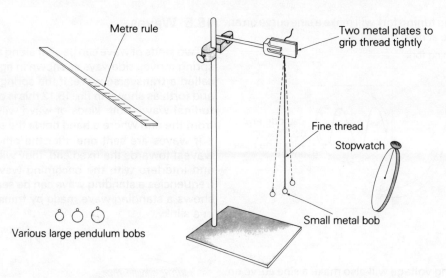

Metre rule

Two metal plates to grip thread tightly

Fine thread

Stopwatch

Small metal bob

Various large pendulum bobs

fig. 18.6

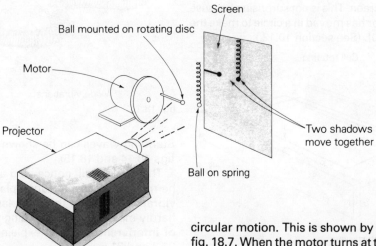

Ball mounted on rotating disc

Motor

Screen

Projector

Two shadows move together

Ball on spring

fig. 18.7

Mass of pendulum bob

If different sized pendulum bobs are swung with small amplitude and the length of the pendulum kept the same, it is found that the period does not change.

Length of pendulum

The longer a pendulum is the slower it will swing. If the pendulum is made four times longer its period will double, if it is made nine times longer its period will treble. This means that

$$\text{period}^2 \propto \text{length}$$
$$T^2 \propto l$$

18.4 Simple harmonic and circular motion

There is a close link between simple harmonic and

circular motion. This is shown by the experiment in fig. 18.7. When the motor turns at the right speed the two shadows move together.

A graph of circular motion is called a sine curve, so curves caused by simple harmonic motion are also sine curves.

A swinging pendulum will trace out a sine curve on a moving piece of paper (fig. 18.8).

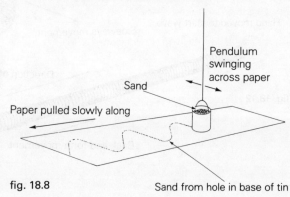

Pendulum swinging across paper

Sand

Paper pulled slowly along

fig. 18.8

Sand from hole in base of tin

A vibrating tuning fork will make a sine curve on an oscilloscope screen (fig. 18.9).

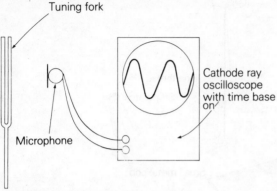

Tuning fork

Microphone

Cathode ray oscilloscope with time base on

fig. 18.9

Alternating voltage will also make a sine curve on an oscilloscope screen. This is not surprising because wire in a generator has moved in a circle to make the voltage (fig. 18.10). (See section 10.12.)

Coil rotating

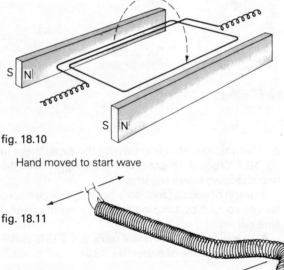

S N

S N

fig. 18.10

Hand moved to start wave

fig. 18.11

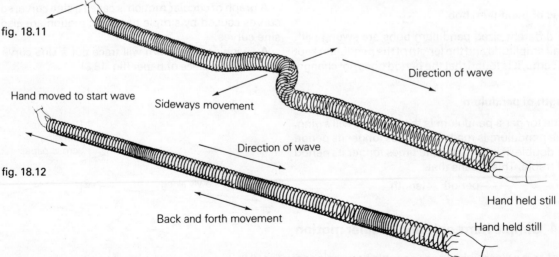

Hand moved to start wave

Sideways movement

Direction of wave

Direction of wave

Back and forth movement

fig. 18.12

Hand held still

Hand held still

18.5 Waves

Two kinds of wave can be sent along a slinky. If the spring moves sideways as shown in fig. 18.11 this is called a **transverse** wave. If the spring moves back and forth as shown in fig. 18.12 this is called a **longitudinal** wave. Both kinds of wave will reflect back from the end where a hand holds the slinky still.

If waves are sent one after the other (a train of waves) towards the fixed end, they will reflect back and interfere with the oncoming waves. At some frequencies a standing wave can be seen. Fig. 18.13 shows a standing wave made by transverse waves in a slinky.

Almost still

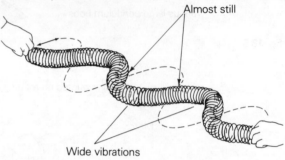

Wide vibrations

fig. 18.13

Standing waves can be shown in other ways, (see figs 18.14 and 18.15).

The person will notice loud and quiet patches as he moves his head through places where the air is vibrating a lot and through places where the air is hardly moving. *Note:* Standing waves are the result of **interference**. This is explained in sections 21.3, 21.4 and 21.5.

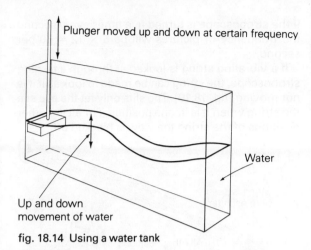

Plunger moved up and down at certain frequency

Water

Up and down movement of water

fig. 18.14 Using a water tank

18.6 Velocity, frequency and wavelength

Velocity, *v* (metres per second)

The velocity of a wave can be found either by measuring how far it moves in a second, or by timing it over a known distance, then using the formula

$$\text{velocity} = \frac{\text{distance}}{\text{time}}$$

Example: A wave moves through 0·9 metres in 3 seconds. What is its velocity?

Calculation

$$\text{velocity} = \frac{\text{distance}}{\text{time}}$$
$$= \frac{0 \cdot 9}{3}$$
$$= 0 \cdot 3 \text{ metres per second}$$

Frequency, *f* (waves per second or hertz)

The frequency of waves can be found by timing a counted number of waves past a point.

Example: 20 waves pass a point in 5 seconds. What is the frequency?

Calculation

if 20 waves pass in 5 seconds
only ⅕th as many will pass in 1 second
∴ frequency = ⅕ × 20
= 4 hertz

Wavelength, *L* (metres)

Wavelength is the distance between similar points on waves which are next to each other (fig. 18.16).

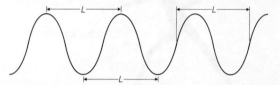

fig. 18.16

The wavelength can be found using a flashing light or a hand stroboscope (see section 18.8). The waves are made to seem still and then the distance between them is measured.

18.7 A formula for waves

The table shows results from a ripple tank experiment.

Velocity V (metres per second)	Frequency f (ripples per second)	Wavelength L (metres)
0·25	4	0·062
0·25	5	0·050
0·25	2	0·125
0·25	3	0·080

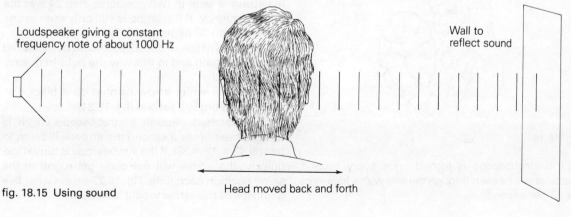

Loudspeaker giving a constant frequency note of about 1000 Hz

Wall to reflect sound

Head moved back and forth

fig. 18.15 Using sound

Notice that if each pair of f and L values are multiplied together, each answer is roughly 0·25. The answers are equal to the velocity of the waves and give us the formula

$$\text{velocity} = \text{frequency} \times \text{wavelength}$$
$$v = fL$$

(metres per second = hertz × metres)

A helpful comparison can be made between waves moving and a man running.

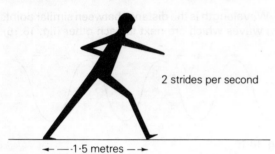

2 strides per second

←—1·5 metres —→

fig. 18.17

In fig. 18.17, because the man takes two 1·5 metres strides per second he moves 3 metres every second. This means that the man's velocity is 3 metres per second. Notice that

$$3 = 2 \times 1·5$$

where 2 per second is the frequency of the man's steps, and 1·5 metres is the 'wavelength' of his stride. Therefore

velocity = frequency × wavelength

18.8 The hand stroboscope

A hand stroboscope has twelve slits and is used as shown in fig. 18.18

fig. 18.18

If the stroboscope is turned once every second, pictures will be seen through the slits with a frequency of 12 per second.

If the stroboscope is turned five times every second the frequency of pictures will be 5 × 12 = 60 per second.

If a vibrating string is looked at through a turning stroboscope, the string can be made to look as if it is not moving (fig. 18.19). The slits only let the eye see the string when it is in one position. For all the other positions of the string the view is blocked off.

fig. 18.19

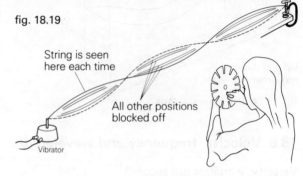

String is seen here each time

All other positions blocked off

Vibrator

If the stroboscope is turned twice as fast, the string will be seen twice in every vibration (fig. 18.20).

String is seen in two positions

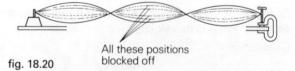

All these positions blocked off

fig. 18.20

A stroboscope can be used to find the frequency of a vibrating string. Suppose the stroboscope is turned 2 times every second to make the string seem still. The frequency of pictures is 2 × 12 = 24 per second. This **might** be the frequency of the string, or it might be half or quarter the frequency because these would also make the string seem still.

If the stroboscope is now turned twice as fast and the string is seen in two positions, then 24 was the right frequency. If the string is still only seen in one position then 48 might be the frequency.

The speed of the stroboscope should be increased again and again and in this way the right frequency can be found.

Suppose a white arrow painted on a black disc revolves 36 times a second (fig. 18.21).
If it is watched through a stroboscope which is turned three times a second the arrow will seem to be still. (3 × 12 = 36). If the stroboscope is turned too quickly, the arrow will not quite get round to the same position each time. Fig. 18.22 shows what five glimpses of the arrow would look like.

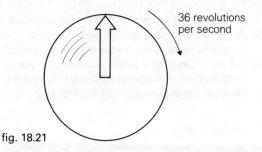

36 revolutions per second

fig. 18.21

Example: A hand stroboscope with 12 slits is turned twice a second to 'freeze' the ripples in a ripple tank. What is the frequency of the ripples?

Calculation

12 slits twice a second = 24 slits a second
∴ frequency of ripples = 24 per second

Note: Care must be taken not to turn the stroboscope too slowly and so get half or quarter the frequency.

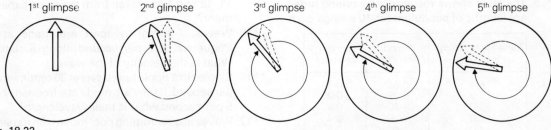

1st glimpse   2nd glimpse   3rd glimpse   4th glimpse   5th glimpse

fig. 18.22

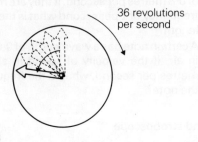

36 revolutions per second

fig. 18.23

The arrow would seem to have moved backwards (fig. 18.23).

Using the hand stroboscope with ripple tanks

Wavelength The stroboscope can be used to make a ripple pattern look still, so that wavelength can be measured.
Note: Care must be taken not to turn the stroboscope too fast and so get half or quarter the wavelength.
Frequency By timing the rate at which a stroboscope is turned to make the pattern look still, the frequency of ripples can be found.

Revision Questions

Formula

$$v = fL$$

Simple harmonic motion (S.H.M.)

  * **1** What quick test is there to see whether or not a thing vibrates with simple harmonic motion?
** **2** Explain whether or not a rubber ball bounces with simple harmonic motion.

Frequency, period and amplitude

** **3** Fig. 18.24 shows four different positions for a mass oscillating on the end of a spring. The centre of oscillation is on line O and the furthest the mass moves is up to line Y and down to line Z.

  a When timed, which of the movements shown by the arrows would give the period?
  b At which position or positions has the mass got maximum speed?

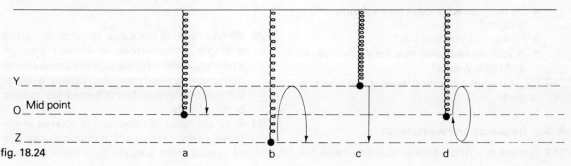

Y

O   Mid point

Z

fig. 18.24   a   b   c   d

c At which position or positions has the mass got maximum acceleration?
d Which is the amplitude, OY or YZ?
e If the oscillation died away, on which line would the mass come to rest?

* 4 In simple harmonic motion what is meant by a frequency, b period, c amplitude?

The simple pendulum

* 5 The table shows results got by timing different lengths of pendulum for 10 swings each.

Time for 10 swings (seconds)	Period (seconds)	Length (metres)
6·4	0·64	0·1
8·9	0·89	0·2
11·0	1·10	0·3
12·6	1·26	0·4
14·0	1·40	0·5
15·3	1·53	0·6
16·6	1·66	0·7
17·7	1·77	0·8

a Plot a graph of period against length.
b Does the graph show that period is proportional to length?
c What would be the effect of doubling the mass of the pendulum bob on the values for period given in the table?

Simple harmonic and circular motion

** 6 Sketch an experiment which might show a close link between circular motion and the simple harmonic motion of a simple pendulum.
* 7 Why does the output of a dynamo often make a sine wave trace on an oscilloscope screen?

Waves

* 8 Explain the difference between transverse and longitudinal waves.
** 9 If two waves are sent towards each other from opposite ends of a slinky
a Do they reflect or pass through one another?
b How could you test this?
c Is your answer also true for sound waves and radio waves?
***10 Explain what a standing wave is and how one is made.

Velocity, frequency and wavelength

*11 A wave in a ripple tank is found to move 0·6 metres in 1·5 seconds. What is its velocity?
*12 A girl counts 30 ripples past a point in 6 seconds. What is the frequency of the ripples?
*13 A boy measures a total distance of 7 wavelengths between ripples as being 0·56 metres. What is the wavelength of the ripples?

A formula for waves

**14 Were the measurements given in questions 11, 12 and 13 all taken from the same experiment?
*15 Waves, 1·2 metres apart are made at a frequency of 2 per second along a slinky. What is the velocity of the waves?
**16 Ripples in a ripple tank travel at 30 centimetres per second. If they are made at a frequency of 5 per second what is their wavelength?
**17 Waves in a swimming pool move with a speed of 0·8 metres per second. If they are made at a frequency of 2 per second what is their wavelength?
**18 A certain note has a wavelength of 0·6 metres in air. If the velocity of sound in air is 330 metres per second, what is the frequency of the note?

The hand stroboscope

**19 One white arrow on a rotating black disc is viewed through a hand stroboscope which has 12 slits and which is turned 4 times a second. Fig. 18.25 shows what is seen. What is the rate of rotation of the disc?

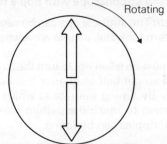

fig. 18.25

**20 When a rotating black disc, on which is marked a single white arrow, is viewed through a rotating hand stroboscope the arrow seems to be moving slowly forward. Explain whether the stroboscope is being turned too quickly or too slowly.
***21 A 12 slit hand stroboscope is rotated at different rates, each of which makes the pattern of ripples from a ripple tank seem to stand

156

fig. 18.26

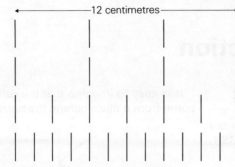

Pattern when stroboscope is turned once every 4 seconds

Pattern when stroboscope is turned once every 2 seconds

Pattern when stroboscope is turned once every second

Pattern when stroboscope is turned twice every second

still. The patterns and rates of rotation are shown in fig. 18.26. What is the frequency, wavelength and velocity of the ripples?

Extra questions

**22 Fig. 18.27 shows a standing wave which is made in a length of rubber tubing, vibrating at a frequency of 4 per second.
  a What is the wavelength of the waves?
  b How fast will waves travel along the rubber tube?

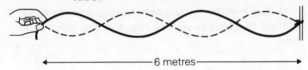

6 metres

fig. 18.27

**23 Describe what life would be like if waves did not pass through each other, but reflected when they met a similar type of wave. Your answer should mention sound, radio and light waves.

**24 A girl bounces up and down on a trampoline, always jumping to the same height and making one bounce every second. Explain whether she is moving with simple harmonic motion.

fig. 18.28   P   O   Q

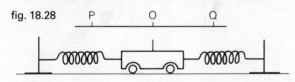

**25 Fig. 18.28 shows a trolley held by two identical springs. The trolley is moved to one side then released, and finally comes to rest. P and Q are the positions where the displacement of the trolley from its rest position is a maximum. O is the mid-point.
  a Complete the following statements: (i) The velocity of the trolley is a maximum at . . . .

(ii) The acceleration of the trolley is a maximum at . . . .
  b The motion of the trolley can be represented by a graph as shown in fig. 18.29.

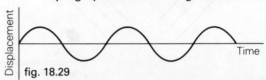

Displacement

Time

fig. 18.29

Show on a copy of the graph (i) the maximum displacement OP, (ii) the time for one complete to and fro movement T.
  c A second similar trolley is firmly attached to the first trolley. (i) What happens to the time for one complete to and fro movement (periodic time). (ii) Give your reason for your answer to (i). (iii) State one other way in which you could alter the periodic time (M.R.E.B.).

***26 A lump of metal hangs on the end of a light spring. When it is pulled down a little, and released, it oscillates with an up-and-down motion which we call 'simple harmonic motion'. Let m = mass of the metal; s = 'spring factor', that is, the **force per unit extension** required to stretch the spring; T = time of one complete oscillation.
  a If m is increased (larger lump) will T become bigger or smaller? Why?
  b If s is increased (stiffer spring) will T become bigger or smaller? Why?
  c Compare the oscillating spring with an oscillating pendulum. The pendulum bob corresponds to the mass on the spring. What provides the equivalent to the spring factor?
  d The same pendulum would oscillate more slowly on the Moon than it does on Earth. Why?
  e But, with the same mass on it, the spring would have the same period of oscillation on Earth and Moon. Why? (O. and C.).

19
Reflection and Refraction

19.1 Reflection of waves by a straight barrier

If straight waves in a ripple tank are sent towards a straight barrier, they will reflect as shown in fig. 19.1.

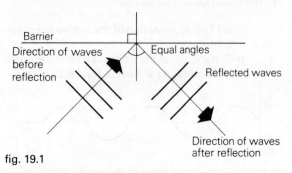

fig. 19.1

If the waves are sent at a different angle towards the barrier, they will reflect so that the new angles are equal (fig. 19.2).

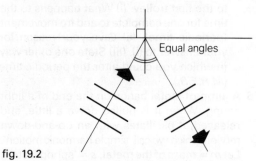

fig. 19.2

When a circular ripple is sent towards a straight barrier it will reflect as shown in fig. 19.3.

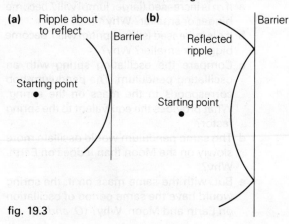

fig. 19.3

158

It is easy to imagine that the reflected ripple has come from a place behind the barrier (fig. 19.4).

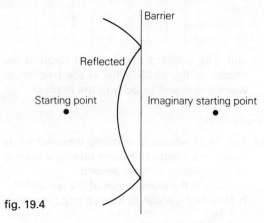

fig. 19.4

Notice that the imaginary starting point is as far behind the barrier as the real starting point is in front.

19.2 Reflection of waves by curved barriers

If a barrier which has a circular curve is used to reflect a straight wave, the wave will reflect as a curve which is almost but not quite circular (fig. 19.5).

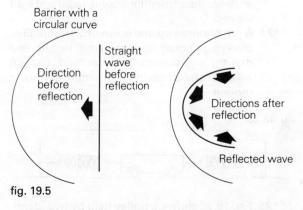

fig. 19.5

To make a reflected wave which really has a circular curve, a barrier with a parabolic shape must be used (fig. 19.6a).

Notice that after a wave has been reflected from a parabolic barrier it moves towards one point of focus (fig. 19.6b). This does not happen when a circular barrier is used (fig. 19.5).

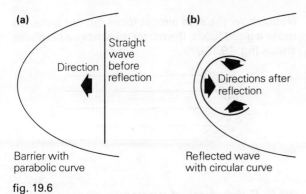

(a)

Straight wave before reflection

Direction

Barrier with parabolic curve

(b)

Directions after reflection

Reflected wave with circular curve

fig. 19.6

19.3 Reflection of light by a plane mirror

Fig. 19.7 shows a ray of light reflecting from a plane (flat) mirror.

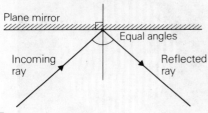

Plane mirror

Equal angles

Incoming ray

Reflected ray

fig. 19.7

If the light is shone at a different angle towards the mirror it will reflect so that the new angles are equal (fig. 19.8).

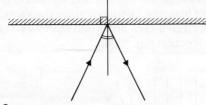

fig. 19.8

We say that the **angle of incidence, i, equals the angle of reflection, r** (see fig. 19.9).

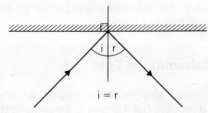

i r

i = r

fig. 19.9

Image in a mirror

When you look into a mirror (fig. 19.10), where is the image (picture) that you see?

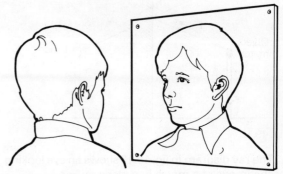

fig. 19.10

A simple experiment answers this question. A match (the 'object match') is fixed in front of a mirror as shown in photograph 19.a. A second match is then put behind the mirror so that it lines up exactly with the image.

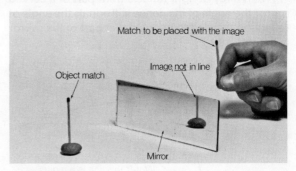

Match to be placed with the image

Image _not_ in line

Object match

Mirror

photograph 19.a

Looked at from above (fig. 19.11) the experiment shows that the object match is as far in front of the mirror as its image is behind the mirror.

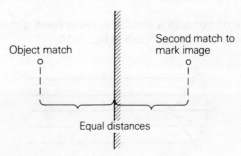

Object match

Second match to mark image

Equal distances

fig. 19.11

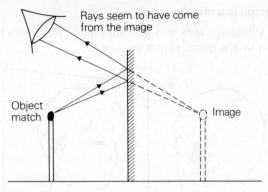

Rays seem to have come
from the image

Object
match

Image

fig. 19.12

The ray diagram in fig. 19.12 shows an eye looking at the image of a match in a plane mirror.
Note: It is much easier to draw reflected rays as if they have come from the image than to try drawing equal angles where the rays reflect.

19.4 Reflection of light by curved mirrors

When a ray of light reflects from part of a curved mirror the angle of incidence still equals the angle of reflection. It helps to imagine that part of the mirror is flat (fig. 19.13).

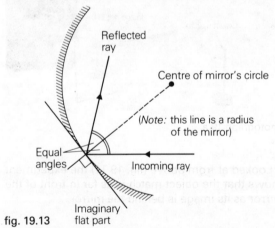

Reflected
ray

Centre of mirror's circle

(*Note:* this line is a radius
of the mirror)

Equal
angles

Incoming ray

Imaginary
flat part

fig. 19.13

If a mirror with a circular curve is used, different rays will reflect as shown in fig. 19.14.

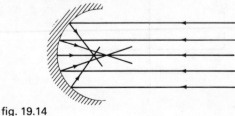

fig. 19.14

Notice how the rays almost focus but not quite. To make a good focus, the mirror must have a parabolic shape (fig. 19.15).

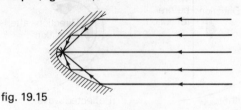

fig. 19.15

19.5 Refraction of waves

Waves in a ripple tank slow down as they move into the shallow water over a glass plate. The result of this is shown in photograph 19.b.

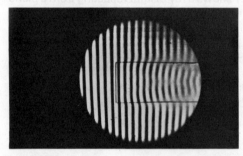

photograph 19.b.

Notice how the waves are closer together in the shallow water. As each wave slows down it is caught up a little by the wave behind until that too is slowed down. Although the velocity and wavelength of the waves get less, the frequency stays the same.

If waves move at an angle into shallow water they change direction (fig. 19.16).

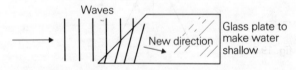

Waves

New direction

Glass plate to
make water
shallow

fig. 19.16

This change in direction is called **refraction**.
Note: It may help to think of how a bull-dozer would change direction if it was slowed down by earth on one side of its front blade.

19.6 Refraction of light

Light shone straight down into water does not change direction, but if shone at an angle to the surface the light will refract (fig. 19.17).

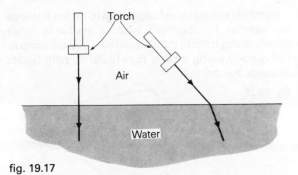

fig. 19.17

Light from an underwater torch shone up towards the surface at an angle also refracts (fig. 19.18). Notice though, that if the light makes a small angle with the surface it will reflect back and not go out into the air. This is called **total internal reflection**.

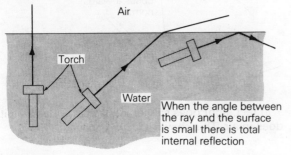

When the angle between the ray and the surface is small there is total internal reflection

fig. 19.18

In writing rules for refraction it helps to have a reference line drawn at right angles through the surface where a ray enters or leaves. Such a line, shown in fig. 19.19, is called a **normal**.

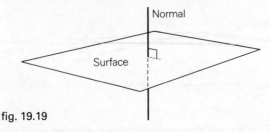

fig. 19.19

Two rules for refraction

(1) When light is shone into water it first crosses the normal and then bends towards it (fig. 19.20).
(2) When light goes out of water it first crosses the normal and then bends away from it (fig. 19.21).
Hint

   into= towards (the words could mean the same)
   out of= away from (the words could mean the same)

Note: These rules for refraction are also true for glass or any other transparent substance.

fig. 19.20

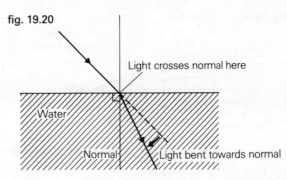

fig. 19.21

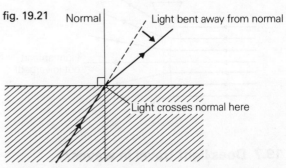

If a ray of light shines right through a glass block it crosses and bends towards the normal when it goes into the glass, then crosses and bends away from the normal when it goes out of the glass again (fig. 19.22).

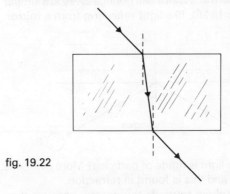

fig. 19.22

In fig. 19.22 the ray left the block parallel to the direction it went in at. This does not always happen as fig. 19.23 shows.

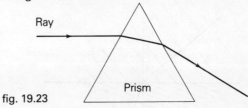

fig. 19.23

It is because light is refracted by glass that lenses focus light (fig. 19.24), or spread it out (fig. 19.25).

161

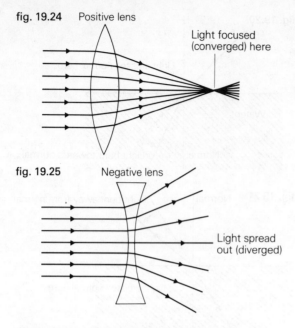

fig. 19.24 Positive lens

Light focused (converged) here

fig. 19.25 Negative lens

Light spread out (diverged)

19.7 Does light travel in waves?

We have seen that light reflects from plane and curved mirrors in much the same way that waves reflect from straight and curved barriers. This is evidence **but not proof** that light travels in waves. If a ball is thrown at a wall it will bounce away at a similar angle (fig. 19.26), like light reflecting from a mirror.

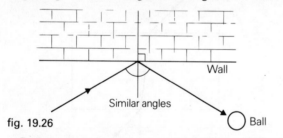

Wall

Similar angles

fig. 19.26 Ball

Perhaps light is made of particles? More evidence is needed and this is found in refraction.

Waves refract **towards** the normal because they slow down (fig. 19.27).

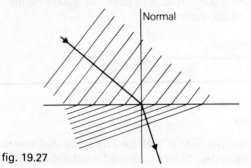

Normal

fig. 19.27

Particles would have to **speed up** to refract towards the normal. For example, when a marble is rolled slowly along a shelf, then accelerates down a ramp to roll quickly along a table (fig. 19.28) its path bends towards the normal.

fig. 19.28

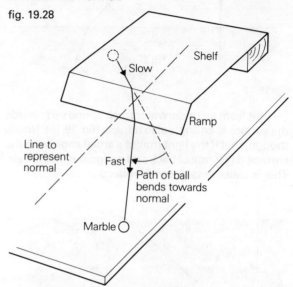

Shelf

Slow

Ramp

Line to represent normal

Fast

Path of ball bends towards normal

Marble

In fact, light goes slower in glass or water than it does in air. This shows it is like a wave.

19.8 Colour

White light can be split into colours by shining it through a prism (fig. 19.29).

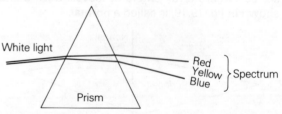

White light

Red
Yellow } Spectrum
Blue

Prism

fig. 19.29

This shows that white light is a mixture of all the different colours. Using a second prism the colours can be brought back together again to make white light (fig. 19.30).

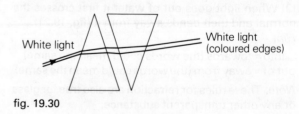

White light

White light (coloured edges)

fig. 19.30

19.9 Adding colours together

If spotlights of red, green and blue light are shone onto a white screen, the place where they all overlap looks white. Where just two colours overlap new colours are made. This is shown in fig. 19.31 and on the cover of this book.

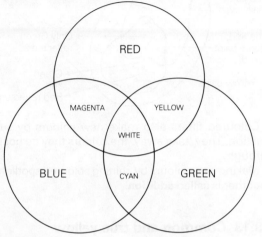

fig. 19.31

Red, green and **blue** are called **primary colours**. They cannot be made by shining any other coloured lights together.

Yellow, magenta and **cyan** are called **secondary colours**. They are made by shining primary coloured lights together.

Complementary colours

It is possible to make white light by shining a primary colour with one of the secondary colours (the one that contains the other two primaries). For example:

$$
\begin{aligned}
\text{red} + \text{cyan} &= \text{white} \\
\text{blue} + \text{yellow} &= \text{white} \\
\text{green} + \text{magenta} &= \text{white}
\end{aligned}
$$

The pairs of colours which go to make up white light are called **complementary colours**.

19.10 Using filters

A blue filter will absorb the red and green parts of white light and only the blue light will 'filter' through (fig. 19.32).

In the same way, a red filter will only let the red part of white light through, and a green filter will only let the green part through.

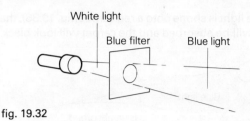

fig. 19.32

Because of this, two primary colour filters together will stop all light (fig. 19.33).

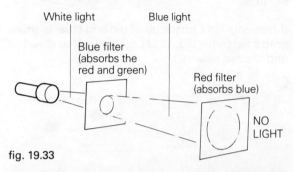

fig. 19.33

If a secondary colour filter is used (fig. 19.34) then the two colours which make up the secondary colour will be let through. Now a second filter may not stop all the light.

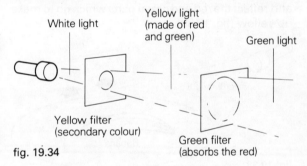

fig. 19.34

19.11 Reflecting colours

Red carpets look red because they reflect the red part of white light, and absorb all the other colours (fig. 19.35).

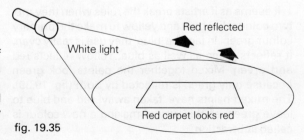

fig. 19.35

163

If blue light is shone onto a red carpet (fig. 19.36), the light will be absorbed and the carpet will look black.

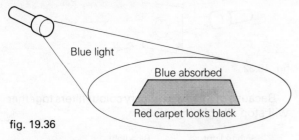

fig. 19.36

If magenta light (made up of red and blue) is shone onto a red carpet (fig. 19.37), the blue will be absorbed and the red reflected.

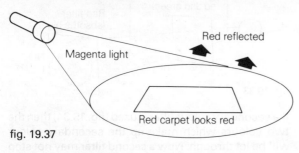

fig. 19.37

Yellow objects absorb the blue part of white light and reflect the red and green parts which go to make up yellow (fig. 19.38).

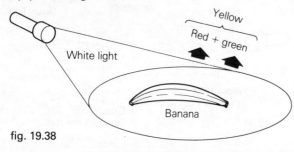

fig. 19.38

The different colours of all objects can be explained in this way.

19.12 Mixing paints

It seems as if artists break the rules when they mix two colours like blue and yellow to make the primary colour green. In fact the 'blue' they use is really cyan. It reflects green as well as blue. Yellow reflects red and green. Mixed together the paints look green because only green is reflected by both (fig. 19.39). The mixed paints have 'taken away' red and blue to leave green, so this way of making a new colour is called **subtraction**.

fig. 19.39

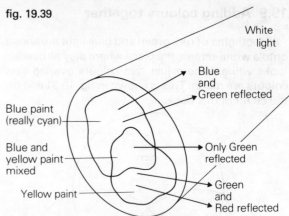

Coloured filters also make new colours by subtraction. They 'take away' the colours they do not let through.

Making new colours by shining coloured spotlights together is called **addition**.

19.13 Common and true yellow

Common yellow, the kind found in spotlights or reflected by paints, contains red and green. True yellow, the yellow from a sodium street lamp or the yellow part of a spectrum, is *not* a mixture of red and green.

Grass lit by common yellow will absorb the red part and reflect green to look its normal colour. Grass lit by true yellow will look grey or black.

Revision questions

Reflection of waves by a straight barrier

* **1** Copy the diagrams in fig. 19.40 and finish them to show how waves in a ripple tank reflect from a straight barrier.

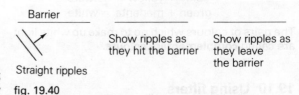

fig. 19.40

* **2** Write a rule for ripples reflecting at a straight barrier.
** **2** A circular ripple increases its radius by 1 metre every second. Draw the shape of the ripple in fig. 19.41 after **a** 2 seconds, **b** 3 seconds, **c** 4 seconds.

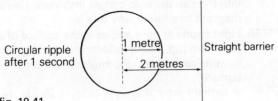

Circular ripple
after 1 second

1 metre

2 metres

Straight barrier

fig. 19.41

Reflection of waves by curved barriers

** **4** Draw diagrams to show how the waves in fig. 19.42 will reflect.

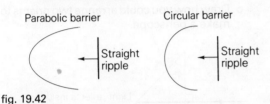

Parabolic barrier

Circular barrier

Straight ripple

Straight ripple

fig. 19.42

* **5** Which shape of barrier will bring a straight wave to the best focus?

Reflection of light by a plane mirror

* **6** If a match is placed in front of a mirror as shown in photograph 19.c where will the image be?

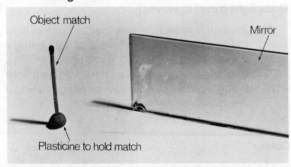

Object match

Mirror

Plasticine to hold match

photograph 19.c

* **7** Fig. 19.43 shows a ray of sunlight falling on a plane mirror. Copy the drawing and show how the ray will reflect. Label the angles of incidence and reflection.

fig. 19.43

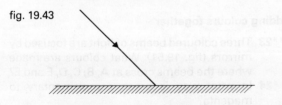

** **8** Fig. 19.44 shows a candle in front of a plane mirror. Copy the drawing, adding to it the candle's image and three reflected rays of light.

fig. 19.44

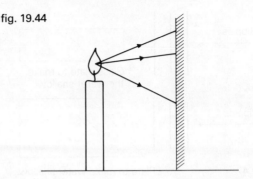

Reflection of light by curved mirrors

* **9** Draw diagrams to show how the rays in fig. 19.45 will reflect.

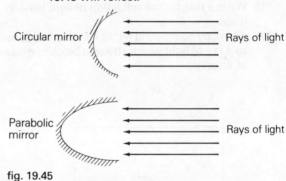

Circular mirror

Rays of light

Parabolic mirror

Rays of light

fig. 19.45

***10** Which shape of mirror will bring the rays in fig. 19.45 to the best focus?

Refraction of waves

****11** Fig. 19.46 shows water waves in a deep tank, going towards the shallow end.
  a Will the waves find it easier or more difficult to move in the shallow water?
  b Will the waves speed up or slow down as they enter the shallow water?
  c Will the waves get closer together or further apart as they enter the shallow water?

Wave

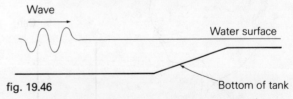

Water surface

fig. 19.46

Bottom of tank

****12** Copy fig. 19.47 and show what the ripples will look like when they have passed into the shallow water over each glass plate.

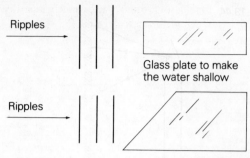

Ripples →

Glass plate to make
the water shallow

Ripples →

Plate to make water shallow

fig. 19.47

Refraction of light

*13 Explain the meaning of the term 'normal' in science.

*14 Write a rule for the refraction of light entering glass.

*15 Write a rule for the refraction of light leaving glass.

*16 Show, by completing fig. 19.48, what happens to a ray of light which strikes a block of glass at an angle.

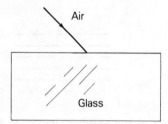

Air

Glass

fig. 19.48

***17 The man in fig. 19.49 cannot see the coin at the bottom of the can. When water is poured into the can the coin comes into view. Use a diagram to explain why this is.

***18 Light shone at right angles at the surface of a 45° prism (fig. 19.50) reflects inside the prism before leaving at right angles from another surface.

  a Explain why the light reflects inside the prism.

  b Draw how you might change the angle of incidence to the first surface of the prism, so there would be no reflection inside the prism.

  c Draw how you could arrange two prisms to make a periscope.

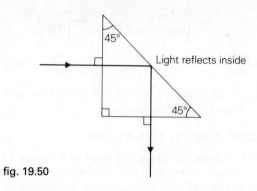

45°

Light reflects inside

45°

fig. 19.50

Does light travel in waves?

*19 Explain if reflection is evidence against light being a particle and in favour of light being a wave.

**20 Explain if refraction is evidence against light being a particle and in favour of light being a wave.

Colour

*21 What evidence is there that white light is made up of colours?

*22 Some say that Joseph's coat of 'many colours' was a white coat. Could there be any scientific truth in this?

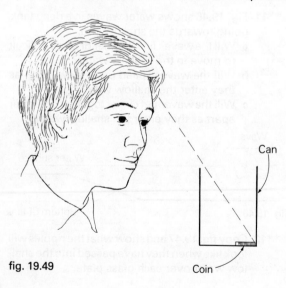

Can

fig. 19.49

Coin

Adding colours together

**23 Three coloured beams of light are focused by mirrors (fig. 19.51). What colours are made where the beams cross at A, B, C, D, E and F?

*24 In what way is green complementary to magenta?

*25 Give examples to show the difference between primary and secondary colours.

fig. 19.51

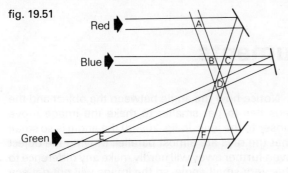

Using filters

*26 What will be seen if white light is shone through a green filter?

*27 Why is the word 'filter' a good description for a piece of coloured perspex which will let light pass through?

*28 What will be seen if white light is shone first through a magenta filter and then on towards a blue filter?

**29 What happens if white light is shone first through a green filter and then through a yellow filter?

**30 What happens to yellow light which is shone towards a blue filter?

Reflecting colours

*31 Why does the grass look green in 'white' sunlight?

32 What colour would a magenta dress look if it was lit by **a red light, **b** blue light, **c** green light?

**33 Describe what would be seen if a red brick on a cyan carpet was lit by yellow light.

Mixing paints

***34 How is it that red, blue and green spotlights shone together can make white, when red, blue and green paints mixed together on an artist's palette make dark brown?

**35 What is the difference between colour addition and colour subtraction?

Common and true yellow

***36 Why does blood look red when lit by a yellow spotlight but black in the yellow light from a sodium lamp?

Extra questions

***37 **a** Parallel, straight waves are produced in a ripple tank, as shown in fig. 19.52. A triangular plate of glass (*ABC*) is placed in the tank so that the water over the glass is very shallow. (i) Copy the drawing and complete the waves in the region *ABC*.

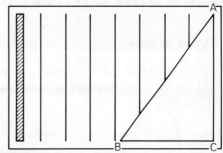

fig. 19.52

(ii) What happens to the wavelength as the waves cross the boundary? (iii) What happens to the frequency as the waves cross the boundary? (iv) If the wavelength is 2 cm and the frequency 10 Hz, what is the velocity of the waves?

b (i) When a beam of blue light falls on a prism the beam is bent as shown in fig. 19.53. Explain this in terms of waves.

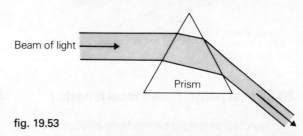

Beam of light

Prism

fig. 19.53

(ii) If red light is used instead of blue, the red light is bent less than the blue light. Explain this. (*O. and. C.*)

**38 Fig. 19.54 represents barriers placed one at a time in a ripple tank. In each case a series of straight ripples arrive at an obstacle. Sketch the position of the ripple after it has travelled a further distance of 2 wavelengths. (*M.R.E.B.*)

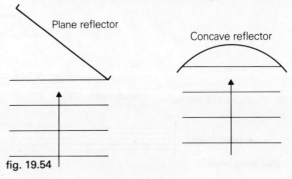

Plane reflector

Concave reflector

fig. 19.54

20
Lenses and Optical Instruments

20.1 Types of lens

There are two main types of lens; **positive** which can focus light (fig. 20.1) and **negative** which will spread light out (fig. 20.2).

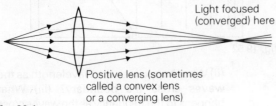

Positive lens (sometimes called a convex lens or a converging lens)

Light focused (converged) here

fig. 20.1

fig. 20.2

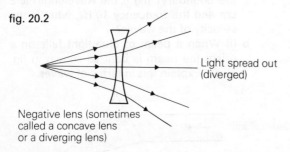

Light spread out (diverged)

Negative lens (sometimes called a concave lens or a diverging lens)

20.2 Focal point, F, and focal length, *f*.

In ray diagrams light comes from an object, O, and focuses to make an image, I. Fig. 20.3 shows how the image gets closer to a positive lens as the object is moved away from it.

fig. 20.3

Notice how the angle between the object and the lens has to get smaller to make the image move closer to the lens. In fig. 20.3(d) the angle is so small that the rays are almost parallel. Moving the object even further away will hardly make any difference to this very small angle, so the image will not get any closer to the lens than it already is.

The closest place an image can get to a positive lens is called the **focal point**, F, of the lens. Parallel light passing through a positive lens will form an image at the focal point (fig. 20.4).

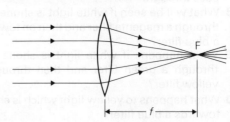

F

f

fig. 20.4

f is the **focal length** of the lens. This is the distance between the middle of the lens and its focal point.

Parallel light shone in the opposite direction through the lens will form an image at the other focal point, which is at the same distance on the other side of the lens (fig. 20.5).

Light can be made to retrace its tracks, so if an object is put at the focal point of the lens, rays of light from it will leave the lens parallel (fig. 20.6).

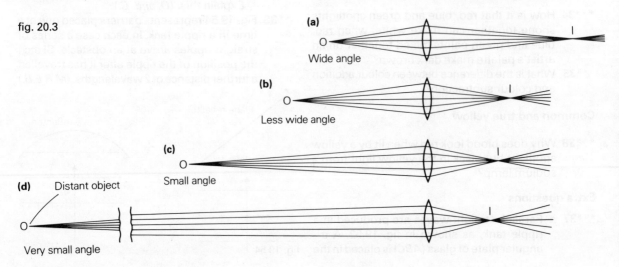

(a)
O
Wide angle
I

(b)
O
Less wide angle
I

(c)
O
Small angle
I

(d)   Distant object
O
Very small angle
I

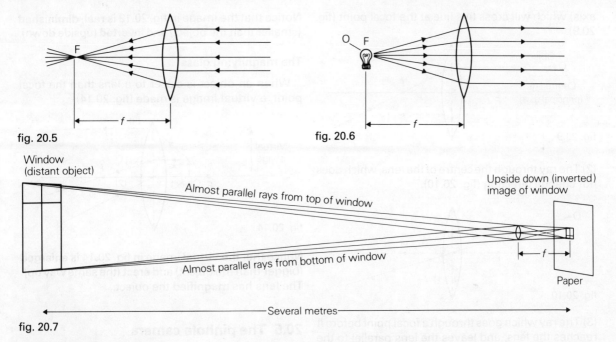

fig. 20.5

fig. 20.6

Window
(distant object)

Almost parallel rays from top of window

Almost parallel rays from bottom of window

Upside down (inverted)
image of window

Paper

f

Several metres

fig. 20.7

Finding the focal length

Stand several metres from a window, inside a room. Focus light from the window onto a piece of paper (fig. 20.7). The distance between the lens and paper will be the focal length.

F and f for a negative lens

Because no real image can be made with a negative lens, the diverged rays of light have to be drawn back to an imaginary or **virtual** image. The focal point, F, of a negative lens is at the position of the virtual image when parallel light is shone at the lens (fig. 20.8).

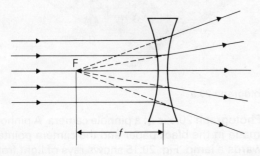

fig. 20.8

The focal length, f, is the distance between the middle of the lens and its focal point. Because this is a **virtual** distance, the focal length of a negative lens has a negative value. (For example; $f = -0.2$ metres).

20.3 The power of a lens

$$\text{the power of a lens} = \frac{1}{\text{focal length}}$$

where focal length is measured in **metres** and the power is measured in **dioptres**, (D).

Example 1: A positive lens has a focal length of 0·2 metres. What is its power?

$$\text{power} = \frac{1}{f}$$
$$= \frac{1}{0 \cdot 2}$$
$$= 5 \text{ dioptres}$$

Example 2: A negative lens has a power of −20 dioptres. What is its focal length?

Calculation

$$\text{power} = \frac{1}{f}$$
$$-20 = \frac{1}{f}$$
$$\therefore f = -\tfrac{1}{20} \text{ metres (or } -0 \cdot 05 \text{ metres)}$$

20.4 Scale drawing

There are three rays from an object, which if marked on a scale drawing will help fix the position of the image.

(1) The ray parallel to the centre line (or principal

axis) which will cross this line at the focal point (fig. 20.9).

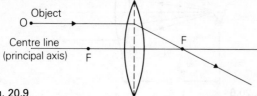

fig. 20.9

(2) The ray through the centre of the lens, which does not change direction (fig. 20.10).

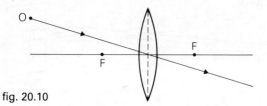

fig. 20.10

(3) The ray which goes through a focal point before it reaches the lens, and leaves the lens parallel to the centre line (fig. 20.11).

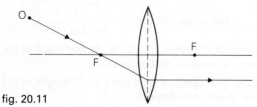

fig. 20.11

If these three rays are drawn on the same diagram (fig. 20.12), they will show the position of the image I.

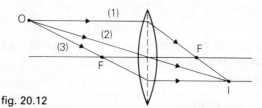

fig. 20.12

Fig. 20.13 shows how three rays can be drawn from the top of a tall object, to fix the position and height of the image.

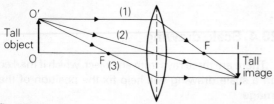

fig. 20.13

Notice that the image in fig. 20.13 is **real, diminished** (smaller than the object) and **inverted** (upside down).

The magnifying glass

When an object is closer to a lens than the focal point, a virtual image is made (fig. 20.14).

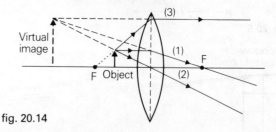

fig. 20.14

Notice that the **virtual** image in fig. 20.14 is **enlarged** (bigger than the object) and **erect** (the same way up). The lens has **magnified** the object.

20.5 The pinhole camera

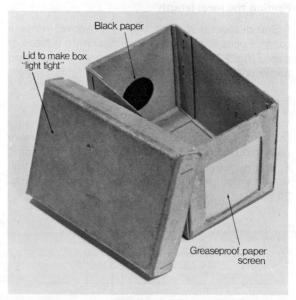

photograph 20.a

Photograph 20.a is of a pinhole camera. A pinhole is made in the black paper and the camera pointed towards a lamp. Fig. 20.15 shows rays of light from the top and bottom of the lamp filament, entering the camera to make a **diminished, inverted** image on the screen.

If the camera is moved away from the object the image gets smaller. If the camera is moved closer the image gets bigger (fig. 20.16).

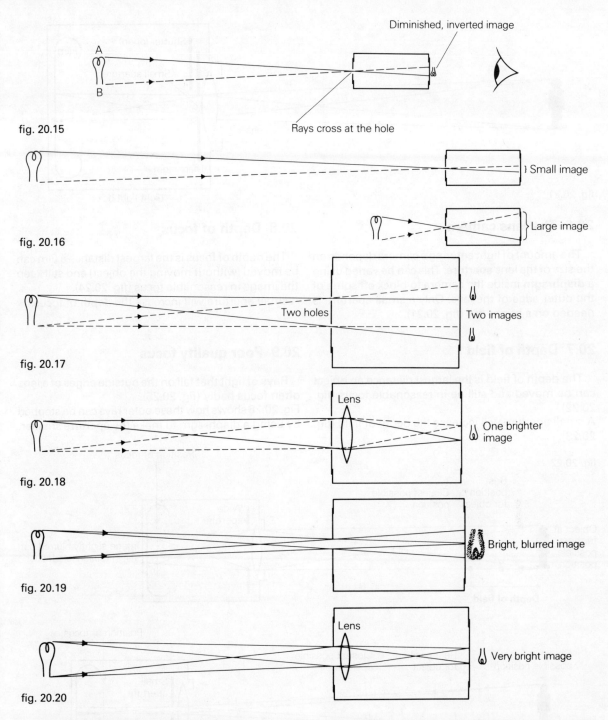

fig. 20.15

Diminished, inverted image

Rays cross at the hole

fig. 20.16

Small image

Large image

fig. 20.17

Two holes

Two images

fig. 20.18

Lens

One brighter image

fig. 20.19

Bright, blurred image

fig. 20.20

Lens

Very bright image

If two pinholes are made in the black paper, two images are made on the screen (fig. 20.17).

If a lens is put into the camera the two images can be brought together to make one brighter image (fig. 20.18).

If one large pinhole is made in the black paper, a bright but blurred image is made on the screen (fig. 20.19).

The large pinhole can be thought of as many small pinholes giving lots of overlapping images which make a blur. These images can be brought into one very bright image by using a lens (fig. 20.20).

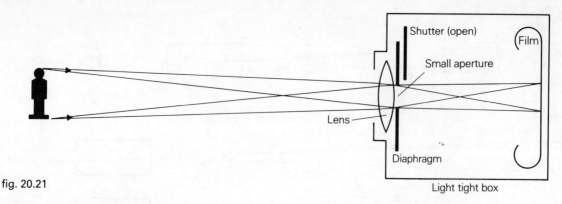

fig. 20.21

Light tight box

20.6 The lens camera

The amount of light entering a camera depends on the size of the lens **aperture**. This can be varied using a **diaphragm** inside the camera to block off some of the outer edge of the lens. Only a small aperture is needed on a bright day (fig. 20.21).

20.7 Depth of field

The depth of field is the largest distance an object can be moved and still be in reasonable focus (fig. 20.22).
A small aperture will increase the depth of field (fig. 20.23).

20.8 Depth of focus

The depth of focus is the largest distance a film can be moved (without moving the object) and still keep the image in reasonable focus (fig. 20.24).
A small aperture will increase the depth of focus.

20.9 Poor quality focus

Rays of light that fall on the outside edges of a lens often focus badly (fig. 20.25).
Fig. 20.26 shows how these outer rays can be stopped by using a diaphragm to make the aperture smaller.

fig. 20.22

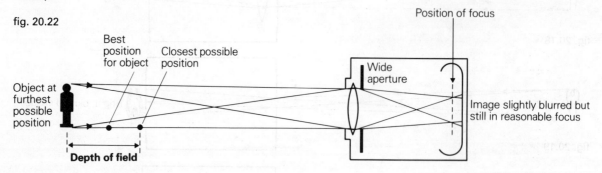

fig. 20.23

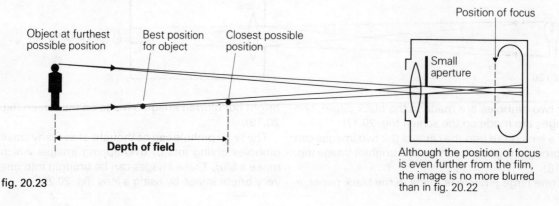

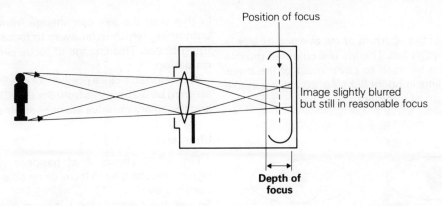

fig. 20.24

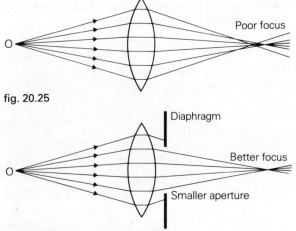

fig. 20.25

fig. 20.26

Note: Not only does a smaller aperture block off rays which would focus badly, it also increases the depth of field and depth of focus.

20.10 Shutter speed and exposure time

The slower the **shutter speed** of a camera, the more light will get to the film. The length of time for which light falls onto the film is called the **exposure time.**

The disadvantage of a long exposure time is that a blurred picture is made if the object being photographed moves, or if the camera shakes.

To get more light into the camera on a dull day either the exposure time must be long or the lens aperture large. Both have their disadvantages and the choice usually depends on whether the subject is moving or still.

20.11 The eye

Fig. 20.27 is a cross section of a right eye viewed from above.

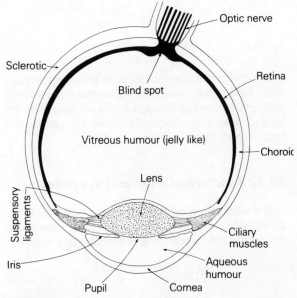

fig. 20.27

Blind spot

Light is focused by the cornea and lens onto the retina. An image is seen when messages travel from nerve endings in the retina along the optic nerve to the brain. At the place where the optic nerve leaves the eye there are no nerve endings and this is a **blind spot.**

An experiment will show that you have a blind spot. Cover your left eye with your hand and use your right eye to look at the cross in fig. 20.28. Move the book slowly towards you keeping your eye focused on the cross. You should notice that when the book is about 0·2 metres from your eye the star will vanish.

x   *

fig. 20.28

Pupil

The **pupil** is the aperture of the eye and its size is controlled by the **iris**. The iris is a coloured muscle which adjusts by itself to cover most of the outer edge of the lens in bright light (fig. 20.29). It acts like the diaphragm of a camera.

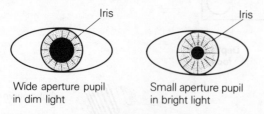

Wide aperture pupil in dim light

Small aperture pupil in bright light

fig. 20.29

In dim lighting the pupil is large. Although this lets more light into the eye, it cuts down the depth of field and lets light pass through the outer edges of the lens to make a poor focus. This is why it is difficult to read in poor light.

20.12 Accommodation and eye defects

The **ciliary muscles** form a ring round the lens (fig. 20.30). When these muscles contract, the **suspensory ligaments** are slackened and the lens gets fatter.

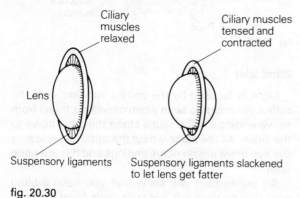

Ciliary muscles relaxed

Ciliary muscles tensed and contracted

Lens

Suspensory ligaments

Suspensory ligaments slackened to let lens get fatter

fig. 20.30

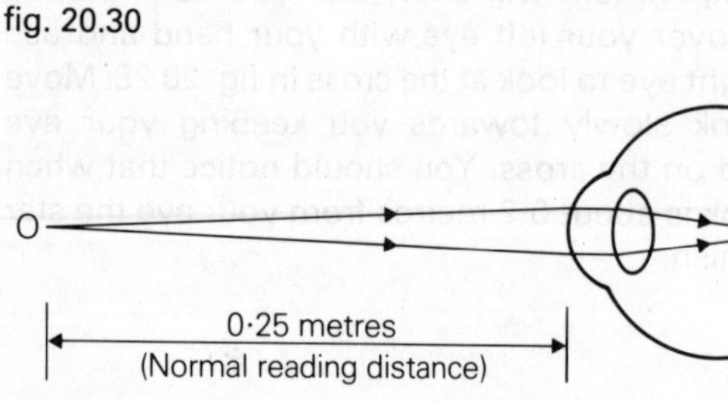

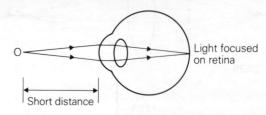

O

0·25 metres
(Normal reading distance)

fig. 20.31

In this way the eye can change from focusing on something which is far away to focusing on something closer. This change of focus is called **accommodation.**

A comfortable close position for reading is normally taken to be 0·25 metres from the eye. Closer than this and the ciliary muscles are over-strained.

Short sight

Fig. 20.31 shows what happens when a **short** sighted person tries to focus on an object 0·25 metres from his eye.

To see the object clearly, it must either be held a **short** distance from his eye (fig. 20.32), or he must wear negative lens glasses (fig. 20.33).

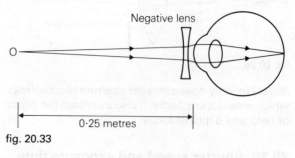

O

Light focused on retina

Short distance

fig. 20.32

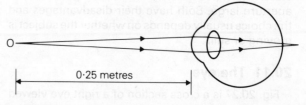

Negative lens

O

0·25 metres

fig. 20.33

Long sight

Fig. 20.34 shows what happens when a long sighted person tries to focus on an object 0·25 metres from his eye.

The object will look less blurred if it is held a **long** distance from the eye (fig. 20.35), but to see it in clear focus, positive lens glasses must be worn (fig. 20.36).

O

0·25 metres

fig. 20.34

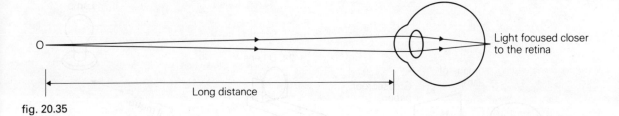

Light focused closer
to the retina

Long distance

fig. 20.35

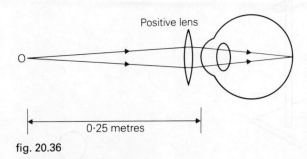

Positive lens

0·25 metres

fig. 20.36

A telescope turns the small angle made by a distant object into a large angle so that the object looks closer. Fig. 20.39 shows rays from the top and bottom of a distant object, passing through a telescope. Notice how the angle is made larger.

Because light which started down from the top of the object, leaves the telescope in an upward direction the image is upside down. This telescope is only useful for astronomy, for then it doesn't matter which way up things are!

20.13 Telescopes

The top and bottom of an object which is near make a large angle with the eye (fig. 20.37).

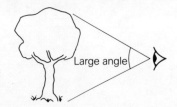

Large angle

fig. 20.37

When the object is a long way away the angle is small (fig. 20.38).

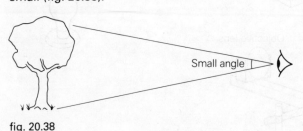

Small angle

fig. 20.38

20.14 Setting up an astronomical telescope

A weak positive lens (+ 2·5 dioptres) is fixed near to one end of a telescope mount. The mount is lined up with a distant lamp and the image of the lamp focused onto a piece of greaseproof paper (fig. 20.40).

A powerful positive lens (+14 dioptres) is then used to magnify the image which is on the paper (fig. 20.41). Both eyes are relaxed as this is being done so that both the actual lamp and the magnified image are in focus at the same time.

The greaseproof paper is then taken away and the telescope is now set up in **normal adjustment** (fig. 20.42).

Note: For seeing things the right way up, a **terrestrial telescope** can be made using three lenses.

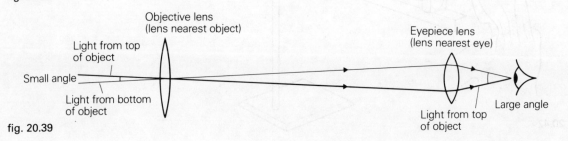

Objective lens
(lens nearest object)

Eyepiece lens
(lens nearest eye)

Light from top
of object

Small angle

Light from bottom
of object

Light from top
of object

Large angle

fig. 20.39

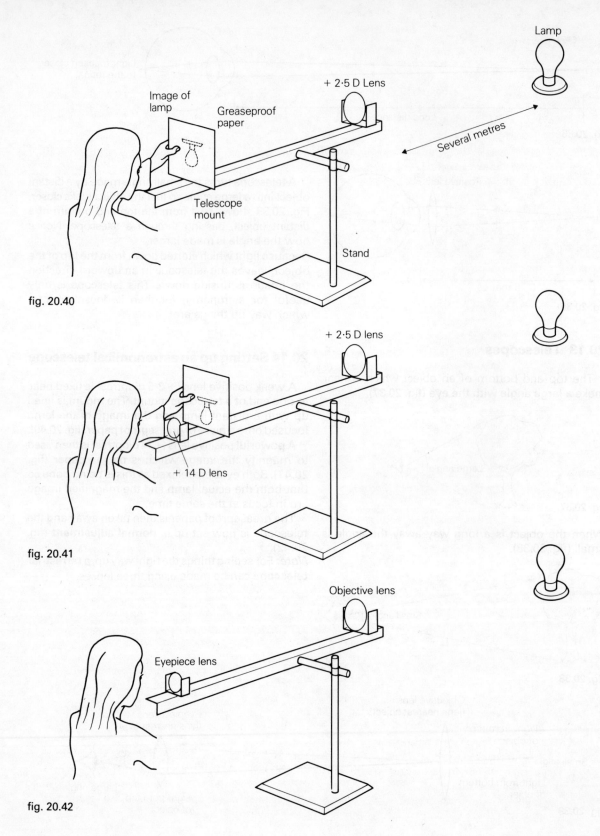

Lamp

Image of
lamp

Greaseproof
paper

+ 2·5 D Lens

Several metres

Telescope
mount

Stand

fig. 20.40

+ 2·5 D lens

+ 14 D lens

fig. 20.41

Objective lens

Eyepiece lens

fig. 20.42

Revision questions

Formula

$$\text{power of a lens} = \frac{1}{\text{focal length}}$$

Types of lens

* **1** Fig. 20.43 shows two types of lens. Copy the diagrams, label each lens and show rays of light passing through them.

fig. 20.43

Focal point, F, and focal length, f

** **2** Copy and complete the three unfinished diagrams in fig. 20.44 to show the rays after they have passed through the lens in each case.

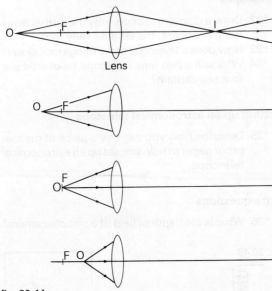

fig. 20.44

* **3** Copy and complete the diagrams in fig. 20.45 to show the rays after they have passed through each of the lenses. Label the focal point and focal length in each case.
* **4** Describe how you could quickly find the focal length of a positive lens.
** **5** Jane says, 'I know that parallel rays of light will focus at the focal point of a lens, but how can rays of light from a window be parallel?' She draws the sketch in fig. 20.46 which shows why she does not understand. Copy and improve her diagram to help her understand about parallel rays.

fig. 20.45

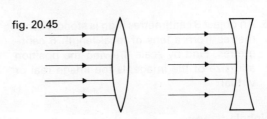

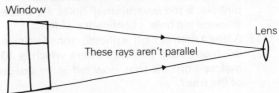

fig. 20.46

The power of a lens

* **6** A positive lens has a focal length of 0·5 metres. What is its power?
* **7** The focal lengths of two lenses are +0·8 metres and +0·2 metres. Which lens is the more powerful?
* **8** A lens has a focal length of −0·25 metres
  * **a** What is its power?
  * **b** What type of lens is it?
** **9** A lens has a power of +5 dioptres.
  * **a** What is its focal length?
  * **b** What type of lens is it?
10 A lens has a power of − 12·5 dioptres. What is its focal length?
* **11** A lens has a power of +20 dioptres. Is it more likely to be a fat or a thin lens?
12 What is the power of a watch glass?

Scale drawing

13 Copy fig. 20.47 and add to it 3 rays which will fix the position of the image.

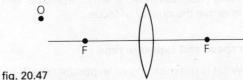

fig. 20.47

14 An object 4 centimetres high is stood 5 centimetres from a lens of focal length 3 centimetres. Find by scale drawing the position and size of the image. Is the image real or virtual?

177

***15 An object 3 centimetres high is stood 4 centimetres from a lens of focal length 6 centimetres. Find by scale drawing the position and size of the image. Is the image real or virtual?

The pinhole camera

*16 Why is the image in a pinhole camera upside down?

17 Draw diagrams to show what happens to the image in a pinhole camera when, **a several more pinholes are made near the original pinhole, **b** the several small holes are made into one big hole, $\frac{1}{2}$ centimetre wide.

**18 A tree 4 metres high is photographed using a 0·2 metre long pinhole camera which is 10 metres from the tree. How tall is the image of the tree?

The lens camera

**19 What advantages has a lens camera over a pinhole camera for taking photographs?

**20 What advantages has a pinhole camera over a lens camera for taking photographs?

*21 Sketch the inside of a lens camera and label the important parts.

Depth of field

**22 What is 'depth of field' and how does it depend on the lens aperture?

Depth of focus

**23 What is 'depth of focus' and how does it depend on the lens aperture?

Poor quality focus

*24 Why do some lenses make a poor quality focus? Explain how a small aperture will improve the quality of focus.

Shutter speed and exposure time

*25 What is the meaning of 'exposure time'?

*26 How will an increase in shutter speed affect the exposure time?

**27 In a photograph taken by a teacher of the children in her class, only those in the centre of the room are in good focus. Children sitting near the front or the back of the room look blurred. In what ways could the teacher have got all her class in focus?

The eye

**28 How does the cornea play a part in focusing light onto the retina?

**29 Although a pupil may widen to let the same amount of light into an eye on a dull day as on a bright day, it is easier to read small print on a bright day. Why is this?

Accommodation and eye defects

**30 Ruth looks at figs. 20.31 and 20.34 and says, 'I think that people with short sight might have long eyes and people with long sight might have short eyes'. Why does she think this?

**31 A person has to hold a letter at arms length to read it.
   a Is she short or long sighted?
   b Does she need positive or negative lens glasses?

Telescopes

*32 Draw a diagram to show why the further away lamp posts are, the smaller they look.

***33 How does a telescope make things look closer?

*34 Why will a two lens telescope be of little use to a sea captain?

Setting up an astronomical telescope

**35 Describe how you can use a piece of greaseproof paper to help you set up an astronomical telescope.

Extra questions

**36 What is the depth of field of a pinhole camera?

fig. 20.48

Lamp filament

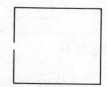

**37 Fig. 20.48 shows a simple pinhole camera held up to a lamp. An image of the lamp filament is seen on the screen.
   a Copy the diagram and show clearly on this the formation, position and size of the image.

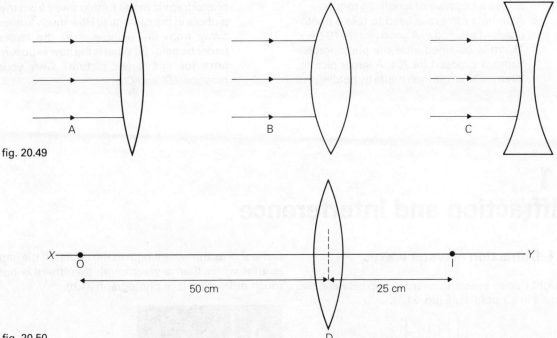

fig. 20.49

X ——•————————————————————————————•—— Y
  O   I
     |←———— 50 cm ————→|←— 25 cm —→|

fig. 20.50   D

b What difference in the image would be seen
(i) if the lamp were moved away from the
pinhole camera? (ii) if the pinhole were
increased to about twice its size?

c What would you see on the screen if the
pinhole was enlarged to a diameter of 2
centimetres?

d If a suitable converging lens were placed in
front of the enlarged hole what would you
see on the screen? (*M.R.E.B.*)

***38 a** In each of the parts of fig. 20.49, drawn to
the same scale, rays of light are shown
striking a lens. Copy the drawings and
show in each case possible directions of
the rays when they come out of the lens.

b Lens D in fig. 20.50 forms an image I of a
very small bright object O.
(i) If the small object is raised 2 cm above
the line XY, where is the new image position? (ii) Draw a sketch to show how the
lens forms the image of the object in its new
position. You should show the path of two
rays from the object. (iii) If the object is
moved a short distance further away from
the lens, what happens to the image?

c Draw a suitable diagram to show how such
a lens can be used as a magnifying glass.
The rays in your diagrams should show the
direction in which the light waves travel.

d What evidence leads us to believe that light
is a wave motion?

e On the basis of the *wave theory,* explain
how light is converged by a lens. (*O. and
C.*)

***39** One type of camera has a shutter, called a
focal-plane shutter, which consists of two
blinds which travel across in front of the film
as in fig. 20.51

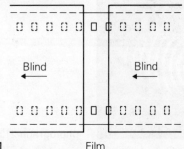

fig. 20.51   Film

The slit between the blinds allows light to fall
on the film. The length of time for which light
falls on any part of the film is determined by
the width of the slit and the speed of travel of
the blinds.

a If the slit is 2 mm wide and each part of the
film is exposed for $\frac{1}{125}$s, how fast are the
blinds travelling?

b How long does it take for the slit to travel

179

across a negative of length 25 mm?

c A pinhole camera is used to take a photograph of a window. A good picture 10 cm × 15 cm is obtained after the photographic paper is exposed for 70s. A larger picture, 20 cm × 30 cm, is then made by holding the photographic paper further away from the pinhole in the camera. (i) How much further away from the pinhole must the larger paper be held? (ii) What is the new exposure time for this larger picture? Give your reasons. (*O. and C.*)

21
Diffraction and Interference

21.1 Diffraction of water waves

Straight ripples are sent towards a gap between two barriers in a 'ripple' tank (fig. 21.1).

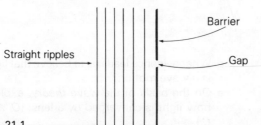

fig. 21.1

Photograph 21.a shows how the ripples curve and spread out as they pass through the gap.

photograph 21.a

This spreading of waves at the edge of a barrier is called **diffraction**. Notice that the gap is about the same size as the wavelength of the ripples. If the gap is a lot wider than a wavelength then there is not much diffraction (see photograph 21.b).

photograph 21.b

21.2 Diffraction of light

If light is shone through a thin slit scratched in black aquadag paint on a glass slide (fig. 21.2), it will spread out slightly to make a blur on a screen.
If a wider slit is used, the light will not spread out so much. This is what happened with the ripples in a ripple tank when the gap was made wider (photograph 21.b).

21.3 Interference of water waves

Two sets of circular ripples are made in a ripple

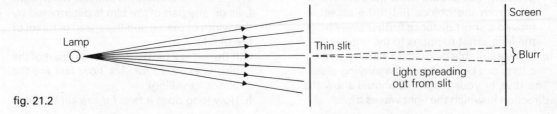

fig. 21.2

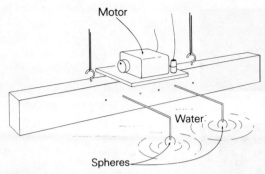

fig. 21.3

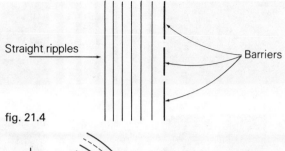

Straight ripples → | ← Barriers

fig. 21.4

tank using the apparatus shown in fig. 21.3. Photograph 21.c shows the pattern which is made. This is called an **interference pattern**. It happens because in some places the waves add together to make even bigger ripples, and in others they cancel to leave almost no ripples at all.

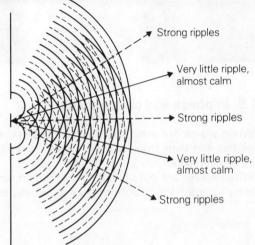

→ Strong ripples

→ Very little ripple, almost calm

→ Strong ripples

→ Very little ripple, almost calm

→ Strong ripples

fig. 21.5

photograph 21.c

Because curved ripples can also be made by diffraction at a single gap, another way to get an interference pattern is to send straight ripples towards two gaps (fig. 21.4).

Fig. 21.5 shows how the diffracted ripples overlap to make an interference pattern.

The full curves stand for the crests (or tops) of ripples and the dotted curves stand for the troughs (or dips)

in between. Wherever two crests cross or two troughs cross there are strong ripples. Where crests meet with troughs the water is almost calm.

21.4 Interference of light

Light is shone through two slits scratched in black aquadag paint on a glass slide (fig. 21.6).

Photograph 21.d shows the pattern which is seen on the screen.

Photograph 21.e shows what is seen if one of the slits is covered up. 21.e is the diffraction pattern of a single slit. 21.d is the interference pattern of two lots of diffracted light overlapping.

fig. 21.6

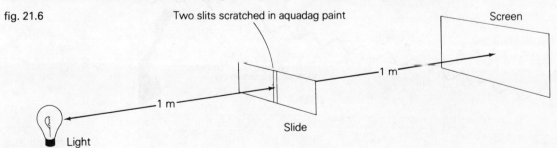

Two slits scratched in aquadag paint

Screen

1 m

Slide

1 m

Light

181

photograph 21.d

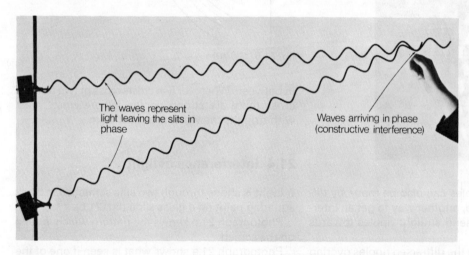

photograph 21.e

21.5 In phase and out of phase

When waves are in step so that their crests come together and their troughs come together, we say they are **in phase**.

When waves are out of step so that the crests of one try to cancel the troughs of another, we say they are **out of phase**.

Photograph 21.f is of waves marked on clear plastic and shows how waves of light might arrive at a screen in phase. (This is called **constructive interference** because the waves interfere to **construct** a bigger wave).

Photograph 21.g shows how light might arrive at a

The waves represent light leaving the slits in phase

Waves arriving in phase (constructive interference)

photograph 21.f

Waves arriving out of phase (destructive interference)

photograph 21.g

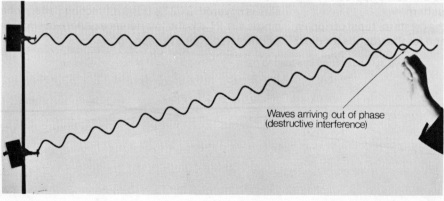

screen out of phase. (This is called **destructive interference** because the waves interfere to **destroy** one another).

Note: The **standing waves** described in section 18.5, were caused by interference of waves going in opposite directions.

21.6 The wavelength of light by Young's slits

Light seems to be a wave because it will refract (section 19.6), diffract and interfere like ripples on water.

The wavelength of light can be found using the two slits (sometimes called **Young's slits**) that were shown in fig. 21.6. A top view of the experiment (fig. 21.7) shows light leaving the slits and arriving at a screen in phase to form a bright fringe (or line) at B.

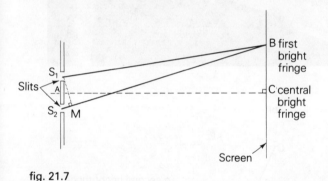

fig. 21.7

The distance S_2M must be exactly one wavelength for the light from S_2 to add constructively to the light from S_1. It can be shown that

$$\text{wavelength of light, } S_2M = \frac{S_1S_2 \times BC}{AC}$$

21.7 A diffraction grating for water waves

Instead of ripples from two gaps overlapping to give a diffraction pattern, a lot of gaps can be used (photograph 21.h) to make a different kind of diffraction pattern.

Strong ripples can be seen in directions where the waves are in phase and form what are called **wavefronts**. This is explained in fig. 21.8a and b.

A wavefront is at a tangent to waves from each gap and it is only possible to get wavefronts at certain angles.

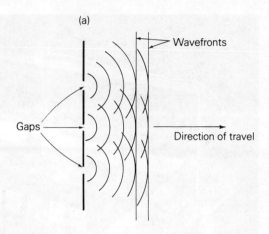

(a)

fig. 21.8

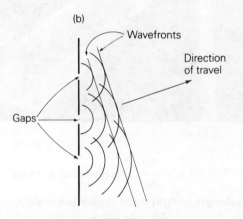

(b)

21.8 A diffraction grating for light

A diffraction grating for light is made by marking or scratching lines onto glass or clear plastic (fig. 21.9).

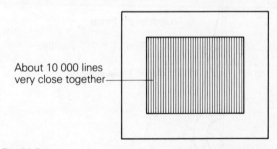

About 10 000 lines very close together

fig. 21.9

Wavefronts to the waves from each slit (or gap), go to make bright fringes in certain directions. Fig. 21.10a and b shows wavefronts from a few gaps going to the first bright fringe and to the second bright fringe.

183

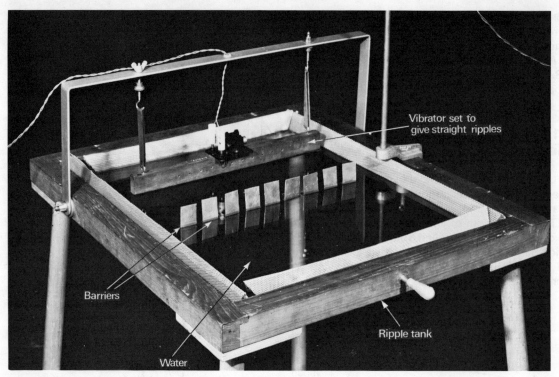

photograph 21.h

Notice that $\sin \theta_1 = \dfrac{AB}{AC}$. This gives the formula

wavelength of light = slit separation $\times \sin \theta_1$
$(AB = AC \sin \theta_1)$

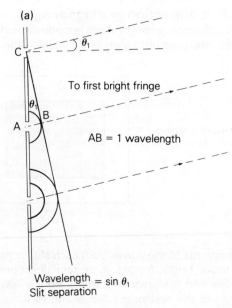

To first bright fringe

AB = 1 wavelength

$\dfrac{\text{Wavelength}}{\text{Slit separation}} = \sin \theta_1$

fig. 21.10

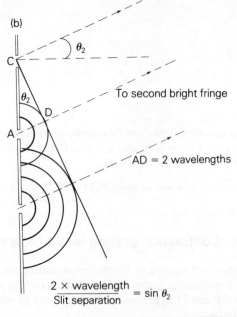

To second bright fringe

AD = 2 wavelengths

$\dfrac{2 \times \text{wavelength}}{\text{Slit separation}} = \sin \theta_2$

As was shown in section 19.8 white light is made up of different colours. Each colour has a slightly different wavelength, so that each colour's wavefronts move in a slightly different direction (fig. 21.11). This is why white light is spread into a spectrum by a diffraction grating.

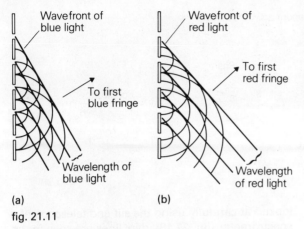

Wavefront of blue light

To first blue fringe

Wavelength of blue light

(a)

Wavefront of red light

To first red fringe

Wavelength of red light

(b)

fig. 21.11

In fact, if a lamp is looked at through a diffraction grating, several spectra are seen each side of the light. These spectra are numbered first order, second order and so on (fig. 21.12).

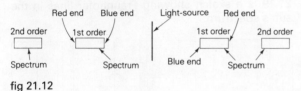

2nd order

Red end   Blue end

1st order

Spectrum

Spectrum

Light-source   Red end

1st order   2nd order

Blue end

Spectrum

fig 21.12

21.9 The wavelength of light by diffraction grating

The wavelength of each of the colours of light can be found using a diffraction grating. Fig. 21.13 shows the experiment for green light.

The girl sees a first order fringe to the right of the light. The angle θ_1 that it makes with her eye can be found by holding a pencil in line with the first green fringe and measuring distance, x, with the metre rule. If the distance between the slits of the grating is known then the wavelength of green light can be calculated using the formula

wavelength of light = slit separation × sin θ_1

21.10 Line spectra

A hydrogen discharge tube is looked at through a diffraction grating (fig. 21.14).

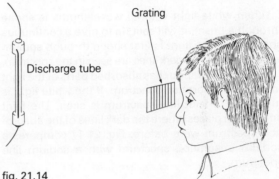

Grating

Discharge tube

fig. 21.14

Instead of each order spectrum being a continuous rainbow of colours, each is made up of bright, spaced out lines (fig. 21.15).
Line spectra from different gases show bright lines in different positions.

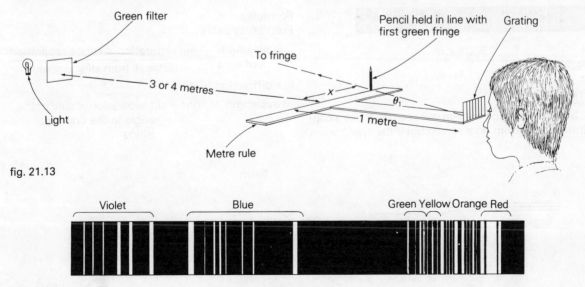

Green filter

To fringe

Pencil held in line with first green fringe   Grating

3 or 4 metres

x

θ_1

1 metre

Light

Metre rule

fig. 21.13

Violet   Blue   Green Yellow Orange Red

fig. 21.15   Hydrogen spectrum

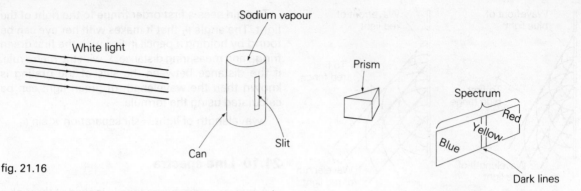

fig. 21.16

21.11 Absorption spectra

When white light with all wavelengths is shone through a prism, it will split up to give a continuous spectrum. If the light is first shone through sodium vapour (fig. 21.16), dark lines are seen in the spectrum.

The sodium vapour has absorbed parts of the light to give an absorption spectrum. If the white light is turned off a faint line spectrum is seen. The faint lines are in places where the dark lines of the absorption spectrum were before. Fig. 21.17 compares a sodium absorption spectrum with a sodium line spectrum.

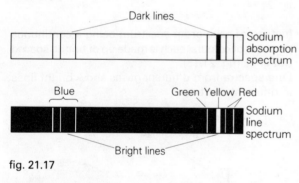

fig. 21.17

Fraunhofer lines

Sunlight through a prism will seem to make a continuous spectrum on a screen but if the spectrum is looked at carefully using the slit and telescope of a spectrometer (fig. 21.18), dark lines are seen in the spectrum.

These dark lines are named **Fraunhofer lines** after their discoverer. The lines are there because hot gases round the sun absorb parts of the light. Fig. 21.19 is a sketch showing Fraunhofer lines in the sun's spectrum.

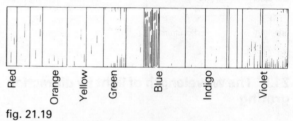

fig. 21.19

Revision questions

Formulae

For Young's slits:

$$\frac{\text{wavelength of light}}{} = \frac{\text{slit separation} \times \text{fringe separation}}{\text{distance from slits to screen}}$$

For diffraction grating:

wavelength of light = slit separation × sine of the angle to the first order fringe

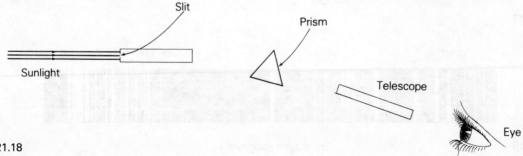

fig. 21.18

Diffraction of water waves

** **1** Photograph 21.i shows waves entering a model harbour.

    a What is happening to the waves?

    b Why are the waves closer together inside the harbour? (Hint: section 19.5).

* **2** Fig. 21.20 shows straight ripples going towards a gap between barriers in a ripple tank. Copy the diagram and draw the waves after they have gone through the gap.

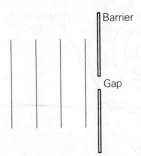

fig. 21.20

** **3** What difference would you notice to the diffraction of ripples in fig. 21.20 if the ripples were five times closer together and the gap was five times wider?

Diffraction of light

*** **4** Light is shone through a wide slit to make a bright patch on a screen (fig. 21.21). Describe and explain what is seen on the screen as the slit is made slowly narrower until it closes completely.

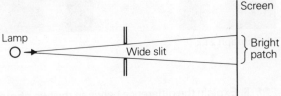

fig. 21.21

Interference of water waves

** **5** Fig. 21.22 shows two sets of overlapping ripples in a ripple tank. Trace or copy the picture and draw in the interference pattern.

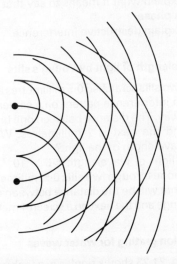

fig. 21.22

** **6** What would happen to the interference pattern if the two sets of ripples in fig. 21.22 were moved further apart?

Interference of light

* **7** One of the two photographs, 21.j and 21.k, shows the pattern made by light shone through two slits onto a screen, and the other shows the pattern when one of the slits is covered up. Which is which?

photograph 21.j

photograph 21.k

** **8** Explain the difference between the two photographs, 21j and 21.k.

** **9** What will happen to an interference pattern if the two slits are made closer together?

In phase and out of phase

* **10** Explain what it means to say that waves are **in phase**.
* **11** Explain destructive interference.

The wavelength of light by Young's slits

** **12** Two slits scratched 0·5 millimetres apart make an interference pattern on a screen 2 metres away. The distance between one bright fringe and the next is 2 millimetres. What is the wavelength of the light?

** **13** If light of wavelength $4·5 \times 10^{-7}$ metres is shone through two slits 0·5 millimetres apart, what will be the distance between one bright fringe and the next on a screen 4 metres away?

A diffraction grating for water waves

** **14** Fig. 21.23 shows ripples in a tank which have come from four gaps between barriers. Trace or copy the drawing and use it to explain why strong ripples can be seen in certain directions.

* **15** What is a wavefront?

fig. 21.23

A diffraction grating for light

* **16** How is a diffraction grating for light made?

** **17** Why must the lines on a diffraction grating be much closer together than the barriers in a ripple tank?

* **18** Fig. 21.24 shows a wavefront moving towards a bright fringe in a spectrum. Which order spectrum?

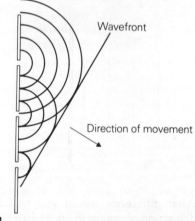

Wavefront

Direction of movement

fig. 21.24

** **19** Look at the diagram of diffraction grating spectra in fig. 21.25 and explain which has the longer wavelength, red or blue light.

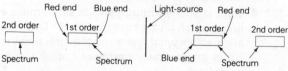

fig. 21.25

The wavelength of light by diffraction grating

***20** Fig. 21.26 shows an experiment to find the wavelength of green light, using a grating with 3000 lines per centimetre. x was found to be 16 centimetres. Calculate **a** the slit separation, **b** the angle θ_1, **c** the wavelength of green light.

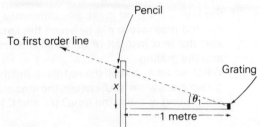

fig. 21.26

Line spectra

*21** What is the difference between a spectrum which can be made with an ordinary lamp and the spectrum which can be made with light from a discharge tube?

Absorption spectra

22 Fig. 21.15 (section 21.10) showed a line spectrum for hydrogen. If white light was shone through a hydrogen discharge tube and then through a prism describe the spectrum which might be made on a screen.

23 Fraunhofer lines led scientists to search for an unkown element which was eventually discovered and called helium. Why do you think scientists thought that this gas existed?

Extra questions

***24** A pupil looks carefully at an interference pattern which has been made by shining white light through two slits. He sees coloured edges to the bright fringes.
  a Explain why he sees coloured edges.
  b Sketch the fringes and label their edges to show the colours he sees.

25 What would be the effect on an interference pattern with light, of making the two slits wider but keeping them the same average distance apart?

26 In fig. 21.27 white light is used to obtain interference fringes by 'Young's double slit' method.

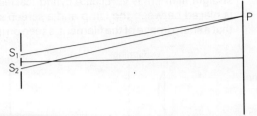

fig. 21.27

  a P is the position of the third bright fringe. Explain why a bright fringe is observed at P.
  b What would be the effect on this fringe if the slit separation were increased?
  c What would be the effect on this fringe if the distance between the slit and screen were increased.
  d The distance between slit and screen is 2 metres. The double slits are 0·5 millimetre apart. If the average value of the wavelength of white light is 5×10^{-7} metre calculate the distance between the fringes. (*M.R.E.B.*)

***27** Explain the importance in the development of scientific thought of Young's observation of the effect of passing light through two small openings. Include in your answer a description of what was done. (*O. and C.*)

***28** **a** In a scientific paper Professor P states that he has invented some very small lamps which give out a weird bluish-grey light of wavelength 4 cm travelling at a speed of 800 metres per sec. On reading the paper a person A says 'Impossible'; a person B says 'It all seems highly improbable, but I'm going to get some of the lamps and check P's statement'. Give some reasons why A may be right.
  b Suppose that you took the same view of the matter as B, and that P's values for wavelength and speed are not far out. Suggest *simple* methods for checking the order of magnitude of P's values and describe, with experimental details, how you would obtain a more reliable check.
  c If conditions were to change such that *all* light travelled at 800 metres per sec., how would this affect, (i) the timing of track events in running-sports, by the customary stop-watch method, (ii) checking the result of a horse-race by the photo-finish method? Give reasons for your answers. (*O. and C.*)

**29 In fig. 21.28 the lamp is set up so that its bright, straight filament is vertical. A cylindrical lens is placed between the lamp and a screen so that a sharp image of the filament is seen on it.

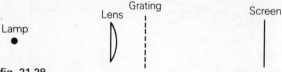

Lamp

Lens

Grating

Screen

fig. 21.28

a A diffraction grating with its rulings vertical is put near the lens as shown in the diagram. What will be seen on the screen?

b Suppose the diffraction grating is replaced by another which has twice as many rulings per centimetre. How will this affect what is seen on the screen?

c In terms of the wave nature of light, explain what is seen on the screen.

d What would be the effect of putting a sheet of green glass between the lens and the grating?

e What would be the effect of using a sheet of red glass instead of the green glass?

f Explain if it would make any difference if the red glass were put between the lamp and the lens instead of between the lens and the grating.

g What would happen if the red glass and the green glass were put between the lens and the grating at the same time? (*O. and C.*)

22
Waves and Particles

22.1 X-rays

An X-ray tube is shown below. (fig. 22.1)

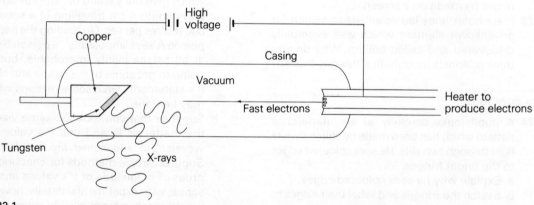

fig. 22.1

Electrons are accelerated from the heater towards the tungsten by a high voltage. Fast electrons crash into the tungsten and about $\frac{1}{250}$th of their kinetic energy turns into X-rays. Most of the energy changes to heat and is conducted away from the tungsten by the thick copper.

22.2 X-ray diffraction

X-rays passed through a crystal will form a diffraction pattern on a screen (fig. 22.2). This shows that X-rays, like light, are waves.

X-rays reflect off from different layers of atoms in

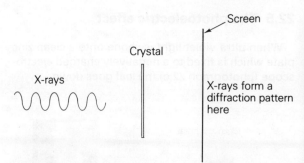

fig. 22.2

the crystal. If the reflected rays are in phase (fig. 22.3) then they will make a bright patch on a screen or photograph.

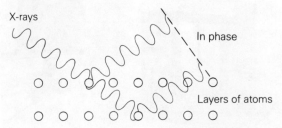

fig. 22.3

If the reflected rays are out of phase (fig. 22.4) then they will cancel each other and not make a bright patch.

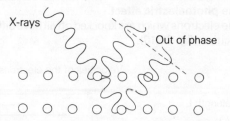

fig. 22.4

X-rays only reflect in phase in certain directions from a crystal. This is shown by photograph 22.a of X-rays which have been diffracted by a diamond crystal. If the structure of the crystal is known then the wavelength of the X-rays can be calculated from the position of the spots in the diffraction pattern.

22.3 An X-ray diffraction pattern from powdered crystals

If powdered crystals are used instead of a single crystal then a pattern of rings will be made (photograph 22.b).

photograph 22.a

photograph 22.b

This happens because there are many tiny crystals in the powder. For every crystal which makes a dot at the top of the screen there will be another which will make a dot at the same angle but towards the bottom of the screen (fig. 22.5).

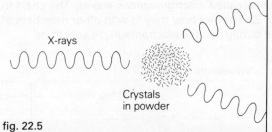

fig. 22.5

There will also be other crystals which will make dots at the same angle towards each side of the screen (fig. 22.6).

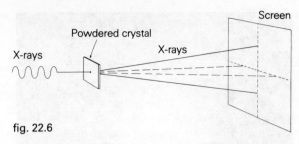

fig. 22.6

And other crystals which will make dots at the same angle towards the corners of the screen and in every other direction. All these dots make a circle (fig. 22.7).

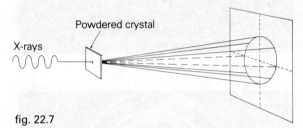

fig. 22.7

The same sort of effect can be got by spinning a grating so that it moves through every possible angle while you look at a lamp (fig. 22.8).

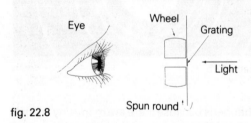

fig. 22.8

22.4 The electromagnetic spectrum

X-rays have a shorter wavelength than light but travel at the same speed. They belong to a family of waves called *electromagnetic waves*. The chart in fig. 22.9 shows how they fit with other members of the family into the *electromagnetic spectrum*.

22.5 The photoelectric effect

When ultra violet light is shone onto a clean zinc plate which is fixed to a negatively charged electroscope (photograph 22.c) the leaf goes down.

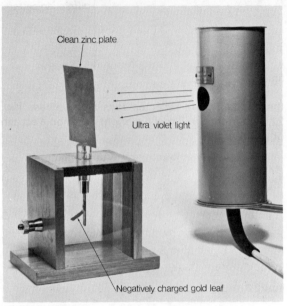

photograph 22.c

The electroscope is discharged by ultra violet light knocking electrons off from the zinc. This is an example of the **photoelectric effect**.

The electrons which are knocked off all have different velocities (fig. 22.10).

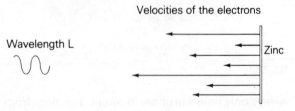

fig. 22.10

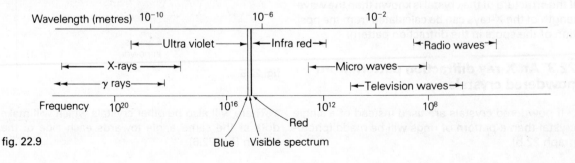

fig. 22.9

Electrons from the surface move the fastest: ones from just below the surface are slower (fig. 22.11).

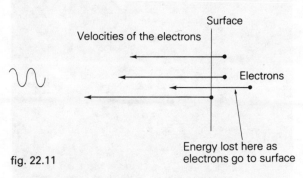

fig. 22.11

If brighter ultra violet light is shone onto the zinc, then electrons are knocked off more often but their speeds are no faster than before. If the wavelength of the ultra violet light is made longer, then slower electrons are knocked off of the zinc plate. If the wavelength is made shorter, then faster electrons are knocked off (fig. 22.12).

fig. 22.12

The energy of the fastest electrons and the time that light should need to shine for to give them this energy can be calculated. However if light shines for less than this calculated time fast electrons can still be knocked off.

These photoelectric experiments show that light energy travels in 'lumps' or 'particles' and that their energy depends on the wavelength of the light. A particle of light energy is called a **photon.**

22.6 Matter waves

Section 22.5 showed that light which is thought of as waves behaves like particles and carries its energy in photons. It is interesting that some other things which are thought of as particles behave like waves.

Electrons fired through gold foil (fig. 22.13) made the diffraction pattern shown in the photograph 22.d.

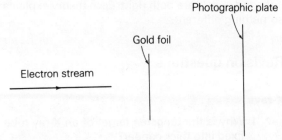

fig. 22.13

This is like the X-ray diffraction photograph in section 22.3. The electrons have reflected in phase in some directions and out of phase in others as if they were waves.

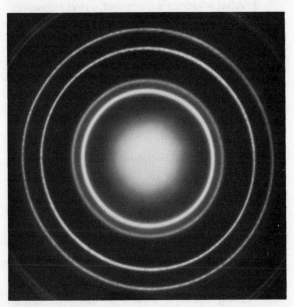

photograph 22.d

All moving particles; electrons, protons, neutrons, air molecules and even cricket balls have wave properties. For large particles, however, the wavelength is too small to notice. Because moving matter has a wavelength this section was headed 'Matter waves'.

Is light a wave or a particle?
Is matter a particle or a wave?

It depends what you need to explain. An underground map or a street map of London will help you explain to a friend how to travel from St. Paul's to Hyde Park. Which map is right? The answer is both.

One map shows the underground route and the other shows the route by road.

In the same way the wave and particle theories of light and matter are both right. Each theory explains something different.

Revision questions

X-rays

* **1** Why is the tungsten target of an X-ray tube fixed into thick copper?
* **2** Is the tungsten target of an X-ray tube made more negative or more positive than the heater?

X-ray diffraction

* **3** What evidence is there that X-rays are waves?
* **4** Fig. 22.14 shows an X-ray beam reflecting from A and B. Explain whether or not this would cause a bright patch on a photograph.

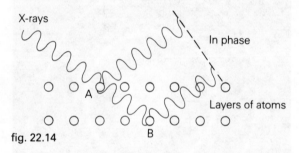

X-rays

In phase

A

Layers of atoms

B

fig. 22.14

An X-ray diffraction pattern from powdered crystals

* **5** Photograph 22.e shows an X-ray diffraction pattern of aluminium. Explain if this was made using a single crystal or using powdered aluminium.
* **6** Explain why light looked at through a spinning grating gives a pattern which is like the X-ray diffraction pattern obtained from powdered crystals.

The electomagnetic spectrum

* **7** How does the speed of X-rays compare with the speed of radio waves?
* **8** How does the wavelength of X-rays compare with the wavelength of radio waves?
* **9** Which is the odd one out; gamma rays, sound waves, light waves, infra red waves?

photograph 22.e

The photoelectric effect

* ****10** Light from an ultra violet lamp is used to knock electrons off a zinc plate. The fastest electrons are found to move at 100 000 metres per second. What will be the effect on this speed of **a** making the light dimmer, **b** making the light brighter, **c** using light of a shorter wavelength, **d** using light of a higher frequency?
* ****11** What evidence is there that light energy travels in 'lumps' like particles?
* ***12** What name is given to a particle of light energy?
* ****13** Why is it dangerous to be hit by X-rays and not by radio waves even though they belong to the same family of waves?

Matter waves

* ***14** What is the name of the effect that shows light is like a particle?
* ***15** What evidence is there that light is a wave?
* ****16** What evidence is there that electrons (which we think of as particles) can behave like waves?
* ****17** Are electrons waves or particles?

Extra questions

* *****18** If the high voltage used to accelerate electrons in an X-ray tube is increased how will this affect the wavelength of the X-rays produced?
* *****19** The X-ray tubes used by dentists are only about 8 centimetres long but some X-ray tubes which work on millions of volts can be

12 metres long. Why is a long tube needed when very high voltages are used?

**20 If a Geiger-Müller tube connected to a scaler is placed in the path of X-rays (fig. 22.15) the scaler will begin to count. How is this possible when X-rays are like waves?

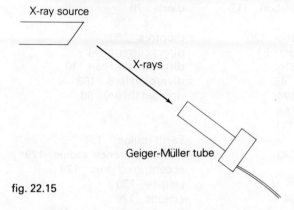

X-ray source

X-rays

Geiger-Müller tube

fig. 22.15

**21 Write a paragraph about the following statement and explain what is the *something* that is referred to:

'The photoelectric effect tells us something about the nature of light.' (*O. and C.*)

**22 When ultra violet light is shone onto a zinc plate attached to a positively charged electroscope the leaf does not go down. Why not?

***23 A pupil who has learned that light is sometimes like a wave and sometimes like a particle, says that it must be a particle moving along in a wavy line. Explain why the pupil is wrong.

Index

Answers to numerical questions

1 Forces (page 6)

2	10 N, 15 N, 20 N
3(a)	2·5 N
11	3·5 Hz
12	100 N, 50 N
13	0·33 m
14	8 N
15	9·6 N

2 Volume and Density (page 12)

1(a)	50 m^3 (b) $50\,000\,000 \text{ cm}^3$
3	Wood 750 kg/m^3, Iron 8 000 kg/m^3, Glass 3 000 kg/m^3
6	1·2 kg/m^3
9(a)	$10\,000 \text{ m}^3$ (Above a 1 m^2 table)
(b)	12 000 kg (More than a ton!)

3 Atoms and Molecules (page 18)

11	$1·45 \times 10^{-9}$ m

4 Pressure (page 23)

3	5000 N/m^2
4	15 000 N/m^2
5	5000 N/m^2
12	10·34 m
14	100 000 N/m^2
15	3 cm^2

5 Movement and Force (page 36)

3	$\frac{1}{50}$ s
4	250 cm/s
5	40 cm/s
7	35 cm/s
8	11·2 cm/s
9	625 cm/s^2
10	4 m/s^2
11	0·5 m/s^2
13	11 cm/s
14	100 cm/s^2
15	35 m
16	15 000 m
18(a)	5 m/s^2 (b) 937·5 m
19(a)	32 m/s (b) 156 m
20(a)	18 m/s (b) 96 m
21	14 m/s

22(a)	2·5 m/s^2 (b) 20 m
27	$\frac{1}{3}$ m/s^2
28	2 m/s^2
29(a)	3 m/s^2 (b) 6000 N
30(a)	80 N (b) 5 N
31	5 N/kg
32	10 kg
34	3·2 m
35	5 m, 20 m, 45 m
36(a)	4 s (b) 40 m/s
37(a)	60 m (b) 35 m/s
46	18 kg m/s
47(a)	3600 N s (b) 3600 kg m/s (c) 4 m/s
49	5 m/s
50	0·29 m/s
51	0·5 m/s
53	1·6 m/s
59(b)	0·4 s (c) 0·72 m
60(a)	2·5 m/s^2 (b) 400 s (c) 200 km

6 Energy and Force (page 47)

3(a)	3000 J (b) 180 J (c) 1440 J (d) 15 000 000 J
4	3200 J
5	3 J
6	11 J
7	30 J
8	10 N
9	162 J
10	6400 J
15	50 J
16	120 J
17	4·4 J
20(a)	3000 J (b) 1500 W
21(a)	1620 J (b) 270 W
22(a)	2400 J (b) 2400 J (c) 8·9 m/s
25(a)	0·6 m (c) 1 J (d) 2 m/s (e) 0·67 m/s (f) 1 J before, 0·33 J after
26(b)	(i) 6000 N (ii) 180 000 J (iii) 205 000 J (iv) 120 000 J

7 Kinetic theory (page 56)

7	100 cm^3
8	5 cm^3
9	500 000 N/m^2

10	8611 m
11	415 m/s
14(a)	5 (b) 10 000
18	1 cm^3
19(b)	10^{-10} m
20(a)	$\frac{1}{3}$ (b) 3×10^{-10} m
21(d)	5882 N/m^2 (f) 49
22(a)	960 kg

9 Current electricity (page 74)

8 B 0·1 A, C 0·1 A, D 0·1 A, E 0·45 A,
F 0·3 A, G 0·15 A, H 0·15 A

Switches closed	A^1	A^2	A^3
X only	0	0	0
Y only	0	0	0
Z only	0	0	0
X and Y	0·4	0·4	0
Y and Z	0	0	0
X and Z	0·2	0	0·2
X, Y and Z	0·6	0·4	0·2

14 A 4·5 V, B 2·25 V, C 2·25 V, D 3 V,
E 1·5 V, F 1·5 V, G 3 V

15 $R_1 = 2\,\Omega$, $R_2 = 6\,\Omega$

16 (a) 1 A, (b) 6 Ω, (c) 6 V, (d) 1 A, (e) 3 Ω,
(f) 4 A

17 9 C

18 5 A

19 6 J

20 4800 J

21 24 W

22 0·25 A

23 20 V

24(a) 2·5 Ω, (b) 3·75 Ω, (c) 5 Ω

29(a) 1·1 A, 2·2 A (b) 0 A, 2·2 A

30(a) 0·2 A at P, Q and R, (c) 3 V, (d) 0 V

10 Magnets and Electromagnetism (page 90)

31 48 V

32 3 V

33 0 V

34(a) 30 A, (b) 0·3 A

11 Alternating Electricity (page 99)

6 50 V

7 336 V

13(c) (i) 1000 Hz

13 Heat energy (page 109)

3 30°C

4(a) 42 000 J, (b) 4200 J

6 3600 J/kg°C

7 25 m

8 48°C

9(a) 200 J/kg°C

10(b) 30 J/s,
(e) The specific heat capacity of water is
approximately 4·5 times greater than that of
aluminium.

11(a) 50 J, (b) 750 J, (c) 166·7 J/kg°C

14 Circular motion (page 113)

6(a) 9 m/s^2, (b) 18 N

7 1960 N (approx)

8(a) 8019 m/s, (b) 84 min

12(b) (iii) 50 m/s^2
(iv) 350 N

15 Electrons and Electron Streams (page 123)

23 $8·9 \times 10^{-31}$ kg

24(a) 1200 C, (b) 2×10^8 C/kg, (c) 8×10^{-28} kg

16 Astronomy (page 135)

31 $3·6 \times 10^{22}$ N

41(b) 45°

17 Radioactivity (page 146)

23(a) 1 a.m.u. (b) 1 a.m.u.

28 3 protons, 4 neutrons, 3 electrons

29 $^9_4$Be

33 $^4_2\alpha$, $^{\ 0}_{-1}\beta$

34 $^{216}_{84}$Po

35 $^{14}_7$N

42 600, 75

43 6 N

44 3 years

54(d) 0·24 mg of strontium, 0·76 mg of yttrium

18 Oscillations and Waves (page 155)

11 0·4 m/s

12 5 Hz

13 0·08 m

15 2·4 m/s

16 6 cm

17 0·4 m

18 550 Hz

19 24 Hz

21 f = 6 Hz, L = 4 cm, v = 24 cm/s

22(a) 3 m, (b) 12 m/s

19 Reflection and Refraction (page 164)

37(a)   (iv) 20 cm/s

20 Lenses and Optical Instruments (page 177)

6   2 D
8(a) -4 D
9   0·2 m
10 $-0·08$ m
12   0 D
14   The real image is 6 cm high and 7·5 cm from the lens
15   The virtual image is 9 cm high and 12 cm from the lens
18   0·08 m
39(a)   250 mm/s,   **(b)** 0·1 s
      (c) (i) Twice as far
      (ii) 280 s

21 Diffraction and Interference (page 186)

12 5×10^{-7} m
13   3·6 mm
20(a) $3·3 \times 10^{-6}$ m,   **(b)** 9°   **(c)** $5·3 \times 10^{-7}$ m
26(d)   2 mm